A Jewel in the Crown

Hilda and Rudolf Kingslake to whom this volume is dedicated.

A Jewel in the Crown:
Essays in Honor of the 75th Anniversary
of The Institute of Optics

Edited by

Carlos R. Stroud Jr.

MELIORA PRESS

An imprint of University of Rochester Press

First published by the Meliora Press
University of Rochester Press
668 Mount Hope Avenue, Rochester, NY 14620, USA
www.urpress.com

and at Boydell & Brewer, Ltd.
P.O. Box 9, Woodbridge, Suffolk IP12 3DF
United Kingdom

ISBN 1–58046–162–X

Library of Congress Cataloging-in-Publication Data

A jewel in the crown : essays in honor of the 75th anniversary of the Institute of Optics / edited by Carlos R. Stroud, Jr.
    p. cm.
  Includes bibliographical references and index.
  ISBN 1–58046–162–X (acid-free paper)
  1. Optics—Research—History.   2. University of Rochester. Institute of Optics—History.   I. Stroud, Carlos.   II. University of Rochester. Institute of Optics.
  QC363.J49 2004
  535′.072′074789—dc22

                                        2004013871

British Library Cataloguing-in-Publication Data
A catalogue record for this book is available from the British Library

Printed in the United States of America.
This publication is printed on acid-free paper.

Dedication

This volume of essays celebrating the seventy-fifth anniversary of the founding of The Institute of Optics is dedicated to Rudolf and Hilda Kingslake, whose association with the Institute spanned almost the entire period. They arrived in 1929 and remained very closely associated with the department for seventy-four years until their deaths a few days apart in 2003. Their many contributions to the Institute, the community, and to optics in general are described in several essays, in particular in the biographical essay by Brian Thompson. Here we simply note that the qualities that their lives exemplified are those that are central to our academic program: scholarship, service, and a dedication to bridging the gap between fundamental and applied optics. The Kingslakes were also kind and generous people loved by all who knew them.

We owe a special debt to Hilda Kingslake. She was the author of a history of the first fifty years of the Institute, and of a later updated history through 1987. We have included here chapters from those volumes as twelve of our seventy-five essays. Her scholarship and elegant presentation set a high standard for this and any future histories.

Table of Contents

Preface

The history of The Institute of Optics is rich and complex, a story of remarkable accomplishments and remarkable people. There are few academic programs in any discipline that have played as large a role in the development of a profession as the Institute has in optics. A very large fraction of the country's leaders in optics—academic, industrial, and governmental—received their training in the Institute. These alumni are notably attached to their alma mater, returning often to Industrial Associates meetings, alumni gatherings, and to live in the Rochester area. Our task is both to record the facts of this history and also to try to cast some light on why this relatively small program has been so successful in research and education in its first seventy-five years.

A simple recitation of the chronology cannot possibly capture the character of the people who have made up the Institute, nor the atmosphere and attitudes that define the environment that led to so many successes. To convey these things we need the voices of the people who actually have made up the Institute for all these years. We have attempted to capture these voices in a collection of 75 essays by a wide variety of authors who lived, and in many cases made, the history. We are fortunate that Hilda Kingslake recorded much of the early history in a previous volume celebrating the fiftieth anniversary[1], and in a 1987 updated volume[2]. We include 12 essays from her earlier writings. We also have the text of a speech that Brian O'Brien gave describing research in the Institute supporting the military during World War II. There are excerpts from oral reminiscences of several who have many years of association with the department.

One can not capture the reality of an institution by telling only about the serious moments. The humor, the fun, and the social life are very much a part of what determines any successful academic environment. We have included a number of essays and photographs that capture these aspects of life in the Institute. We have even included excerpts from a spoof spy thriller novel set on the fourth floor of Bausch & Lomb during the War.

I am enormously indebted to the more than two dozen authors who contributed essays to this volume. Their efforts will be appreciated by all who through their writings relive the events that they describe. I make no guarantee that every essay is consistent with every other, even when they describe the same events. Memories have a way of distilling the essence of an event from the perspective of the one remembering. The essence and the perspective are perhaps a more accurate reflection of important things than are numbers and dates. To a very large degree the exact numbers and dates are available. The University Archives, housed in the Rare Books and Special Collections Department of the Rush Rhees Library and ably looked over by Nancy Martin, holds a large collection of documents, photographs and other memorabilia of the Institute. This collection has recently been augmented by the Rudolf Kingslake Archive organized and described by Brian J. Thompson and Martin L. Scott. A descriptive register of the Kingslake papers will soon be accessible via www. library.rochester.edu/rbk/rarehome.htm.

The person who was most instrumental in gathering the materials for this book was Kathleen Youngworth, (Ph.D., 2003). She spent countless hours going through the archives, excerpting important documents, and selecting the photographs for this volume. We are all indebted to her for her skillful and enthusiastic efforts. Maria Schnitzler helped with compiling the materials and also contributed one essay. Christopher Ditchman and Melissa Mead helped by generating high-resolution electronic copies of the many photographs. Sandi Boulter in the University Public Relations Department helped by providing materials, and Tom Rickey assisted with copy editing.

The photographs have been gathered from many sources, mainly from the archives of the University and of the Institute of Optics. Others have been contributed by the students, faculty, staff and alumni of the Institute. We are grateful to them for their assistance. Three photographs are reprinted from the old Rochester Times Union newspaper with permission from Gannett Company. Two photographs by George Burns reprinted from the Saturday Evening Post. We were informed that the photographer owned the copyright, but were unable to contact him or his heirs.

Finally, we must gratefully acknowledge the financial assistance of two optics institutions that have been around Rochester even longer than The Institute of Optics: Eastman Kodak and Bausch and Lomb. These two companies provided funds that helped get the department started 75 years ago, and they have stepped forward again to help fund this history and the anniversary celebration. We thank them for their generosity.

CARLOS STROUD
June, 2004

References

1   Hilda G. Kingslake, *The Institute of Optics: the first fifty years, 1929–1979*, (Rochester, N.Y.: College of Engineering and Applied Science, University of Rochester, 1979).

2   Hilda G. Kingslake, *The Institute of Optics, 1929–1987*, (Rochester, N.Y.: College of Engineering and Applied Science, University of Rochester, 1987).

PART I

BEGINNINGS: 1900–1939

I. Beginnings: 1900–1939

It was no coincidence that The Institute of Optics was founded in Rochester, nor that it was founded in the years following World War I. The rapid growth of optics-related industry in the United States—eye glasses, scientific, surveying and military instruments, and more recently consumer photography—made it intolerable to be dependent on Europe for the essential materials and trained technicians needed to support these industries. In particular, the dependence on German sources for these vital supplies had proven unsatisfactory in the war. France and England had recently set up their own optics institutes in response to the same pressure. There was widespread sentiment that the country needed its own school to supply trained optical scientists and engineers as well as to carry out basic research in the subject area. George Eastman and Edward Bausch decided that the school should be in Rochester and helped to support its founding.

In this section we have a series of essays describing the founding of the Institute and its early years. We are fortunate to have eyewitness accounts by Hilda Kingslake, who came over from England with her new husband, who was a founding faculty member of the new Institute. Hilda was the daughter of one of the founding faculty members of the Optics Section at Imperial College of the University of London, A. E. Conrady, and herself a member of the first graduating class of that department. Although Hilda was never a faculty member of the Institute, she, like her husband, was closely associated with it for the first seventy-four years of its existence.

Hilda Kingslake wrote a history of the first fifty years of the Institute and revised it in 1987 to include the first fifty-eight years. In this section we include three essays from her history describing the events immediately preceding the founding through the first decade of the new Institute. In addition, we have a biography of Rudolf and Hilda Kingslake by Brian J. Thompson, and a short biographical sketch of early faculty member Jane Dewey by Carlos Stroud. Susan Houde-Walter provides insights into the interrelated foundings of The Institute of Optics and the Optical Society of America. Even in the Great Depression years of the 1930s, there was a bit of frivolity to leaven the serious business of getting the new Institute developed. Carlos Stroud describes the beginnings of the optics picnic and other diversions during this period.

1. Rush Rhees and His University: 1900–1930

Hilda Kingslake

Rush Rhees was President of the University of Rochester when The Institute of Applied Optics was founded in 1929. He was then almost at the end of a long and distinguished term of service which began in 1900, when the University was a very small private college restricted to undergraduate teaching in arts and science. In 1900, there were 157 students and 17 on the faculty, and the buildings consisted of little more than Anderson Hall, built in 1861, Sibley Library, built in 1876, and the Reynolds chemistry laboratories, built in 1887—all on what is now known as the Prince Street campus or the "old campus." The Alumni Gymnasium, also on the Prince Street campus, opened in the fall of 1900. Present-day students and faculty know little about this strong, quiet, circumspect, somewhat stern but kindly Baptist minister from New England, who once taught mathematics and for whom the present University library is named. The story of how, within 10 or 12 years, he found the wherewithal to buy additional land and add several major buildings on the Prince Street campus is well recorded. These were the Eastman Building for physics and biology (1905), Carnegie Building for applied science (1911), the Memorial Art Gallery (1913), and Anthony Memorial and Catharine Strong halls for women (1914).

Experience as a member of the board of directors of the Mechanic's Institute very soon made Rhees aware of a great need for university-level technological training in the Rochester area. He spent a year-long sabbatical leave in Europe for the specific purpose of investigating facilities for higher education in applied sciences and returned to Rochester with a goal of development for the University very clear in his mind. Again, it has been well recorded how, within another 20 years, he secured the millions of dollars required to transform completely the University; how he established a complete and superior school of music (1924) and a very fine medical school (1925), how he introduced a program of graduate education and a department of engineering in the College of Arts and Science. By 1929, moreover, Rhees had nearly built a complete new campus for men in arts and science due to be dedicated in 1930; he was also augmenting the facilities of the old campus for women students,

Benjamin Rush Rhees, President of the University of Rochester 1900–1935.

Eastman Building, Prince Street Campus.

who he decided should be educated separately from the men. The opening of The Institute of Applied Optics in the fall of 1929, with only two on the faculty, was to all outward appearances a very minor event indeed, and it is not at all surprising that in the University as a whole this innovation made little, if any impression. However, from its start, the Institute was regularly listed in the University bulletins and was given special attention in the President's Annual Reports to the Trustees for many years. Although the founding of the Institute was well reported in student publications and in the city press, no mention of

James P. C. Southall.

the founding appears in the hundred-year history of the University; reference is made only to the Institute's part in the war.

Why did Rush Rhees at this very complex time in University development trouble with this unfamiliar, little understood venture? It was all in keeping with his sincere desire to be of service to the scientific industries and the community of the Rochester area, whence the University derived so much of its support.

In 1910, J. P. C. Southall, at that time a professor at Alabama Polytechnic in Auburn and later Professor of Physics at Columbia University, published a book entitled *Principles and Methods of Geometrical Optics*. In the preface he pleaded for more attention to geometrical optics in particular and to all optics in general. He drew attention to the fact that "the great province of applied optics was almost exclusively German territory, so that nearly all the outstanding developments of modern times in both the theory and construction of optical instruments are of German origin." He regretted that English-language books ignored the great German theoreticians.

In 1912, Perley G. Nutting, then at the Bureau of Standards and later at Eastman Kodak Company, published a little book entitled *Outlines of Applied Optics*. In the preface he stated that more texts were urgently needed. He pleaded for more serious teaching of optics, especially applied optics, "usually ignored by students of pure optics." He was convinced that no richer field awaited the investigator in pure optics than in applied optics, "which presents brainracking and alluring problems" worthy of university teaching and research.

In 1914 Europe was plunged into World War I. The German blockade and the allied counter-defense of the seas very soon affected transoceanic commerce between the United States and Europe. A famine of superior optical instruments and optical glass immediately developed, so that all too soon the truth of Southall's words came home to both England and the United States.

In 1915, envisioning ultimately the founding of the Optical Society of America, a number of optically concerned members of the Rochester companies and professions established the "Association for the Advancement of Applied Optics," with every intention of its becoming, as soon as possible, the first local section when the national society should be formed. A year later, in 1916, the National Society was founded.

In 1917, the problem of finding personnel to cope with the often unfamiliar precision optical equipment required by the wartime government became so acute in England and France that, while the war was still in progress, a Department of Applied Optics was opened at the Imperial College of Science and Technology, a college of the University of London. The faculty appointed were experienced and progressive personnel taken from war work in industry and the Ministry of Munitions. Within a year the university-level Institut d'Optique was opened in Paris. In December 1917, Southall, by now a Professor of Physics at Columbia University and teaching more optics than at all usual, published an article in the *Scientific American*, reviewing the progress of advanced education and research in optics that started in London and Paris, he expressed the hope that Columbia might realize the advisability of undertaking a similar program in this country.

On February 6, 1918, Mr. George Eastman addressed the following letter to Dr. Rhees, in reaction to a letter he had received from Professor Southall:

> Dear Dr Rhees:
>   The enclosed letters from Mr. Dey and Professor Southall raise the question in my mind whether Rochester is not the place for a School of Applied Optics instead of New York. If you are interested, I should be glad to arrange for Dr. Mees, Mr. Barnes, and Mr. Dey to go and see you about it.
>   Since beginning this letter, I called up Mr. Edward Bausch and he says that he had some talk with you about such a project several years ago and that he had not materially changed his attitude toward it which was very favorable.
>   Yours very truly,
>   (signed) Geo. Eastman

It must, therefore, have been in 1917, or even in 1916, that Edward Bausch had first approached Rhees. Bausch and his business associate Adolph Lomb, were charter members of the young Optical Society of America, together with Southall and a number of others influential in the field of applied optics. All were imbued with the thought of establishing a university department solely devoted to teaching and research in optics. At the third annual meeting of the Optical Society of America, held at Baltimore in December 1918, only 10 months after Mr. Eastman's letter to Rhees, the Council referred to "the School of Optical Engineering shortly to be organized in connection with the University of Rochester." At that time, Dr. Rhees had indeed received Mr. Eastman's suggestion very favorably, but he had not yet gone beyond suggesting that the first step would be to find a director. In fact, Rhees was only just beginning to feel his way through preliminary conversations and correspondence.

The years 1920 to 1930 were, of course, the years of greatest change in the whole history of the University to this day. Nevertheless, Rhees revived the 1918–1919 discussions; many relevant and serious questions had to be answered. Almost from the beginning, it was quite agreed that the Institute should be in Rochester at the University. Other decisions were not so easily arrived at. Should the Director be appointed before details of courses and housing of the Institute were decided? Who should be the Director? Should both pure and applied optics be included? Should the Institute be entirely undergraduate, entirely graduate, or partly what was then called a trade school? Or should it be for both undergraduate and graduate work? Most seemed inclined to favor both graduate and undergraduate work; and the training of technicians was very soon eliminated, no doubt in view of the existence of the Mechanic's Institute, now vastly developed into the Rochester Institute of Technology. What size organization should be planned? Should it be autonomous or should it be associated with physics or engineering? All these and other unavoidable questions exercised the minds of everyone, and especially of those expecting to be deeply involved in the final plan.

Dr. C. E. K. Mees, Director of the Research Laboratory at Eastman Kodak Company, although a chemist himself, was a charter member of the Optical Society of America and a member of its Executive Council. At that same meeting of the Council held in Baltimore on December 18, 1918, already referred to in this text, Perley Nutting, Secretary to the Board, reported that it was the hope of the Council that "the school of optical engineering to be organized in connection with the University of Rochester" would take care of the journal and other activities of the Optical Society, that such an institute would "automatically control not only education but publication of the Journal, a Handbook of Optics, and various reference handbooks in applied optics." Quite clearly, Mees took these projections for The Institute of Applied Optics to heart and proceeded to formulate in his mind the accommodation necessary for such a comprehensive program of activity. In May 1919, Mees presented a grandiose proposal for a four-storey building, 70 by 100 feet in area, complete with library and workshops. He estimated the cost of the operation for the first five years to be $400,000, equivalent to several million dollars today. This ambitious plan apparently gave everyone concerned a good deal to think about, as little more was done until 1925.

The 1925–26 Report of the President included the announcement of the appointment of T. Russell Wilkins as Junior Professor of Physics. A Canadian, aged 35, and a graduate of McMaster University in Canada, he took his doctorate at Chicago under R. A. Millikan, in what at that time was definitely "modern physics." His thesis was "Multiple Valence in the Ionization of Alpha Rays." This appointment proved to be an important step on the way to the establishment of The Institute of Optics.

In 1926 or early 1927, a subcommittee consisting of T. R. Wilkins of the University, L. A. Jones of Eastman Kodak Company, and W. B. Rayton of Bausch & Lomb, was appointed "to outline courses to be offered in the proposed Institute of Applied Optics of the University of Rochester." Their report, submitted on June 3, 1927, listed two main lines of study: (a) the training of students in the theory of optics and optical instruments so that there may be an adequate supply of men versed in the theory and skilled in the design

Lloyd Jones, Eastman Kodak Company.　　*Wilbur Rayton, Bausch & Lomb.*

of optical instruments: "This will make available to the industries of the country the best and latest knowledge in the field"; and (b) the training of optometrists (see Chapter III). The report also stated: "It is further hoped that among those who complete the work offered in the School of Optics some will be desirous of continuing their work. Then it is quite possible that in the future a postgraduate school can be developed in which advanced training may be given and research work in the field of optics may be encouraged." Also, "The Committee has kept in mind in a broad way the general organization of courses in the University of Rochester so that courses already given may be utilized in so far as possible but where these existing courses are not in harmony with the general scheme new courses have been indicated." The courses included physical and geometrical optics, physiological optics, physics for optics students, scientific German, French or history, mathematics, some chemistry, psychology, machine drawing and shop work, materials used in optical instruments, radiation and electrical measurements, and the design of optical systems. The optometry students did less optical theory and added elementary anatomy and physiology, pathology of the eye and, of course, optometric instruction and clinical practice. For all students, there were the regular freshman general education courses and some electives usefully related to the required courses.

The committee estimated that—in addition to the staff for purely optometric courses and in addition to any necessary increase in faculty in physics and other departments teaching courses to optics students—the minimum personnel for teaching specialized courses for students in optics would be three: one for advanced geometrical and physical optics courses, one for physiological optics, and one to supervise and teach shop work. It was recommended that in the beginning The Institute of Optics be under the supervision and direction of one who was essentially a physicist; that the man obtained for the teaching of geometrical and physical optics should be chosen also in consideration of his executive ability and that he would later become dean of the school.

Bausch & Lomb Building, the new shared home of the Department of Physics and Institute of Applied Optics, 1930.

On August 1, 1928, an agreement was signed between the University of Rochester, Eastman Kodak Company, and the Bausch & Lomb Optical Company, whereby the University agreed "as soon as reasonably possible hereafter" to establish and maintain an institute of optics "for the training of students in the various fields of optical science" and to prepare candidates for work in the optometric and ophthalmic fields . . ." A statement followed to the effect that a committee of three scientific representatives of the three parties to this agreement had drawn up a four-year course of study for both optics and optometry students, and that this course was approved by each of the parties.

The University agreed to set apart, without cost, the whole fourth floor of the Bausch & Lomb building being erected for the Department of Physics, with facilities and service staff to be available for use by The Institute of Applied Optics. The University also agreed to keep separate records and accounts for The Institute of Applied Optics, including estimated costs of the time given by the physics faculty and staff. The University further agreed that, to a reasonable extent, employees of the companies should be allowed to attend lectures and share other benefits of the existence of an institute of optics.

The agreement named two committees, representing the three parties to the agreement, to oversee the affairs of the Institute: a conference committee of three, which was really the professional scientific advisory committee, and a finance committee. The University further agreed to confer a B.S. in optics or its equivalent on students satisfactorily completing the course and to confer M.S. and Ph.D. degrees upon students fulfilling the requirements.

Finally, the two companies agreed to contribute up to $10,000 each to equip the Institute with apparatus, and up to $20,000 each per year for five years to cover the operating costs beyond what the University itself would contribute. The whole agreement was to become effective on July 1, 1928, and to remain in force until June 30, 1933. The parties also agreed to endeavor to continue The Institute of Applied Optics beyond that date under terms to be agreed upon.

The agreement was signed by Rush Rhees, President of the university, W. G. Stuber, President of Eastman Kodak Company, and Edward Bausch, President of the Bausch & Lomb Optical Company.

It was almost another year before any faculty were appointed and over a year before classes in applied optics began. On February 19, 1929, Dr. Rhees wrote to Dr. Wilkins, asking him to formulate "in conference with Dean Hoeing and also with Jones and Rayton a form of announcement for our new courses in optics." He suggested that a special circular and a statement be prepared for announcement in the college papers and the city press. An announcement appeared in the Democrat and Chronicle on March 15, 1929, in bold headlines over a well-written article.

President Rhees, in his Annual Report for 1928–29, stated that "five noteworthy developments have marked the record of the current year. One has been the execution of an agreement between the Bausch & Lomb Optical Company, the Eastman Kodak Company, and the University of Rochester for the conduct and maintenance of an Institute of Optics in association with the College of Arts and Science and particularly with the department of physics of that College." He proceeded for two pages of that report to describe the teaching to be given. He stated that by the end of the 1928–29 academic year he had not been able to find a director—but "we are fortunate in having secured the consent of Professor T. Russell Wilkins to serve as acting Director. Associated with him on the Conference Committee will be L. A. Jones and W. B. Rayton." Rhees reported that the Departments of Physics, Physiology, and Psychology and specialists of the cooperating industries would conduct special classes for students in physiological optics until a man could be found, "so far a vain search."

"Our problem has been complicated," Rhees continued, "by the fact that in recent years in this country, as well as in England and in Germany, most men who devote themselves to physics prefer to work in the fascinating new fields of atomic structure and allied problems." Rhees, in fact, had run into the basic problem which had led to the need for special university departments of optics. Rush Rhees retired in 1935 and was succeeded by an unusually young man, Alan Valentine, from Yale.

2. Common Origins of The Institute of Optics and the Optical Society of America

Susan Houde-Walter

In the early nineteenth century optical instrument makers were almost entirely based in Europe. This was the age of the simple landscape camera lens and the first achromatic microscopes. There were optical designers, but the theory of imaging was primitive. Real glasses had to be begged from glaziers and refractive indices were largely unknown, as were curvatures. Instrument makers used trial and error and jealously guarded and copied each other's designs. The situation was radically improved by a multi-decade, interdisciplinary collaboration between Carl Zeiss, Ernst Abbe, and Otto Schott in Jena, Germany. Together they developed and applied diffraction imaging theory, glasses to correct secondary spectrum, and many precepts of sound optical design and testing. By the 1860s, Germany became a hotbed for optics manufacture, particularly microscopes.

John Jacob Bausch was a German optician's apprentice who decided in 1850, at twenty years of age, that he could have a better life in America. He headed for New York City on a forty-nine-day boat journey and from there made his way to Buffalo, New York. There was a cholera epidemic in Buffalo, and he could not find any work in any event. The employment scene was not much better in Rochester, but he managed to survive for a few years, whereupon he decided to open a spectacle shop of his very own. Unfortunately, most Americans did not use spectacles. His business languished, but he was helped by a German-born friend, Henry Lomb, who joined him and contributed his own earnings to the Bausch family. After the Civil War, spectacles became better accepted, business improved, and "Bausch & Lomb, Inc." expanded into instrument making. The improvements in German microscope design encouraged them to hire a microscope maker from Berlin named Ernst Gundlach. Photographic lenses were next, and soon after, Bausch & Lomb became the exclusive American manufacturer of anastigmats for Zeiss.

Rochester in the 1880s had small optical companies bubbling up all over. Mr. Gundlach apparently did not get along well with management at B&L and was involuntarily retired a few years after his hire. He and a schoolteacher friend started an optical goods store operating from their home, just down the street from the B&L factory. Their company moved several times, but was known to produce microscopes and objectives. Gundlach himself eventually left that company to start another company in the same business. Wollensak and Ilex were also started by former B&L employees to make photographic shutters, in 1882 and 1910, respectively. In the meantime, the original Gundlach company bought the Korona camera lens company to expand its product line. Later, the company bought the Manhattan Optical Co. and occupied 761 South Clinton Avenue. That address was also occupied by the Rochester Panoramic Co. (1905), the Seneca Camera Co. (1903–10) and the Ilex Optical Co. (1912–16). Wollensak bought the original Gundlach company in 1905. Meanwhile, William Walker founded the Rochester Optical Co. in 1880 to make photographic cameras. The following year, his brother founded a competing company, Rochester

Camera Manufacturing Co. Three other rival camera companies joined forces with the competing brothers' companies in 1899 to amalgamate the Rochester Optical & Camera Co. The merger may have been in response to an aggressive newcomer to the optical scene: George Eastman.

Unlike his counterparts, Eastman did not have a technical background. Rather, he was assistant bookkeeper at a local bank, but he was interested enough in his photographic hobby to travel to London to learn how to make gelatin dry plates. He patented a plate-coating machine and opened for business in 1880, making plates at night and working at the bank in the daytime. By 1888 Eastman's business was strong despite having lost a long patent battle with another optical company over transparent film. Eastman got into camera manufacture, and he acquired Blair Camera, American Camera, and Photographic Materials and moved them into a central location in Rochester.

Several other camera companies were founded in Rochester at that time, including Sunart Photographic Co. (1893), Folmer & Schwing (1887), Gassner & Marx (1898), Vogt Optical (1899), Century Camera Co. (1900), Seneca Camera Co. (1900), Crown Optical Co. (1906), and Rectigraph (1909). Many more were to come.

Throughout this period of expansion in Rochester, applied optics was coming to be recognized as a field of its own. The National Bureau of Standards in Washington, D.C., recognized that it was too big to confine under the aegis of physics, and established an Optics Division in 1903. Perley Nutting joined the bureau the same year. Nutting had just completed his doctorate at Cornell University, but not before he had toured Europe and observed the advanced instrument making and quality of optical glass for himself. Nutting kept up his contacts in Europe when he returned to the United States, and he communicated European advances to others at the bureau. In the several years following Nutting's hire, the bureau published several circulars on optical instruments and optical properties of materials, including Nutting's book, *Applied Optics*. Nutting and several colleagues, including the bureau director, S. W. Stratton, met frequently at the bureau to present original work and to discuss optics in general.

By 1910, Nutting had decided to form a formal society for applied optics and to establish a journal of original papers. He wrote to many friends and colleagues in the United States and Europe. Although many shared his sentiment, no action was taken. Shortly afterwards, Nutting moved to Rochester to join the new research lab at Eastman Kodak.

World War I started in Europe in August 1914. The blockade on Germany meant that optical glass was no longer available to the burgeoning optics industry in Rochester. It became immediately clear that more knowledge of optical theory and more advanced instrument-making skills would also be needed in the United States. The existing Rochester groups on microscope making, optometry and the like did not satisfy this need. Consequently, on November 18, 1915, several interested

Perley Nutting, early proponent of optics in the United States.

individuals, including Nutting and Lomb, met in the Physics Library at the University of Rochester to form an optical society. It was named the Rochester Association for Advancement of Applied Optics. Within three weeks, a constitution and by-laws were written and adopted, and first officers and council elected. The first regular meeting was scheduled for Tuesday, January 4, 1916, on the University campus, and every other Tuesday thereafter between October 1 and May 31. (This schedule is still used by the Rochester local chapter.) Ophthalmologists, optometrists, lens designers, physicists and engineers, and photographers were recruited as new members. The formation of the society was announced in several journals, and an average of forty people attended each of the new meetings. Given the obvious interest and need, it was decided one short month later, in February 1916, to plan a national optics society, with the name Optical Society of America. One year later the OSA was well-enough known that the National Research Council approached OSA for lists of optical equipment manufacturers and suppliers to the federal government.

The first order of OSA business was to start the Journal of the Optical Society of America. The first paper in the journal, "Opportunities for Research," was a broad and heartfelt appeal to the scientific community by F. K. Richtmyer from Cornell University. In it he said that the OSA "should not be content to hold meetings a few times a year and to publish a journal. The opportunities extend far beyond these functions. . . ." He entreated OSA members to identify and promote important topics of investigation, to encourage university research, and he reminded readers that even seemingly minor problems could reveal important discoveries, such as Hertz's discovery of photoelectricity. A lens designer at Bausch & Lomb, Herman Kellner, was the first appointed editor for JOSA. Originally trained and practicing in Germany, Kellner was meticulous in his efforts to establish and maintain the highest scientific standards for the journal. Individuals familiar with his efforts reported that many submissions were bottlenecked on his desk while others were rejected as substandard. He and Nutting agreed to set the tone in the first issues as one of highest possible technical quality and original work only. The result was a thin but first-rate journal.

The first regular meeting of the OSA was held on December 28, 1916. There were twelve contributed papers on vision, lens design, image theory, color measurement, light sources, microscopy and glass technology. Eight of the twelve contributions came from industry. The second scheduled meeting was cancelled because of war, but the "third" annual meeting was held in 1918 almost immediately after the war ended. With war very fresh on everyone's minds, the council considered limiting admittance "in accordance with nationality and residence," but ultimately decided to keep the meeting open.

Plans for the founding of an "Institute of Optics" were simultaneously afoot at the University of Rochester. It would take eleven more years to come to fruition, but in 1918 Nutting suggested that the Institute of Optics should be intimately involved with publication of JOSA, and oversee a handbook of optics and various reference books on applied optics. It is interesting to note that many OSA officers served on the advisory committee to found the Institute of Optics. Thus the links between OSA and the Institute of Optics were established very early in their respective histories.

Nutting left Rochester to head the research lab at Westinghouse before the first national meeting took place. Nevertheless, he had made indelible marks by founding both the Rochester section of the OSA and the OSA itself, plus contributing to the foundation of the Institute of Optics. OSA has grown enormously since then, as has the optics industry in Rochester and the academic effort at the University of Rochester (witness the Center for Visual Science, the Laboratory for Laser Energetics, the Center for Optics Manufacturing,

Meeting of the Optical Society of America, 1921.

the Center for Electronic Imaging Systems, all offshoots of the Institute of Optics). Vestiges of Nutting's influence can still be seen by the deep commitment students and faculty have to OSA volunteerism and governance of the society. And even as OSA has grown into a truly international society, it may be possible to say that you can take OSA out of Rochester, but you cannot take Rochester out of OSA. Our beginnings are entwined.

Material for this article was drawn from the following three sources:

1   Hermann Beyer, "100 years ABBE's microscope theory and its significance for practical microscopy," *Jena Review* 3 (1973).
2   Rudolf Kingslake, "The Rochester Camera and Lens Companies," printed by the Photographic Historical Society, Box 9563, Rochester, NY 14604 (1974).
3   "Fifty-Year History of the Optical Society of America," *JOSA* 56:3 (1966).

Susan Houde-Walter received her M.S. and Ph.D. from the Institute of Optics in 1983 and 1987, respectively. She has been a member of the faculty of the University of Rochester since 1987.

3. Founding Years: 1929–1933

Hilda Kingslake

Guided no doubt by his scientific advisors in Rochester, Rhees in 1929 continued his search, now in England, for qualified faculty for the planned Institute of Applied Optics.

At Brown's Hotel in London, he interviewed two young men, both only 26 years old, who he decided to appoint to the faculty. Continuing with his 1928–29 Report to the Trustees, he was able to announce: "I have been fortunate in finding a man ideally trained for geometrical optics and optical design. He is Rudolf Kingslake, MSc. (London), a graduate of the Technical Optics department at the Royal College of Science, a unit of Imperial College of Science and Technology, London, and he has accepted our appointment to be Assistant Professor of Geometrical Optics and Optical Design. . . . He has published eight papers in the Transactions of the Optical Society of London and elsewhere. By training and experience, he is admirably fitted to contribute largely to the development and significance of our new enterprise." Kingslake's appointment as Assistant Professor was confirmed at the Board of Trustees' meeting on June 15, 1929.

Rhees continued in the 1928–29 Report: "We have invited another young English scientist to accept appointment as Assistant Professor of Physical Optics. He is A. Maurice Taylor Ph.D. (Cantab), . . . author jointly with E. I. G. Rawlins of a book, *The Infrared Analysis of Molecular Structure*. His training and interests are such as admirably to complement those of Mr. Kingslake, and promise much strength for our new Institute." A. M. Taylor's appointment, for some reason, was not confirmed by the Board of Trustees until their meeting on November 7, 1929. Rhees continued: "For the instruction of students in optical shop methods, we are fortunate in having the services of Mr. Herbert E. Wilder, who served in the same capacity in the former Rochester School of Optometry. From the staff of that discontinued school, we have also taken its Dean, Mr. Ernest Petry, to be our Lecturer on Theoretical and Practical Optometry. His experience coupled with his thorough training and his high professional ideals make him an invaluable colleague in the new work." Rhees concluded: "In as much as the Institute is new, its courses will not be given in full until four classes of students have been enrolled for them. For the professional courses in optometry, the first students

Rudolf Kingslake, about 1930.

A. Maurice Taylor, 1930.   *Ernest Petry.*

were accepted in 1926. . . . Three classes of such students are now in attendance . . . As yet the enrollment is small because the youth who have contemplated optometry as a career have not hitherto been required to satisfy college entrance requirements . . ."

With regard to accommodation, Rhees stated, "For the present, work for The Institute of Applied Optics is conducted on the old campus. By September 1930, however the work will be carried on on the new campus. . . ."

Following the appointment of Kingslake and Taylor, Wilkins was able to publish the *Special Bulletin* on The Institute of Applied Optics for 1929–30, as requested by Dr. Rhees. It was an attractive five-inch by eight-inch illustrated booklet of 36 pages. He listed the faculty and the various courses to be offered, together with descriptive paragraphs introducing some of the less familiar subjects to the reader. It was an impressive publication. This was the first of a succession of small bulletins published in the Wilkins years. Then began a long series of special bulletins and notices of summer sessions, all most attractive, large, illustrated, and eye-catching. The University's next problem involved the immigration laws. The waiting list from England was about nine months long at that time, which meant that the two appointees could not start teaching until the spring! Authorities were informed of the dilemma, and in view of the urgency of teaching in optics, they issued extended visitor's visas on the condition that both returned to England as soon as classes were over. Meanwhile, their names were kept on the immigration lists so that they could enter legally as alien residents in time for the 1930 term. Kingslake and his wife, also a graduate of Imperial College with three years experience in optical industry, arrived at the beginning of October and Taylor a few weeks later. Kingslake arrived to find The Institute of Applied Optics consisting of one small office in the old Eastman Building, where physics and biology were taught. Acting Director T. R. Wilkins, a very large man, and his secretary, Helen Tobin, a recent Rochester graduate, seemed to fill the office. Helen Tobin remained secretary to the directors for the next 43 years, retiring in July 1972. Space in that one office was somehow found for Kingslake and, a few weeks later, for Taylor, too! Lectures were to be given in the Eastman Building; and as soon as at all possible, laboratory work was to start in the as yet unpartitioned, unfurnished top floor of the new Bausch & Lomb building for physics on the partially built new campus three or four miles away on the old site of Oak Hill Country Club. John Leone, a very young man of great good will, was appointed technician and general factotum as soon as teaching at the new campus began. He continued in this capacity until retirement in 1976; he died the same year.

The partitioning of the floor was completed as soon as possible. Petry's clinic rooms and offices for optometry were divided off at the east end, and the glass workshop was at the west end, leaving the center for the work in applied optics. Offices, student laboratories, research labs, one small classroom, and a small darkroom were all, surprisingly, quickly made ready for use. For large lectures, the physics department theater was to be used. However, the space was already too limited, so that photometric and photographic labs were located on the third floor in space lent by the physics department. A metal workshop for making small research apparatus and special laboratory equipment was also on the third floor and shared with physics. Clarence McVea was the machinist in charge for some years, to be succeeded by Paul John, a very precise gentleman who had just two standards, good and perfect. One had to specify which was required.

Both Kingslake and Taylor not only had to prepare several courses of lectures, lecture by lecture, as they plunged straight into the teaching of seniors in optometry without any preparation; they also had to equip laboratories with a minimum of apparatus, some of it generously given by interested companies. For a time, Kingslake was teaching 16 hours a week. One student assistant, an M.S. graduate student in optics and physics, T. A. Russell, helped with laboratory work. Russell later went on to Eastman Kodak.

Arthur L. Ingalls, who in 1932 earned the first B. S. in Optics from the University of Rochester. After a very productive career in optical engineering at a number of places including Bausch & Lomb and the University of Michigan he looked forward to attending the celebration of the 75th anniversary of the Institute, but he died at age 91 in the spring of 2004.

Within a month after their arrival, the stock market collapsed, and the financial state of so many businesses and individuals was immediately complicated. It is very remarkable that the three parties to the agreement with regard to financing The Institute of Applied Optics stood by their five-year contract, so that the Institute, nevertheless, worked steadily though slowly ahead through the Depression years.

In late October 1929, Wilkins drove Kingslake and Taylor to the fourteenth annual meeting of the Optical Society of America at Cornell University and took every opportunity to introduce them to members of the optical profession in this country. Dr. Rhees attended the opening session of the meeting to announce in person the founding of The Institute of Applied Optics and the appointment of the first faculty, the first of their kind in this country. Almost certainly of greater importance than even this announcement was Dr. Wilkins' presence at the reading of a paper by Brian O'Brien, who was in charge of radiation research at the J. N. Adams Memorial Hospital at Perrysburg, New York, near Buffalo. Wilkins was immensely impressed and convinced that O'Brien was the man The Institute of Optics should have to teach physiological optics. In his annual report to the President for 1929–30, Wilkins was able to express great satisfaction at the appointment of Brian O'Brien (Ph.D. Yale 1922), 31 years old, to teach physiological optics, visual sensitometry, and colorimetry. He was named Professor by the Board of Trustees. Wilkins also reported the appointment, part-time, of Gustave Fassin, an employee of Bausch & Lomb, to teach mechanical design of optical instruments. A Belgian who had taught at the Technical School of Ghent and had had charge of workshops in the Societe Belge d'Optique, he was an original and competent designer. The faculty was now essentially complete and able to cover the projected program of teaching and research. Humanly, it was also an interesting, cosmopolitan, and very congenial team, with everyone well under 40 years of age and tackling a new kind of assignment.

Wilkins further reported that the University Field Secretary recently appointed, Charles R. Dalton, was giving great attention to making the existence and program of The Institute of Optics known to high-school students. At that time, there were three freshmen and one sophomore in optics who, of course, were not yet attending classes in the Institute. In optometry there were six freshmen, three sophomores, four juniors, one senior and one special case. Optometry applications were large, but unexpected University requirements greatly reduced the number accepted. The optometry student listed as a special case was an experienced married man, a bank teller who had lost his job because of a bank failure in the Depression. In due time, he graduated at a high level in optometry and thoroughly enjoyed his new profession.

The appointment of Brian O'Brien and Gustave Fassin rendered the top floor of the Bausch & Lomb building yet more inadequate. The glass shop had to be moved, and was reassembled in Gavett Hall, the engineering building. O'Brien immediately established an extensive laboratory for both undergraduates and graduates at the west end of the building. He brought with him, on indefinite loan, many thousands of dollars' worth of apparatus accumulated in the course of his radiation studies. The sponsoring companies of The Institute of Applied Optics continued to render great assistance with special apparatus, and O'Brien soon attracted graduate students.

The academic year 1930–31 did not show as much improvement in student registration as was hoped for, but Dalton's work in the schools gave promise of a larger enrollment for 1931–32. During the year, several special courses for people from industry and others were again given in introductory geometrical optics, mechanical design of optical instruments, spectroscopy and radiometry, advanced physical optics, the design of optical systems, and the theory of photographic processes for a

Gustave Fassin.

The Optics glass shop.

total registration of 143, nearly all from the scientific laboratories of the sponsoring companies. The largest attendance at courses given by members of the faculty was in geometrical optics and in the design of optical systems, fully bearing out Nutting's and Southall's assurances of the great need for applied geometrical optics, still not taught in regular university departments. One young Kodak attendee was a future president of the Eastman Kodak Company, but probably not entirely due to his attendance at this course! A course in photographic processes given by Mees, Jones, and others of the Eastman Kodak Company had by far the largest audience, for it was a unique opportunity for many in both industry and the University to hear a whole course on the subject.

In the 1931–32 report, Wilkins was able to announce great activity in research, quite evident from the gratifying list of publications and papers submitted for future publication, chiefly by O'Brien, his students, and assistants. A question with regard to the appropriateness of O'Brien's radiation work in the University was dropped since it had placed him on several government committees and resulted in a paper to the American Physical Society on some physiological effects of light, all of which attracted attention in scientific circles to the Institute.

An optical bench, much needed for lens testing, instruction, and investigation, was jointly designed by Kingslake and Fassin and was taking more than half the time of the instrument maker. It is still in use in the Institute.

Mr. Petry had been appointed by the State Board of Regents to the State Board of Examiners in optometry. He was also extending clinical practice work to be of service to students, faculty, and staff. The city at large was made more aware of the existence of the Institute through an illustrated article written by Wilkins for the monthly publication of the Chamber of Commerce in the March 1931 issue.

Dr. Sedgwick, anatomist at the medical school, had been added to the list of part-time lecturers. Dr. Paul Foote, Secretary of the Optical Society of America, had requested an article for the Journal, which was to appear in June 1931. He also reported that the council of the Society was "delighted with the progress which the organization had made," and planned to hold the 1932 annual meeting in Rochester in the fall.

The General Electric Company had sent Mr. F. K. Moss to give a series of three lectures on "The Science of Lighting for Seeing," which was very well attended and much appreciated. Research fellowships, to be established by several companies, were under discussion. The medical school was interested in O'Brien's work in physiological optics. In fact, The Institute of Applied Optics was beginning to take its place in the scientific world. The academic year 1931–32 marked the fourth year of the operation of the five-year agreement. It was also the year of Mr. Eastman's death.

In January 1932, a dinner was held at Todd Union, the student dining center at the time, for representatives of the sponsoring committee, administrative officers of the University, and the faculty of The Institute of Applied Optics. A rather complete report of the activities and achievements of the Institute was given at this time by the acting director, T. R. Wilkins.

In January 1933, W. B. Rayton prepared a statement for Dr. Rhees entitled "The Future of Optics in America." He first analyzed the state of affairs optically for optometry and ophthalmology, and concluded that the United States was up to date and well abreast of European achievement in those fields. Turning to consideration of achievements in applied optics, he drew attention to the facts that although the United States had the largest telescope, the glass had to be imported; that there probably was an over-production of college-trained people, but a scarcity of qualified people interested in the performance of optical instruments because "Americans" seemed to have taken scant interest in teaching and studying geometrical optics. After further discussion, he concluded: "There are very few colleges in this country giving attention to geometrical optics and the theory of optical instruments; amongst them M.I.T. and the University of Rochester are outstanding. The work at the University has only just begun. . . . It would be a severe disappointment . . . if the work at the University of Rochester were to be discontinued or seriously curtailed."

Also in January 1933, Dalton presented to the President the results of a survey he had requested concerning the caliber and geographical distribution of students in applied optics and optometry admitted in the last five years. The results were as follows and bore out the observations of the faculty.

The students admitted to courses in applied optics were on the whole "markedly" superior to those in the men's college as a whole. With regard to geographical distribution: of 31 students enrolled in optometry, only two were from Rochester and seven were from outside New York State, so that optometry was evidently a drawing power for students from outside the city "comparable to the Eastman School of Music." In applied optics, 10 of 19 enrolled students were from outside the city, above the average for the men's college. Rhees, in his 1932–33 Report to the Trustees presented in the spring of 1933, reviewed the history of The Institute of Applied Optics, and drew the attention of the Trustees to Wilkins' report for the year. Rhees announced that the sponsoring companies regarded their financial responsibility for the work of the Institute as terminated, while at the same time expressing a growing confidence in the importance and value of the project. In his will, Mr. Eastman left a great amount to the University. Remembering, Rhees said, Eastman's great interest in starting The Institute of Optics and his continuing interest—he might have added that as a very unwell man, Eastman made a careful tour of the Institute, speaking with each professor, shortly before he died—Rhees expressed the thought that "as much of the work should be carried on as experience proves is specially valuable."

Following considerable discussion with the sponsoring companies, with Columbia University, and with the State Department of Education in Albany, it was decided, judging by recent registrations at both Columbia and Rochester, that one school of optometry in the state was apparently adequate to supply the need and that this should be at Columbia. The closing of the optometry division in The Institute of Optics received considerable attention in the press. The *Campus* (weekly student newspaper) published an article and a very fine editorial explaining the University's reasons and reasonableness in closing the optometry courses, while retaining the courses in applied optics.

Wilkins, in his report submitted to the President for the academic year 1932–33, explained the changes proposed for 1933–34 in view of the Trustees' decision. He presented figures for registration, both in applied optics and optometry, for the years 1929–33. In 1932–33, 32 optometrists were registered, along with 19 students in applied optics, and 153 who attended extension lectures. There were 10 physics graduate students doing their research in optics. Following advice of the Board of Trustees, the Institute enrolled no further freshmen in optometry, but current students were allowed to complete their course.

The syllabus in applied optics was to continue as organized for the next year although more prominence would be given to Fassin's work. Plans were made to exhibit during commencement instruments designed and completed during the previous year for use in research involving optics: a recording microdensitometer, a rotating spark gap, an underwater spark as a source of ultraviolet, an infrared spectrometer, a quartz double monochromator for studies in photochemistry, and a Wilson cloud chamber. Members of the Department of Physics and Chemistry and The Institute of Optics were involved in the design and building of these instruments, and represented excellent early examples of the continuing cooperation and involvement of the Institute with other departments in the University.

Theodolite sighting of stratospheric balloon.

So far about 40 papers had been published by the faculty and their students in various fields. The Institute had cooperated with the medical school in making possible delicate and precise work in a number of fields, including experiments measuring absorption bands, possibly due to vitamin A, and determinations of bile by spectrophotometric methods. In the early 1930s O'Brien and his students began a series of studies on lunar reflection in various regions of the ultraviolet, and concluded that the moon was blanketed with fine dust, now a much more interesting conclusion than at the time in view of recent exploration on the moon itself.

The year 1933–34 was a more eventful year for the Institute's host Department of Physics than for Optics: Professor Henry Lawrence, for 33 years senior professor, retired in 1934 and was succeeded by Lee A. DuBridge. Meanwhile, Professor Wilkins, Acting Director of The Institute of Optics, took six months' sabbatical leave in the second term of the year, and O'Brien became Acting Director of the Institute in his absence. Taylor also took six months' leave of absence to work at Cornell. Thirteen reports of investigations and research were presented at various scientific meetings in 1933–34. It is interesting to note that the double monochromator for infrared refractive indices, designed and calibrated by the Kingslakes, was eventually used at the University by Franz Urbach in the course of his historic development of infrared phosphors during World War II.

O'Brien reported that The Institute of Optics had been requested to undertake, with the Bausch & Lomb Optical Company and the National Bureau of Standards, the spectrographic study of the ultraviolet and of the solar spectrum in connection with the proposed stratospheric flight of the National Geographic Society and the United States Army Air Corp. The stratospheric balloon "Explorer II" ascended to a record height of 72,000 feet from the Black Hills near Rapid City, South Dakota, on November 11, 1935. The flight was witnessed by O'Brien and Fassin, who ran an experiment on the flight to measure the vertical distribution of ozone in the upper atmosphere. On the same flight, Wilkins provided equipment to study cosmic-ray tracks on film.

In the late 1930s O'Brien set up an evaporating unit for metallizing mirrors, and when later the thin-film anti-reflection coatings were introduced, he adapted his machine for this purpose. Later his students made many successful films with this simple equipment.

4. Optometry and the University of Rochester: 1917–1936

Hilda Kingslake

Optometry is that branch of applied optics limited to measurement and correction by means of spectacles, of abnormal refraction of the eye. Unwittingly optometry played a vital role in crystallizing the final decision by the University of Rochester to found without further delay an Institute of Applied Optics.

In 1917 Ernest Petry, self-appointed Dean of the Rochester School of Optometry which he founded in 1911 or 1912, contacted Dr. Rhees with regard to the problem confronting his school of a hundred students and six faculty members. In 1908 the State of New York, following the lead of other states, began to regulate the practice of optometry, thereby placing small private optometry schools in considerable jeopardy. Rhees had at least some knowledge of this School of Optometry, for in his 1916–17 Presidential Report he stated: "I have to report the resignation of Assistant Professor Howard D. Minchin, who has accepted the position of President of the Rochester School of Optometry. Professor Minchin came to the University as Instructor in Astronomy and Physics in 1903. Since 1906 he has been Assistant Professor. In recent years he has interested himself increasingly in the rapidly developing profession of optometry. The representatives of that profession in Rochester have recognized that interest in the honorable appointment to which they have called him." Minchin was at that time in good standing in the world of optics in Rochester, for he was a charter member and serving on the council of the young Association for the Advancement of Applied Optics. He was also a charter member of the more recent Optical Society of America.

In 1923 another State law was passed whereby on and after January 1930 all newly qualified optometrists in New York State had to be graduates, B.S. or B.A., of a recognized university and certified in optometry. In the early 1920s an M.S. alumnus and Assistant in Physics, Gordon H. Gliddon, became a part-time teacher in physical optics at the Rochester School of Optometry while holding a regular job at Eastman Kodak Company. It would seem that the School of Optometry was trying to strengthen the academic standing of its faculty. However this 1923 law doomed the separate existence of such schools, and conversations between the University and Petry were accelerated. The subject, very understandably, also became a matter for discussion with regard to the proposed Institute of Applied Optics. Since optometrists qualifying in 1930 had to have a university degree, it was necessary that they enter as freshmen in 1926, becoming seniors in 1929–30.

Rhees, interested as always in all useful knowledge, persevered, consulting with Southall of Columbia where some teaching in optometry was already offered, with departments in his own University with the State of New York, and with A. E. C. Drescher and Adolph Lomb of the Bausch & Lomb Company. Even so, more years elapsed before the final decision in 1928 to found an Institute of Applied Optics.

Between 1923 and 1925 the University, through the Dean of the College of Arts and Science, the Treasurer, and others concerned, came to an agreement with regard to such matters as curriculum for optometry, transfer of equipment, and use of the faculty of the School of Optometry. In 1926 most of Petry's equipment was temporarily moved from its quarters at 38 South Washington Street to the Carnegie Building for Applied Science on the Prince Street campus, and two members of the faculty—Ernest Petry himself and his instructor in optical shop work, Herbert E. Wilder—were retained to teach their own specialties.

The following information was given on page 105 of the 1926–27 Annual Catalog of the University, in the section on courses for the bachelor's degree and under the title of Optics: "It is the intention of the College to develop advanced work in optical theory and practice as part of the work of the department of physics. A first step in this direction is the

Herbert Wilder, optical shop instructor.

organization of a course which will enable students to meet the requirements of the State of New York for registered optometrists." The Bulletin described the requirement of the State laws for optometry, and the sequence of courses that was to be offered by the University to obtain the necessary degree of B.S. in Optometry. It further stated that only freshmen would be admitted in 1926–27 in optometry. Exactly the same notice appeared in the 1927–28 Annual Catalog of the College of Arts and Science. Ernest Petry and

Members of the first class in Optometry.

Herbert Wilder were listed in both years among the faculty as, respectively, Lecturer in Optometry and Instructor in Optometry.

Plans for an Institute of Applied Optics began to move ahead again, now under considerable pressure since the University was admitting freshmen students in optometry who would need lectures and laboratory work in geometrical and physical optics at least by 1929. The history of the years 1926–36 are recorded in the following chapter on The Founding of The Institute of Applied Optics. A total of 40 students had obtained the degree of B.S. in optometry when the department was closed in 1936, at which time all teaching in optometry in New York State was concentrated at Columbia University. Several of our optometry alumni have a fine record of service and contribution to the University of Rochester.

5. Jane Dewey: Pioneer in Quantum Optics

Carlos Stroud

The newly founded Institute for Applied Optics at the University of Rochester is not a place that you would expect to find a woman who was an expert in the emerging discipline of quantum mechanics. After all quantum mechanics is not usually listed among the subfields of applied optics, and the University of Rochester did not formally eliminate its separate Women's College and become truly coeducational until 1955—twenty-six years later. But, as unlikely as it might seem, there on the list of faculty of the Institute for the year 1929–1930 is Jane Dewey, special lecturer in quantum and wave mechanics.

Jane Dewey was certainly well qualified for the position. Born in 1900, she received her bachelors degree from Barnard College of Columbia University in 1922, and her Ph.D. in physical chemistry in 1925 working with F. G. Keys at Massachusetts Institute of Technology. She followed this with two years of postdoctoral studies at the Institute for Advanced Studies in Copenhagen, Denmark, working with Nobel Laureate Niels Bohr and Werner Heisenberg. She then studied with Professor Karl Compton at Princeton as one of the first group of National Research Council postdoctoral fellows. In 1929 Schrödinger's wave equation was only three years old, Einstein and Bohr were in the process of carrying out their famous debates on the interpretation of the new theory, and the new Institute had lectures by a woman who was one of the few scientists in the country competent to teach the subject, and almost definitely the only woman in the country who was so qualified.

In September 1929 Jane Dewey arrived in Rochester accompanied by her father, the famous educational philosopher John Dewey, and her husband, Alston Clark. Her husband, also a physicist, was a student at Cornell University, and the lectureship in Rochester was apparently the closest job that she could find. The "two-body problem" that plagues modern professional couples was an important factor in her life. Her father commented on his impressions of Rochester in a letter to his other daughter, Louise Romig.[1]

> Rochester is a nice town and they are developing the University—Kodak Eastman [sic] has given them 23 million dollars, and they have a new medical school—buildings alone cost 2 million.

Jane's appointment was described by University of Rochester President Rush Rhees in his 1929 annual report to the Board of Trustees as " being under the direction of the department of Geology assisted by several other departments upon the problem of the development of the technique of the quartz spectrograph to determine in small quantities the chemical substances not normally looked for in chemical compounds and to apply this technique to certain minerals."[2] She was actually working under the direction of T. R. Wilkins, the acting director of the Institute of Applied Optics. She reports in a letter to her father a few days after she arrived:[3]

> . . . I'm fairly well settled but not working very hard. In time I think they will start me a class of some kind, I spoke to Wilkins—my boss—about it and he said that not all members

of the department were here and he wanted to get them together on what advanced work would be given. I think he wants it to be in the Institute of Applied Optics rather than the physics department. This is not a place where you get up anything yourself, I wanted some apparatus moved and the mover declined to move it without Wilkins say so. He was very polite about it but that is what it came down to. Everything I want, no matter how slight has to be ordered through Wilkins. I have a swell office—filled with junk—but facing southeast and with three windows, but I declined to work in the room my apparatus is in as it is hermetically sealed. They said they would put in ventilation but I have seen no signs of it. I wanted to move the apparatus into my office but they preferred to put in ventilation, or said they did, we'll see what happens. Fortunately Wilkins is very good natured and has no intention of being domineering—he just runs everything because he can't imagine any other way of doing things.

This disagreement concerning laboratory space is not entirely unknown in modern universities, but it appears to be a sign of things to come. She left the University of Rochester in 1931 to join the faculty of Bryn Mawr College as assistant professor of physics. There she was soon promoted to associate professor and assumed the chairmanship of the Physics Department, but her marriage with Alston Clark broke up, and she applied for a leave due to health problems. Bryn Mawr then replaced her with a male professor. This was the deepest part of the Depression so that she was unemployed for four years until she landed a part-time evening teaching position at Hunter College in 1940. During the war she held an industrial position at U.S. Rubber Company, and then joined the staff of the Army's Aberdeen Proving Grounds where she remained until she retired.

While she was in the Institute she published one experimental paper based on the work that she had done at Princeton.[4] It is perhaps ironic that her interests in semiclassical approximations to wave equations and the Stark effect in highly excited atoms would put her in the center of intellectual activity today, as Professors Alonso, Bigelow, Eberly, and Stroud are all currently working on closely related problems.

References

I would like to acknowledge the assistance of Harriet Furst Simon of the Center for Dewey Studies of the Southern Illinois University and Donald Glassman of the Barnard College Archives for assistance in gathering materials for this essay.

1   Letter from John Dewey to Louise Romig dated September 21, 1929 in the Center for Dewey Studies of Southern Illinois University, Carbondale, IL 62901.

2   Annual Reports of the President and Treasurer to the Board of Trustees of the University of Rochester, Rochester, NY 1929, pp 11–12.

3   Letter from Jane Dewey Clark to John Dewey (undated) in Center for Dewey Studies of Southern Illinois University, Carbondale, IL 62901.

4   Jane M. Dewey, "The Intensity Maxima in the Continuous Spectrum of Helium," *Phys. Rev.* 35, 155 (1930).

6. In Memory of Hilda and Rudolf Kingslake: Two Lives Devoted to Optics*

Brian J. Thompson

Hilda and Rudolf Kingslake died within two weeks of each other in February 2003. Hilda died on February 14, two days before her 101st birthday, at the Episcopal Church Home in Rochester, N.Y. She had been ill for a number of years. Rudolf died February 25 at age 99, also at the Episcopal Church Home. They had been together in early life as students since 1921 and together in marriage since 1929. They both had every confidence that they would be together now.

Hilda Gertrude Conrady was born in London, England, on February 16, 1902. She was the eldest daughter of Alexander Eugen and Annie Conrady (née Bunney). A. E. Conrady, as he was usually called, was professor of optical design in the newly established Technical Optics Department of the Royal College of Science, a unit of the Imperial College of Science and Technology in London. (At home and amongst friends, Conrady used his middle name, Eugen.) Hilda was part of the first full-time class in the Technical Optics Department program. She studied under her father and was part of the first graduating class in 1923. Hilda continued her work in optics in the department as a research scholar. While there, she published regularly on such topics as the Foucault knife-edge test and primary spherical aberration, in journals including the *Transactions of the Optical Society (GB)*, *Proceedings of the Optical Conferences* (e.g., 1926), and the *Photographic Journal*. The authorship, in the style of the time, was "Miss H. G. Conrady, A.R.C.S. D.I.C." Later, after her marriage to Rudolf, she would sign Hilda Kingslake née Conrady and, much later, Hilda Conrady Kingslake.

The Kingslakes attending a workshop.

---

*This obituary was originally published in *Optics and Photonics News* **14**, 10 (2003), and is reprinted here with permission.

Hilda Kingslake, November 1979.

Rudolf Kingslake was born Rudolf Klickmann August 28, 1903, to Martin and Margaret Klickmann (née Higham). He was the eldest of five children. Martin Klickmann changed the family name to Kingslake May 15, 1917. (Rudolf in reminiscing told me that the boys at school used to call him "Queenspond"!) After being educated in private schools, Rudolf attended Imperial College in the same program that Hilda had already enrolled in and thus came under the tutelage of Professor Conrady. Hilda, with a twinkle in her eyes, never let Rudolf forget that he graduated the year after she did, and that she carried the Conrady genes. What a team to carry forward, and significantly expand on, the Conrady tradition of optical design. Rudolf graduated with his bachelor's degree in 1924 and earned his master's degree in 1926. In 1950 he was awarded a doctor of science. After graduation in 1926, he continued for another year as a Beit Fellow before joining Sir Howard Grubb, Parsons and Co., in Newcastle-on-Tyne, as an optical designer. After that he moved to the International Standard Electric Co. in London.

Rudolf Kingslake with a mechanical calculator at the Eastman House Museum.

A major turning point in both their lives and careers occurred when the president of the University of Rochester, Rush Rhees, visited England in the early summer of 1929, specifically to recruit faculty members for The Institute of Optics. Rhees entertained, interviewed, and successfully recruited Rudolf to the Institute over dinner at Brown's Hotel. The appointment as assistant professor of geometrical optics and optical design was confirmed by the board of trustees June 15, 1929, on the recommendation of the president, who wrote: "He [Rudolf] has published eight papers in the Transactions of the Optical Society (G.B.) and elsewhere. By training and experience he is admirably fitted to contribute to the development and significance of our new enterprise."

The Kingslakes were married September 14, 1929. They sailed to America, arrived in Rochester, and started their 74-year careers of exceptional and distinguished service to the field of optical science and engineering and to the professional international community of scholars. Their many contributions to the life of the University and to the greater Rochester community are well regarded, recognized and documented.

Rudolf had a lifelong career in association with The Institute of Optics and developed the teaching materials for the first courses in lens design and geometrical optics formally offered in the United States. He served the University as a full-time faculty member until 1937, when he joined Eastman Kodak as head of the Lens Design Department at the invitation of Dr. Mees, head of Kodak Research Laboratories. For the first year, Rudolf divided his time between The Institute of Optics and Eastman Kodak; he continued as a part-time professor until well into his eighties. The year before his move to Kodak, the Kingslakes spent a sabbatical at Imperial College under an exchange arrangement that brought L. C. Martin to Rochester. With Rudolf's unusual sense of humor, he said, "Martin and I exchanged jobs, houses, and cars . . . but not wives." It is worth noting that L. C. Martin "communicated" Hilda's first paper in the *Transactions of the Optical Society (GB)* in 1924.

The Kingslakes made separate and joint contributions to the development of optics and to the literature, particularly through publications in the various journals of the Optical Society of America. Both were made fellows of the society. Rudolf was elected president in 1947–48, and later became an honorary member of OSA. In 1973 he was awarded the Ives Medal. Both Kingslakes received awards and commendations from many civic and professional societies. In particular, Rudolf received major awards from the Society of Motion Picture and Television Engineers (SMPTE), the International Society for Optical Engineering (SPIE), the Society for Photographic Scientists and Engineers (SPSE, now the Society for Imaging Science and Technology), and the Rochester Engineering Society.

Hilda's technical papers are still cited and have lasting value. Her insightful contributions on the history of our field are equally valuable, including her *Fifty-Year History of the Optical Society of America 1916–1966* and *The First Fifty Years, The Institute of Optics 1929–1979*, together with its sequel, *The Institute*

Hilda Kingslake was active in community life in Rochester, founding a library service for shut-ins. She was known as the "Book Lady".

The Kingslakes and six Directors of the Institute: M. P. Givens, R. L. Hopkins, L. W. Hyde, B. J. Thompson, K. J. Teegarden, and N. George.

of Optics 1929–1987. Finally, I return to another important joint publication in *Applied Optics* titled "Alexander Eugen Conrady 1866–1944."

Professor Conrady had published part one of his book, *Applied Optics and Optical Design,* in 1929, but was not able to complete the second part before his death. However he left a well-advanced, handwritten manuscript that the Kingslakes were able to use to complete part two. It was published in 1960, "edited and completed by Dr. Rudolf Kingslake," and containing a foreword by Hilda G. Conrady Kingslake.

Several generations of full- and part-time students in The Institute of Optics, attendees at summer schools in Rochester and at courses around the country and abroad have benefited from Rudolf's teachings. Many others have benefited from the excellent expository writing in his lecture notes and many books, including *Lenses in Photography, Lens Design Fundamentals, Optical System Design* and *A History of the Photographic Lens.* In addition, there is enduring value in the edited multi-volume series *Applied Optics and Optical Engineering: A Comprehensive Treatise.*

Rudolf and Hilda Kingslake were warm, friendly, modest and caring. They retained their senses of humor throughout their lives. At an 80th birthday celebration, Rudolf said, "There is nothing special about being 80—after all, anyone can have an 80th birthday, all they have to do is live long enough." Finally, there is Kingslake's first law: "In optics it is easy to do something roughly but very difficult to do it well." Rudolf and Hilda, you both did it exceptionally well.

Brian J. Thompson has been a member of the faculty of the University of Rochester since 1968. He served as Director of the Institute of Optics from 1968 until 1975. He is currently Provost Emeritus of the University of Rochester, Rochester, NY.

7. A Little Fun on the Side

Carlos Stroud

The traditions that were established in the new Institute of Applied Optics were not all of the academic sort. One of the earliest social traditions was the optics picnic. Initially, the Institute was rather small and closely tied to the Department of Physics, so annual picnics were held jointly. These early picnics looked like something out of an old English movie with the ladies in long dresses and the gentlemen in coats and ties. The meals were set with silver and china. A picnic tradition was started that still is eagerly celebrated today, albeit in a somewhat changed form. By the 1970s the picnics had lost their formality, but were attended by everyone even remotely connected with the Institute. The setting was the campground on George Fraley's place in Mendon. In that period the newest faculty member in the department was responsible for organizing the fall picnic each year, and each did his best to out-do his predecessor. There were faculty-student touch football games, volleyball, softball, horse shoes, Frisbees, and even a demonstration cricket match. The food gradually became more elaborate, graduating from hamburgers, to chicken, to elaborate barbecues with pork and beef turning on spits above in-ground pits.

A number of memorable events occurred at these picnics. There was a famous tortoise-hare race between graduate students Mary Citron and Eric Krisl that is described in a separate essay in this volume. Another occurred in September 1976 when the Rochester winter got an unusually early start. A canvas screened tent was set up to protect the food from the weather and insects, but it proved an inadequate shelter against the sudden gust of wind and rain that descended just as dinner was served. The tent was crowded with people filling their plates from the contributed dishes when a violent gust pulled loose the guy ropes and the tent began to collapse. Brian Thompson, newly promoted to dean of the

Optics-Physics Picnic, June 1934.

Bonfire at the Optics Picnic at Fraley's campground.

*Dean Brian Thompson saves the picnic by holding
up the tent pole.*

College of Engineering and Applied Science, proved equal to the occasion, grabbing the falling central support pole and holding up the tent until the ropes could be reattached. It was not the first or the last problem that dropped from the sky demanding his urgent attention during the period he served as director, dean, and provost.

Perhaps the premiere social events in the history of the city of Rochester were George Eastman's Sunday afternoon parties at his mansion on East Avenue. Soon after Rudolf

Duncan Moore serves up corn at the Optics Picnic.

Volleyball at the Optics Picnic 1974.

and Hilda Kingslake arrived in Rochester, they received an invitation to attend one of these gatherings. Rudolf described to me how they arrived at the grand side entry and were ushered in to meet Mr. Eastman standing at the bottom of the grand staircase greeting his couple hundred guests. Soon after the party began, Eastman, with a few of his closest male friends, vanished upstairs to partake in a poker game while the other assembled guests enjoyed a musical performance in the living room below.

Another interesting social institution active at the University in the 1930s was the X Club. Frederick Seitz, then a young assistant professor in the physics department, and later serving in many roles including president of Rockefeller University, describes in his autobiography the function of this club. He points out that at that time, the University was rapidly changing its character from a local undergraduate teaching school to a national research university. Most of the senior faculty had been hired as teachers with heavy course loads and little opportunity to carry out original research. The new younger faculty were given lighter teaching loads and expected to carry out top-level research. The senior faculty continued to have heavy teaching loads. Not surprisingly, there was some tension in social situations. Several of the younger faculty from many different disciplines joined together to form a club which met regularly with their wives for an evening lecture and social gathering. Brian O'Brien and Seitz were both members of this group.

8. Years of Change: 1934–1939

Hilda Kingslake

The years from 1934 through 1939 were years of great change, not only for The Institute of Applied Optics but also for the University. Dr. Rhees in 1933 expressed his wish to retire. He was 73 years old and had been President for 33 remarkable years. However, he continued in office until 1935, when Alan Valentine was appointed. The first major change for The Institute of Optics was, of course, the termination of the courses in optometry. The class of 1936 was the last to graduate, six in number. Ernest Petry's work with the University was concluded at the end of the 1935–36 year, but Herbert Wilder continued to have charge of the glass workshop until his retirement in 1938. Wilkins paid great tribute to Petry in his 1932–33 Report to the President, drawing attention to his long service to optometry and education. Petry died in 1960 and Wilder in 1953. Had he been able to look into the future, Wilkins would also have reported that several of the 40 optometry graduates had become immensely loyal to the University, giving outstandingly of their time, their funds, and their labor in University campaigns.

The first change in the faculty of applied optics came when A. M. Taylor resigned at the end of the 1933–34 year to return to England. He finally became head of the physics department at Southampton University; he died in May 1979, aged 76. His place was taken by J. Stuart Campbell (Ph.D. Caltech), whose particular interest was vacuum ultraviolet spectroscopy. Unfortunately, he died suddenly in September 1939. C. L. Critchfield, with similar interests, filled the unexpected gap for 1939–40, after which F. W. Paul was appointed Instructor; later to become Assistant Professor of physical optics. His major interest was infrared spectroscopy, and he continued with the University until 1947, working with O'Brien throughout the war.

Physics and Optics faculty and graduate students, 1934.

During the academic year 1936–37, L. C. Martin, on the faculty of the Department of Technical Optics at the Imperial College in London, changed places with Kingslake. Martin was a physicist appointed in 1917 to be lecturer in physical optics and to take charge of the laboratories, a most important part of any department at Imperial College. He had several great interests in optics: color vision, instrumental optics, physical optics, and the nature of the optical image. While here, he gave a course of extension lectures on general optics which was well attended. He is known to many in Rochester because of several books he has published.

On returning to Rochester for the 1937–38 term, much to Kingslake's consternation he was invited by Dr. Mees, head of the Kodak Research Laboratories, to succeed the aging head of the lens design department at Kodak. Because he was loath to leave the University and his work at The Institute of Optics, Kingslake's first reaction was to refuse. Thinking it over, however, he realized that in fact his industrial experience was lamentably brief—that more than anything else, he needed experience in industry for greater competence in teaching an applied subject. Reluctantly, he explained matters to Wilkins and Valentine. It was decided that he would teach prescribed courses as part-time lecturer for the year 1937–38, giving half of his time to Kodak and half to the University.

In 1938, O'Brien was appointed Director of The Institute of Optics, thereby, as President Valentine reported, "providing us with settled administrative leadership for that promising branch of the College." He followed the announcement with half a page of appreciative remarks for Wilkins' very fine directing of the Institute through its early years, so ably that appointment of a permanent administrator was delayed longer than originally contemplated. Wilkins died very suddenly two years later in December 1940.

In this same 1938–39 report, Dean DuBridge stated that The Institute of Optics was being further developed under O'Brien, but that "the Institute is severely handicapped by its inability to locate an adequately trained man to take over the work of Mr. Rudolf Kingslake. The latter, however, is continuing to give as much of this work as his new duties at Kodak allow. This is another illustration," DuBridge continued, "of the unique importance of the work of the Institute, since no other place in the country offers training comparable in this important field." Kingslake was appointed part-time associate professor and gave courses in his own specialty, lens design and system design. DuBridge could not know, nor could anyone else, that a man later to become not only distinguished in geometrical optics and lens design but also a pillar of The Institute of Optics, R. E. Hopkins, was at that moment one of the young M.S. graduate students in the Institute.

DuBridge, in his 1938–39 report, also regretted that the large room in engineering, lent since 1930 for the optics glass shop, had to be vacated to make room for the new Department of Chemical Engineering. The glass shop was moved to the basement of the Library. In 1938, there was another major change in the faculty: Gustave Fassin left town to join another company and so had to relinquish his superb teaching of instrument design at the University. He was a great personality, and his loss was a serious one for the Institute.

In 1939, the last of a series of greater and lesser changes was made: the Institute, so far known as The Institute of Applied Optics, was to be simply "The Institute of Optics," reflecting O'Brien's hope that its program would be inclusive of all optical knowledge, with a correspondingly wide program of research.

Soon after becoming Director, O'Brien took part in interview-type University broadcasts over the radio. He managed to weave in the history of The Institute of Optics, its uniqueness, its range of courses, its equipment, and the fact that the demand for graduates exceeded the supply.

The Annual Report for 1939 submitted by Dean DuBridge drew attention to the "distinguished work" of O'Brien and his students. A grant had been received from the Civil Aeronautics Authority (CAA) for research on problems of vision and flying. Other agencies of the government, both civil and military, were consulting him. The students were also working on a cooperative program with the Smithsonian Institution on measurements of the sun's ultraviolet radiation, and radio-equipped balloons were sent up regularly to the stratosphere for these measurements. Some measurements were made at lower altitudes by airplane, with O'Brien both piloting and making the observations. These experiments provided problems and instruction for both graduate and undergraduate students.

The Institute of Optics
Faculty 1929–1939

Berry, William, 1929–33
Campbell, J. Stuart, 1935–40
Clark, Herbert A., 1938–43
Dewey, Jane, 1929–30
Fairbanks, Floyd C., 1929–30
Fassin, Gustave, 1930–40
Greenwood, Gilbert, 1929–30
Hood, J. Douglas, 1929–30
Jones, Lloyd A., 1929–43
Kingslake, Rudolf, 1929–2003
Kurtz, Henry, 1930–32, 1935–36
Lowry, Earl M., 1929–30
Luckiesh, M., 1930–31

Martin, L. C., 1936–38
Mees, C. E. Kenneth, 1929–43
Moss, F. K., 1930–31
Murlin, John R., 1929–32
Nitchie, Charles, 1934–35
O'Brien, Brian, 1930–55
Petry, Ernest, 1929–36
Rayton, Wilbur B., 1929–31
Sedgwick, H. Jobe, 1930–34
Taylor, A. Maurice, 1929–34
Wilder, Herbert E., 1929–39
Wilkins, T. Russell, 1929–39

The Institute of Optics
Degrees Awarded 1930–1939

Allen, Arthur W., B.S.*, 1933
Allyn, William G., B.S.*, 1934
Armstrong, A. G., B.S.*, 1932
Aronson, Casper J., B.S., 1938; M.S., 1939
Beel, William E., B.S.*, 1934
Benford, James R., B.S., 1935
Bergmann, Cedric O., B.S.*, 1932
Bickel, Edward E., B.S., 1939
Bingham, W. J., B.S.*, 1934
Burrage, R. R., B.S.*, 1930
Chamberlin, J. C., B.S.*, 1931
Craytor, Russell E., B.S.*, 1935
Denton, Arthur H., B.S.*, 1936
Eggleston, John N., B.S.*, 1930
Elliott, Theodore F., B.S.*, 1936
Erckert, S. D., B.S.*, 1930
Estes, Cameron B., B.S., 1938
Evans, John C., B.S., 1939
Evans, Preston G., B.S.*, 1932
Feinberg, Richard, B.S.*, 1933
Fortmiller, Louis J., B.S., 1938
Gienke, E L., B.S.*, 1933
Goldstein, David G., B.S., 1939
Griswold, Mack D., B.S., 1935
Hart, James C., B.S.*, 1935
Harvey, James E., B.S., 1939
Hathaway, F. M., B.S.*, 1931
Hildreth, L. E., B.S.*, 1933
Hoadley, H. Orio, B.S., 1935
Hopkins, Robert E., M.S., 1939; Ph.D., 1945
Hudak, Robert J., B.S., 1939

Hussong, Harold E., B.S., 1935
Hutchings, Franklyn C., B.S.*, 1935
Ingalls, Arthur L., B.S., 1932
Johnson, Fred W., B.S., 1938
Johnson, J. R., B.S.*, 1935
Juengst, W. C., B.S.*, 1936
Levy, S. H., B.S.*, 1933
Lewis, C. P., B.S.*, 1934
Litten, Walter, B.S., 1936
London, Mortimer A., B.S., 1937
Margaretten, Elias J., B.S.*, 1933
Marshall, Henry S., B.S.*, 1934
Milligan, F. H., B.S., 1934
Orden, Alex, B.S., 1937
Orser, W. D., B.S., 1934
Perkins, R. F., B.S.*, 1936
Porter, Melbourne J., B.S.*, 1932
Quick, H. E., B.S.*, 1935
Rogers, Howard F., B.S., 1936
Schiller, A., B.S.*, 1933
Strebel, Gustave A., B.S.*, 1936
Suter, Walter J., B.S., 1934
Tupper, J. L., B.S., 1933
Veit, M. C., B.S.*, 1934
Vermilya, E. B., B.S.*, 1933
Warren, C. D., B.S.*, 1936
Warren, Franklin A., B.S.*, 1934
Weinstein, Jacob D., B.S.*, 1933
Wersinger, R. E., B.S.*, 1935
West, Cedric F., B.S.*, 1935
Weston, Frederick C., B.S.*, 1934
Williams, David L., B.S., 1937
Williams, J. C., B.S.*, 1934

* Degree awarded in Optometry.

PART II

War Years: The 1940s

II. War Years: The 1940s

The Institute of Optics was barely ten years old as the world entered the 1940s with the war already raging in Europe and the United States teetering on the edge of joining the conflict. It was clear to many people that the country would not long be able to stay aloof from the war, and that when we entered, optics would be an essential technology. Brian O'Brien moved quickly to position the new Institute which he directed to play a central role in providing the technology needed. As we will see in the series of essays in this section, the Institute was indeed at the center of optical development during war, with some fifty scientists, engineers, students, and technicians developing new instruments that played important roles in many battles. Hilda Kingslake's provides us with a background of people and chronology, and then a series of essays gives us a more detailed and personal view.

Most of the research was carried out under the support and aegis of the National Defense Research Committee. Brian O'Brien, Fordyce Tuttle, and Wilbur Rayton were all members of Division 16 of the NDRC. In chapter 10 we have excerpts from the official report of NDRC recounting the many contributions made by the Rochester group. Chapter 14 is Brian O'Brien's personal recounting of how this small group in the Institute essentially initiated the whole science of night warfare. Chapter 15 is another remarkable account of how young Ensign Brian O'Brien Jr. used the high-speed streak camera developed by his father and co-workers to take pictures of the first A-bomb test at Bikini Atoll in the Pacific from a vantage point just three miles from ground zero! Other essays give personal accounts by two long-time employees of the Institute of their memories of life in the Institute during and after the war. We also include an excerpt from a spy thriller that gives quite a different account of life on the fourth floor of Bausch & Lomb during the war.

9. Brian O'Brien in War and Peace: 1940–1953

Hilda Kingslake

World War II provided The Institute of Optics with its first opportunity to prove its strength. O'Brien had foreseen the war and was in communication with government agencies in an effort to avoid the serious shortages that occurred during World War I of optical devices and the personnel able to cope with them.

By the end of 1940, The Institute of Optics was already involved with optical problems for government agencies; by the end of the academic year 1941–42, it was becoming more and more deeply involved. Valentine reported to the Trustees "extraordinary demands for direct war service through scientific research. The extent to which he (O'Brien) and the Institute have been able to meet these demands is most impressive. Every effort has been made to maintain normal teaching programs and undergraduate instruction." New courses and a somewhat altered program of study to suit the likely demands of graduating students going into industry war work were introduced. Research students were guided into directions of study of military usefulness. O'Brien managed somehow to cope with an abnormal number of undergraduate students. A few especially appropriate undergraduate courses rendered important by conditions of wartime government needs were substituted for some of the scheduled courses. In 1943, Fordyce Tuttle, later to be assisted by W. Ewald, both from Eastman Kodak Company, began giving very fine evening courses on instrument design.

At the height of activity, some 50 people—scientists, technicians, machinists, research students, and others—were involved in the Institute's program of cooperation with the government, combined with student instruction and research. R. E. Hopkins, first as a young instructor with a B.S. from M.I.T. who had just received his M.S. in The Institute of Optics and later as an assistant professor, was O'Brien's right-hand man for lens design and geometrical optics. Other faculty were Fred Paul, Harold Stewart, Hobert W. French, and John W. Evans. When the NDRC (National Defense Research Committee) was established, O'Brien became associated with section 16.1 on optical instruments. This association began in December 1942 and continued to January 1946. One interesting and historic episode concerned the work on infrared phosphors for night vision devices. The search began for someone who knew how to make infrared-sensitive phosphors. O'Brien thought of Franz Urbach, the recently escaped Viennese expert, but had no idea of his whereabouts. DuBridge told him that Urbach was working in the physics department! He was quietly transferred to The Institute of Optics, where he produced some of the much-needed phosphors, and the development of a series of "metascopes" for night vision by the armed forces became possible—another example of good cooperation between The Institute of Optics and other departments, which has made possible many interesting programs of study.

In 1948, Albert Noyes of the department of chemistry and Brian O'Brien of The Institute of Optics were awarded The Medal of Merit by President Truman, the highest

Portrait of Brian O'Brien by famed photographer Ansel Adams.

civilian award given by the government. O'Brien, his very small faculty, his students, and staff had indeed proved the strength of The Institute of Optics.

In 1947, O'Brien reported to President Valentine on the war effort: he estimated that the Institute had "spent" about one million dollars on the war effort, including overhead allowances to the University. The number of undergraduate students actually increased sharply during most of the war. The fact that courses were tied to the war effort may have given young men a willingness to go on with their studies in preference to more direct war

Brian O'Brien shows Gordon Milne the Icaroscope.

service. Foreseeing extensive involvement in the war, O'Brien had decided to accept no more graduate students for the duration. Five master's degrees and two Ph.D.s were awarded to students already enrolled and who completed their work. The Institute emerged from the war with great momentum but, nevertheless, considerably out of line with the general scheme of things in a university. O'Brien had a very small faculty: only one full-time full professor and a few junior faculty.

Discussions between the administration and interested leaders of industry were revived in 1943, and it was decided that the Institute must go on and should again be assisted with support and grants to students. In 1950, the funding amounted to some $30,000, making possible a greatly enlarged program.

Projects do not automatically come to a close when peace is declared. There remain many half-completed assignments, many good ideas to be further developed. Moreover, scientific personnel in universities connected with the war discovered how much could be achieved by concerted effort and the sharing of different kinds of knowledge and expertise. They had also found out how to finance research students, obtain expensive equipment, supplement university income, and finance attendance at professional meetings. It was indeed a stimulating and challenging time for scholars, and a trying period for university administrations, a complete change of ways and means for the faculty.

Continuing his 1947 report, O'Brien stated that as a result of the war work there had been many requests from government and industries that The Institute of Optics undertake various research programs. He found these projects stimulating for both faculty and students, but realized that too many could affect the quality of teaching and pure research and that a fair balance must be achieved. He expressed the hope that his faculty could be augmented to attract more students, for the graduates were in great demand. Actually, O'Brien was much more interested in guiding research and advanced degree students than in the tiresome details of undergraduate instruction.

A major appointment was made at this time, that of M. Parker Givens, a Ph.D. from Cornell who became one of the great teachers of The Institute of Optics. Competent in many aspects of physical optics, in later years he became interested in holography and modern optics in general. A year later, O'Brien was able to report a most gratifying rise in student registration. Fourteen, he said, should be graduating in 1948, and the total student enrollment was 53, about equally divided through the classes. The demand for graduates at all levels continued to exceed the supply. Among the 18 candidates for M.S. degrees were six regular army officers.

O'Brien referred to two remarkable cameras developed and designed by members of The Institute of Optics since the war. One was started in the closing years of the war by Professor Hopkins and Donald Feder. It was a six inch f/1 lens for night aerial work, giving excellent definition over a curved surface, the film being curved by compressed air between the lens and the film.

Another development was a high-speed camera, first used for observations at the Bikini bomb test, later much improved to make rapid sequences of pictures at speeds up to 20 million frames per second. It was first described at a meeting of the Society of Motion

High speed camera with f/1 lens, curved field, and six inch focal length.

Picture Engineers in 1949. It appealed to the public and received a great deal of publicity, both here and abroad.

Sponsored research and consulting work continued unabated. It seemed impossible to avoid it and had become a way of life. However, controls protecting the faculty, the students, and the University had become necessary. In 1945, a coordinator of research was appointed by the administration to handle all contracts between units of the University and industry, government, or other second parties. The coordinator also presented University needs to foundations and corporations.

Early in his directorship, O'Brien had expressed the intention of keeping the teaching in The Institute of Optics both broad and deep, with adequate theory for both pure and applied work. In keeping with this policy, he appointed David Dexter, already known for his studies in solid state theory. At the time, it was a very forward-looking appointment and an extension of the program of the Institute, a move frowned on by the more conservative of the faculty.

Meanwhile, O'Brien himself became more and more absorbed in problems of government and industry. He finally resigned to take a senior appointment in industry. Later he became entirely independent, but surely never retired! The Institute and its students of the period have much to thank him for.

R. E. Hopkins expressed a very strong conviction in a question-and-answer article in *Optics News:*

> It is my opinion that Brian O'Brien saved The Institute of Optics from extinction. It never could have survived the period just before, during, and five years after the war without him. He was a superb engineer who was able to pick significant problems in optics. His post-war work on solar radiation and the ozone layer was way ahead of his time. His vision research was deep. He did all he could to strengthen activities in geometrical optics, thin films, photometry, and radiometry. He managed to get support and encourage those fields where funds were very difficult to come by.
>
> During the war he really came into his own. He had the ability to inspire a group to enjoy and put out extra effort to accomplish something. He recognized the importance of solid-state physics to optics.

10. National Defense Research Committee

Carlos Stroud

Federal government support for research in optics during the first half of the 1940s was supervised by the National Defense Research Committee, and in particular following reorganization in December 1942, by Division 16 (Optics and Camouflage) of the NDRC. Division 16 was headed by George Harrison. The work of this organization in support of the war effort is nicely documented in a volume titled *Applied Physics: Electronics; Optics; Metallurgy*, edited by C. G. Suits and George R. Harrison (Little, Brown and Company, Boston, 1948). The section on optics, edited by Harrison, describes in some detail the defense-related optics research that was carried out with support from Division 16. The contract under which the book was published explicitly placed rights in the public domain after 1958 so we will excerpt some of the relevant sections to show the role that work in the Institute played in the war effort.

The division was subdivided into four sections: 16.1—Optical Instruments, 16.3—Camouflage, 16.4—Infrared, 16.5—Illumination and Vision. (The missing Section 16.2 was combined with 16.5 early on.) The whole division was directed by a committee whose chief was George Harrison, and whose members included Brian O'Brien and Fordyce Tuttle from the Institute. Brian O'Brien also served as deputy chief of Section 16.5 and Wilbur Rayton served as a member. O'Brien and Tuttle also served on the Committee for Division 17 (Physics).

Harrison begins by reviewing the situation with respect to conventional optical instrumentation:

> While Pearl Harbor found the United States poorly prepared in many respects for a major war, this country did have an adequate set of practical designs for airborne cameras, telescopic sights, binoculars, and nearly all types of other optical instruments. The efforts of NDRC in the field were therefore expended largely on ways to improve and speed up production of existing optical equipment and on methods to utilize that equipment more efficiently.

He points out particular contributions made by the Institute in that area. In particular, he notes the contributions made to applications and production of triple mirrors.

> The military application of triple mirrors to signaling and identification was handled by the Institute of Optics at the University of Rochester. This group also designed and fabricated auxiliary equipment involving triple mirrors, and engaged in such specialized studies as the calculation and application of triple mirrors with an angle intentionally offset to give a known deviation to the reflected light beam.

These triple mirrors are familiar to generations of students who have scrounged in the attic of Bausch & Lomb for the past sixty years. Experiments with these retroreflectors are described in the essay titled "Unusual Labs on River Campus" and elsewhere in this volume.

Harrison also describes work on thin films.

> [T]he bulk of the work in the NDRC thin-film program was done in conjunction with more extensive projects in the field of optics—principally at the University of Rochester,

Triple mirrors in three different mountings.

where spectacular work on a laboratory scale was done on various types of films. Outstanding among the University of Rochester's achievements was the development of a highly successful beam-splitting prism, a special requirement for one military instrument, which reflected one half of an incident light and transmitted the remainder. The use of multiple-layer filters in the prism by depositing high- and lo-index materials on the hypotenuse faces of two right-angle prisms was suggested by the Eastman Kodak Company.

In the chapter titled "New Optical Instruments," Harrison describes the need for precision theodolites:

> The only major weaknesses in American optical equipment were insufficient quantity of precision theodolites and insufficient quality of phototheodolites. Theodolites were needed to lay out map reference points and to make possible topographical surveying, and photo-theodolites to record the course of objects, such as airplanes, weather balloons, and projectiles, through space. The need for theodolites was particularly urgent, because the Corps of Engineers, responsible for surveying and mapping in the Army, had always depended on foreign sources of supply for these instruments. After a study of imported prototypes, theodolites which gave performances as good or better than Zeiss models were designed at the University of Rochester and constructed at the W. and L.E. Gurley Company of Troy, New York.

Of course, binoculars and telescopes were important to the war effort. The Institute played an important role in this area:

> Optical projects related to binoculars and telescopes were assigned to the University of Rochester from early in 1941 until the closing phases of the war. To facilitate the search for dimly illuminated objects at night, the Rochester group developed a series of telescopes which yielded a product of real field (in degrees) and magnification equal to approximately 70, in contrast with a product of 50 in the conventional military instruments. Another primary requirement for a night telescope was a large exit pupil to take advantage of the full area of the pupil of a dark-adapted eye. The full pupil diameter of the average observer

was determined by a series of measurements to be about 7 mm., and a 7-mm. exit pupil was consequently standardized for all instruments intended for night use.

One of the most important night-vision instruments designed by the Rochester group was a 6×42 binocular for pilots of P-61 night fighters. The Rochester design was improved and engineered for production by the Eastman Kodak Company. The Air Forces also wanted a 6×42 telescope, or monocular, for the gunner in P-61 night fighters, and such an instrument, incorporating a Schmidt-type erecting system, was designed at Rochester, where several other experimental models of monoculars and binoculars were developed. The same group was also one of several contractors asked by NDRC to try to improve the

Image through type II-c binocular telescope without anti-oscillation mounting.

Image stabilized with anti-oscillation mounting.

T-76 three-power and the T-44 five-power tank gun sights, the performances of which were considered unsatisfactory by the Ordnance Department. Both instruments were successfully modified, and working models were turned over to the Army.

Holding a pair of binoculars or a telescope steady while flying in a fighter or riding in a tank is nearly impossible. The Institute of Optics also worked on this problem:

> [S]ome type of mechanical holder was necessary for higher-powered, heavier instruments, particularly under unsteadying conditions aboard ships and in aircraft. Known as antioscillation mounts, the mechanical holders had to be individually designed to meet specialized needs for them. The University of Rochester designed such a mount for the six-power night binocular which they designed for P-61 night-fighter planes. The Rochester mount was engineered for production by Eastman Kodak, and pilots later reported that the image of a ground target remained clear and steady, even when they went into a power dive and fired all four 20-mm. guns at irregular intervals. Another mount, equally successful, was fabricated for the monocular gun sight on P-61s.

A reflex sight allowed a gunner to see the image of his target superimposed with a series of concentric circles by reflecting an image of a reticle onto a glass plate inclined to the gunner's eye.

> Four main types of reflex sights were developed at the University of Rochester. The first, for fighter aircraft, was a sight in which the optical path between the reticle and lens was folded twice by plane mirrors in the shape of a figure 4. Two varieties of the sight were designed, because the Army and Navy each required a special type of reticle pattern. The second type of Rochester sight became known as the radar reflex sight and its field of view included the face of a radar screen, and indication from the gyro horizon meter, a reading from the air-speed indicator, and the usual aiming pattern. Wanted by the Navy for airborne use, the radar reflex sight was never used, due to a change in plans and tactics.
>
> The third type of Rochester reflex sight was designed for 40-mm. anti-aircraft guns and included both electrical and daylight illumination for two reticles, one for horizontal tracking and the other for vertical tracking. A second version of the same sight included illumination of the reticles by the light given off by radium-activated phosphor surfaces. While the latter version reached only the laboratory stage of development, substantial orders were placed for the first version in four modifications, known as the M-21, M-22, M-23, and M-24. The fourth type of Rochester reflex sight, designed for especially rough use with mobile 50-mm. machine guns, was mounted on a parallelogram-shaped mechanism to keep it above the muzzle blast and was illuminated by daylight. It was standardized by the Army as the M-18 sight.

A particularly clever and important development in the Institute was the invention of the Icaroscope.

> One of the toughest problems faced by antiaircraft gunners was keeping track of enemy planes which were diving with the full glare of the sun directly behind them. No single filter was applicable to the problem, because any filter dense enough to eliminate the blinding effect of the sun would black out the surrounding sky. NDRC made several attempts to block out the sun's glare from gun sights, which magnified the blinding effect, and eventually met with some success. Harvard Observatory tried to do it with a translucent disk, just large enough to block out the sun's image, which would keep itself always between the sun and the eye of the observer. Eastman Kodak tried a similar photoelectrical and mechanical process which would allow the sun to produce a dense image of itself on a film which ran through the focal plane of the telescope. All of these devices proved too slow to do the required job.
>
> The University of Rochester, originally working independently and later under an NDRC contract, devised a practical antiglare apparatus which made use of an afterglow phosphor.
>
> An important property of such phosphors is 'saturation,' which places a limit on the amount of brightness which can be obtained by increasing the intensity of the exciting

energy. Thus if two areas of a phosphor excited by visible light were exposed, one to skylight and the other to direct sunlight, and were then removed to the dark, the phosphorescent afterglow of the area exposed to the sun would be little, if any brighter than that exposed only to the sky.

The successful instrument, known as the Icaroscope, was placed in limited production by the Navy. It weighed only nine pounds and could be either operated in a simple swivel mount or held by hand. By use of the phosphor, the image of the sun on the viewing screen was only 20 to 50 times brighter than the image of the surrounding sky, whereas to the naked eye it was more than 10,000 times brighter, and planes could be spotted with the instrument at distance greater than 25,000 feet. Near the close of the war a smaller, lightweight model was completed and turned over to the Navy for future applications.

Another project that occupied the fourth floor of Bausch & Lomb Hall was the development of specialized sun glasses.

To furnish protection against either the glare of direct sunlight or the reflection of bright sunlight from clouds, water, or desert sands, the University of Rochester and Bausch & Lomb collaborated in the development of a new type of sun goggles in which a region of minimum density lay across the center of the field, with the density increasing above and below the center of the lenses. A technique for evaporating a hard film of nickel-chromium onto the surface of either clear or tinted glass was perfected to give an almost ideal neutral density. When tests revealed that having a protective film over the lower half of the lenses was a disadvantage, because there was usually not enough light in a car or plane to see the instrument panel clearly through the graded density, new goggles were made up with the film only on the top half. Substantial numbers of the goggles with graded density above the center of vision were manufactured for the Air Forces, and a few hundred with overall gradation.

Harrison makes clear that at the beginning of the war there was a scientific race to make use of "invisible" light, i.e., infrared light, for secure communications and night vision. He writes that "Both the Germans and the Japanese had primitive types of infrared-imaging equipment at the outset of the war, while Allied scientists had equipment which was markedly similar. Research staffs on both sides of the front lines were confronted with the same problem—the perfection of instruments to send and receive infrared light and make it visible to friendly operators only. . . . American scientists won by a large margin in their race to become the first to make practical use of infrared light." The University of Rochester development of the Metascope was at the forefront of this effort. He goes on to explain the nature of an infrared-sensitive phosphor and the way it was used in the Metascope.

An infrared-sensitive phosphor is a material which stores up energy when bombarded by ultraviolet light, visible light, electrons, X-rays, alpha rays, and other energizing agencies. The stored energy is normally released very slowly over a long period of time. If, however, the phosphor in its excited state is subjected to illumination by infrared radiation, the energy is released much more rapidly and in the form of visible light. This phenomenon is the basis of the metascopes, which first excite a phosphor surface, and then stimulate it by infrared radiation to provide a visual image.

Prior to the war the leading research in infrared sensitive phosphors had been carried out by a small group of Viennese scientists including Franz Urbach. It is described in other essays in this volume how Urbach fled the Nazi occupation of Austria and ended up in Rochester just in time to aid the effort to develop the Metascope. Granted an NDRC contract in 1941, he began work on reproducing the earlier work and encountered difficulties obtaining sufficiently pure samples of the rare materials. Eventually he not only

Franz Urbach photographed by the light of the infrared phosphors that he developed. The photograph by George Burns appeared in the Saturday Evening Post magazine.

reproduced the previous results but discovered a group of calcium-strontium-sulfide phosphors activated by europium and samarium. Harrison notes that

> The work on the rare-earth-sulfide phosphors resulted in the discovery of an especially important principle relative to infrared phosphors—infrared sensitization by the interaction of activators. It was found that the two activators did not influence the properties of the phosphor independently, but acted in unison to determine its properties. The dominant activator determined the emission spectrum of the phosphor, while the auxiliary activator determined the stimulation spectrum. The discovery opened a large field of investigation, and application of the activator-interaction principle was the basis for the subsequent success of the program.

The Rochester group then put this advance to practical use.

> Following their successful production of infrared-sensitive phosphors during 1941 and 1942, the optical staff at the University of Rochester, under an NDRC contract, began development work on the equipment necessary to utilize the phosphors for infrared signaling and identification. Between early 1942 and the end of the war the Rochester group designed and built eleven different models of image-forming infrared receivers, known as metascopes. All of these receivers employed phosphors and Schmidt-type optical systems, and six of them were accepted for quantity production by the Army and Navy.

In typical fashion for such a military project the impact was not as great as it might have been due to external factors.

> Tests of the sniperscope under simulated night-combat conditions were conducted by the Army in late 1943, and indicated that the effectiveness of the "seeing eye" would be considerable, particularly in operations against the Japanese, who made a specialty of after-dark infiltration tactics. Although quantity production of the instrument was ordered at that time, the sniperscope became the victim of rather curious security measures, did not see action in the European theater, and was not employed in the Pacific until the last battle of the war. Its use by Army ground forces was held up by the fact that the Navy did not wish to have its own successful use of shipborne infrared equipment endangered by the likelihood of a sniperscope's falling into enemy hands.
>
> Several thousand sniperscopes were shipped to the Pacific in time for the Okinawan campaign, which began on April 1, 1945, or more than a year after the sniperscope had been perfected. Subsequent reports revealed that 30 per cent of all Japanese casualties in the early stages of the battle for Okinawa were attributable to the sniperscope and to the deadly accuracy of the American riflemen, who, for the first time, could see in the dark.

Another item that is familiar to students prowling around in the attic of Bausch & Lomb for the past fifty years is the *fluorescent reflector button*. Its use is described:

> Since night driving and airfield operations in forward areas were hazardous under blacked-out conditions, NDRC encouraged the development of methods to make the borders of roads and runways visible to friendly forces without violating after-dark security measures. One of the most satisfactory wartime solutions was the design of fluorescent reflector buttons which upon being irradiated with ultraviolet light, served as easily discernible roadside markers. The buttons could also be utilized to letter directional signs for night drivers.
>
> Each reflector button was essentially a Schmidt optical system of solid glass or plastic. The button was made in two halves, with the back portion, consisting of the spherical reflecting surface, separated from the focal surface by a solid glass or plastic block. The front element was an aspherical corrector plate. After the focal surface had been coated with an ultraviolet phosphor which had a yellow-green emission under ultraviolet stimulation, the two halves of the button were cemented together. Yellow-green was selected as being close to the color representing the peak sensitivity of a dark-adapted eye.
>
> . . . Several thousand one-inch reflector buttons were produced and employed in field tests, together with a few models of larger Schmidt-type fluorescent reflectors, including some as large as four inches in diameter, which were designed and built by the University of Rochester.

This is hardly a complete catalogue of the contributions to the war effort made at the University of Rochester, but it is clear that from the perspective of the chief of Division 16 of the NDRC the contributions were indeed numerous and important. It is particularly notable that many of these contributions were taken all the way from the posing of the problem, through an innovative solution, to battlefield utilization in a matter of months.

11. Whodunit?

Carlos Stroud

The Institute of Optics was an exciting place during World War II, with some fifty researchers working on a variety of projects that were vital to the war efforts. Approximately half the military optics research projects in the country were centered there. As one might expect in this situation, some attention was placed on security. The fourth floor of Bausch & Lomb was cordoned off with a wire grill and twenty-four-hour guards. George Fraley carried a pistol as he made regular trips to the incinerator in the hospital to destroy surplus classified files. Newly developed instruments were given code names like "Metascope," "Icaroscope," and "Seebackascope."

If this sounds to you like a promising setting for a spy thriller, you are not the first to think so. There exists in the University of Rochester archives a typescript of approximately two hundred pages that tells the story of a Nazi spy ring, a murder, an undercover agent, purloined documents, and a sword fight—all centered in The Institute of Optics. The novel is titled "Amontillado's Arcanum" and is dated October 31, 1945. The author is listed only by a pseudonym, "Spud." Modern research has yet to reveal the real name of the talented author.

The list of characters is mostly familiar to readers of this history of the Institute; almost all were associated with optics during the war. Some were cast as themselves, and others had their names reassigned to fictional characters in the story. The author issues a disclaimer: "Any resemblance between characters in this book and human beings is purely unintentional." Somehow one is led to wonder whether this is a comment on the book or a comment on the people portrayed.

Like many novels of this genre it includes a diagram of the crime scene, in this case the fourth floor of Bausch & Lomb Hall, then the home of The Institute of Optics.

The hero of the novel is a young man named Gale Tristram, nicknamed "Amontillado" like the sherry in Edgar Allan Poe's short story. It is not made clear how he came to be called by this unusual name, but that information may have been made clear on page 6 which is missing from the archival copy of the manuscript. We do learn that "Amontillado was not only good looking but he was capable of making aesthetic love, and as a result, a good many girls were attracted to him." A series of youthful indiscretions, including a notorious incident involving a missing Rembrandt painting, brought him to the attention of the police, who admired his remarkable derring-do and subsequent military heroism enough to think he would be the perfect undercover agent to track down the enemy spy who had been stealing drawings of optical instruments being developed in the Institute.

Soon he is installed as a new technician on the fourth floor of Bausch & Lomb. He is introduced to the whole group of characters, including an undercover FBI agent who inhabited the Institute at the time. Some months earlier the FBI had placed one of its agents, Don Feder, on the staff in a vain attempt to track down the Nazi spy. In short

Cast of Characters

N.D.R.C	Others	Others
Dr. Brian O'Brien	Al Chippendale	Arnold Pehta
Dr. Fred Paul	Jim Eyer	Betty Larson
Dr. John Evans	John Barnes	June Taylor
Robert Hopkins	Helen Parks	Tom Kanwisher
Walter Newcomb	Polly Pitkin	Joyce McChesney
George Schnable	Ruth Oliver	Joy Whitney
Gordon Milne	Louise Rivoli	Elizabeth Schaeffer
Harry Polster	Mrs. Monteur	Butch O'Brien
Joe Magliozzi	Marianne Smith	Inge Renkert
Jim Harvey	Dorothy Kinear	Art Yaeger
Marty Koonen	Mr. Cardinal	Ruth Albert
Louis Fortmiller	Tom Smith	Dick Foster
Ed Spong	John Leone	Doris Greno
Don Feder	Jack Agnolia	Doris Schrader
Mary Banning	Herb Graff	Bill Boyle
Katheryn Harbuz	Hugo Gunther	Policeman
Pauline Coakley	Paul John	One Ear
Helen Tobin	Klinkert	Wartface
Ruth Alberts	Myra Schwartz	Von Heur
Gale Tristram	Carl Moriarty	Bush-man
Police	Madeline Moriarty	Bill Stewart
Roger Harrington	Dr. Urbach	Spud
Ed Schreiner	Mrs. Urbach	
Hobby French	Don Pearlman	
Robert Kesel	Robert Hudson	
Ed Palmer	Henry Henty	
Dave Lanni	Betty Emig	

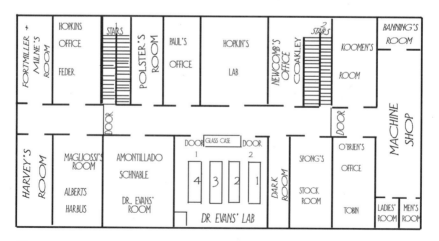

Floor plan of the Fourth Floor of Bausch & Lomb, scene of intrigue and murder.

order more important drawings disappear, and a mysterious murder occurs with Agent Feder stabbed, painted black from head to toe, and suspended by ropes beneath an optical table in Dr. Evan's lab.

There have been many observations in the Institute's labs that at first appear inexplicable, but surely this was among the most bizarre. Our man Amontillado is up to the challenge, but he must use all of his considerable talents—including his experience as the U.S. collegiate fencing champion—to break up the spy ring and bring the culprits to justice. Along the way there were flower pots dropped from the top of Rush Rhees Library, car chases, sniper fire, a sword fight, and a little romance for spice.

Author Spud clearly had talents not usually found among optikers, and a unique way to parody the interesting characters who worked in the Institute during this exciting period.

12. Biography of Brian O'Brien

Walter P. Siegmund and Brian O'Brien, Jr.

Early Years

Brian O'Brien was born in Denver, Colorado, in 1898 to Michael Phillip and Lina Prime O'Brien. His education started in the Chicago Latin School from 1909–1915, and continued at the Yale Sheffield scientific school where he earned a Ph.B. in 1918 and a Ph.D. in 1922. He also did additional course work at MIT and Harvard.

In 1922 he married Ethel Cornelia Dickerman and they had one son, Brian, Jr. After Ethel Cornelia died, he was married a second time to Mary Nelson Firth in 1956.

He was a research engineer with the Westinghouse Electric Co. from 1922 to 1923. During this period he developed, along with Joseph Slepian, the auto-valve lightning arrestor, which is still in use today.

In 1923 he moved to the J. N. Adam Memorial hospital in Perrysburg, N.Y., a tuberculosis sanitarium run by Buffalo's Public Health Dept. Prior to the advent of antibiotics the primary treatment for tuberculosis was fresh air and sunshine. There was some evidence that sun tanning did help in the remission of the disease. However, Perrysburg—40 miles south of Buffalo—had very little sunshine in the winter. Therefore O'Brien, as physicist on the staff, developed carbon arcs with cored carbons that very closely matched the solar spectrum. With this development the patients could have sun therapy year-round. Due to a general interest in the biological effects of solar radiation, he published some of the early work on the ozone layer and erythema caused by the sun.

O'Brien moved to the University of Rochester in 1930 to hold the chair of physiological optics. Shortly thereafter he became the director of the Institute of Optics. His continuing interest in the biological effects of solar radiation led to research in vitamin chemistry. The need for vitamin D, especially in the diet of children, had been recognized for preventing the disease rickets, resulting in the loss of bone calcium and hence deformation of the long bones. At that time there was no

Brian O'Brien, first permanent Director of the Institute of Optics.

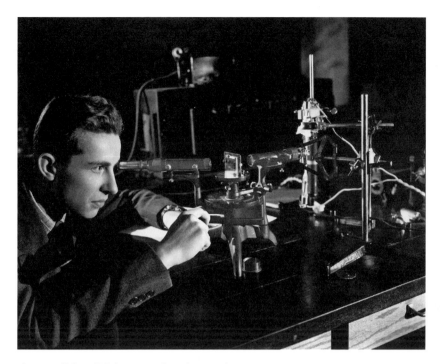

A young Brian O'Brien peers through a grating spectrometer.

synthetic vitamin D, but the dehydrocholesterol in milk can be converted to vitamin D by radiation with ultraviolet light. The carbon arcs developed at Perrysburg were an ideal source of ultraviolet, but for proper irradiation, the milk had to be in a very thin film. Flowing down a solid cylinder produced a suitable film, but the flow volume was much too low to be practical. Free flow from an annular slit might work, but surface tension would collapse the film shortly after leaving the slit. However, if by suitable vanes the milk was given an angular velocity prior to leaving the slit, centrifugal force would counteract the surface tension and a thin free-flowing film would be produced. Thus, a film of high enough flow volume for commercial application was produced, and vitamin D-fortified milk became widespread.

Since photographic materials had been a major tool in much of his work, he became interested in the properties of silver halide emulsions. In order to study the reciprocity effect at very short exposure times, he developed a very high-speed slit camera that later was developed into a framing camera with frame rates up to eleven million frames per second. This was later used to great effect in the nuclear energy program, including the Bikini bomb tests.

Wartime

By observing events in Europe it became obvious to him that the United States would sooner or later become involved in a major war, and so he began to prepare The Institute of Optics for contribution to the war effort. Among the preparations: Major expansion of instrument shop facilities, stocking up on potentially scarce materials such as high-strength aluminum, and expanding development staff.

Early on, the Office of Scientific Research and Development was formed, headed by Vannevar Bush, reporting directly to the White House. Under the OSRD there was formed the National Defense Research Committee with various subdivisions. Section D, handling instrumentation, was formed under George Harrison, and Section D6 was headed by O'Brien.

Because of its very high relative aperture, the Kellner-Schmidt catadioptric system was to be used in many applications during the war. Therefore, a method for mass production of the aspheric corrector plates was needed. Such a method was developed using a heat "dropping" process onto a mold. This used the American Optical "greenblock" molding material, which was machined by a high-precision contouring machine developed at Rochester. The contour of the greenblock included correction for the flow characteristics of molten glass so the top surface of a glass plate heated on the greenblock ended with the correct aspheric shape. All that remained was grinding and polishing the bottom surface plano, and you had a mass-produced Kellner-Schmidt corrector plate.

One of the early uses for a large Kellner-Schmidt system was for a slit lamp for night aerial photography. Fairchild had developed the slit aerial camera, where the ground was imaged onto the film through a slit and the film was in continuous motion at a speed related to the aircraft speed, altitude and the camera focal length, giving a continuous strip photograph of the ground. To use this same principle at night, a line filament lamp was imaged through a large Kellner-Schmidt system projecting a strip of light on the ground. The camera lens imaged this strip of light on the moving film and produced that same strip photograph of the ground.

By far the most prevalent use of the Kellner-Schmidt optics was in the so-called "Metascopes." These were a series of infrared telescopes with Kellner-Schmidt optics, using an infrared phosphor in the image-plane. The term "infrared phosphor" may sound like a contradiction in terms, violating the second law of thermodynamics. However, if electrons can be lifted into metastable states to be triggered out later by infrared radiation, they can then radiate at a shorter wavelength and emit visible light.

It was rumored that an Austrian named Franz Urbach had developed such a "phosphor," but his whereabouts were unknown. Through the various intelligence services O'Brien tried to trace him, but with little success. Some time later, Russell Wilkins, head of the Physics Department, came into O'Brien's office and told him that a refugee physical chemist had shown up in his department, and he had given him some laboratory space, but he really didn't know what to do with him. His name was Franz Urbach, and he had escaped the Nazis!

Urbach had, indeed, developed a phosphor-like material that could convert infrared

Walter Siegmund, student, colleague, and biographer of Brian O'Brien.

radiation into visible light without violating the laws of physics. By doping sulfide phosphors with rare earth elements, primarily europium, many possible metastable states are generated. If electrons are bumped up into these states by high-energy radiation (initially ultraviolet light, but later alpha particles from radium), they will stay there until triggered out by infrared, then fall back to the ground state and, in so doing, emit visible light.

Immediately laboratory space was set up for him in the basement of Dewey Hall, and a crew of assistants was provided. With the spherical image plane of a Kellner-Schmidt optical system coated with this material, and an eyepiece system arranged to view it, one had an infrared viewing telescope. The code word "Metascope" was applied to these devices. A series of these instruments was developed, with several going into large-scale production for use during the war.

For example, the Sampson United Co. in Rochester was contracted to produce the Type A Metascope, but the company had trouble ramping up to the needed production in time for the North African invasion. To solve this, classes were cancelled at The Institute of Optics. The undergraduates were put on a three-shift-a-day basis in the Institute optical shop grinding and polishing the flats on Kellner-Schmidt corrector plates. The faculty went on three shifts at the Sampson United assembly line, and the required number of units was produced for the invasion.

Many other devices were developed for the war effort, including the "Seebackascope" to align a dive bomber between the Sun and a target; the "Icarascope" to reduce the brightness of the solar disc to the point where an attacker coming out of the sunlight could be seen; anti-oscillation mounts for binoculars to increase the range that night fighter

Brian O'Brien, Gordon Milne, and Brian O'Brien, Jr. pack up camera for project Crossroads.

aircraft pilots could identify enemy aircraft, etc. All of this important optical work was performed under O'Brien's section D6 of the NDRC.

Post-War

After World War II O'Brien could return to his interests in basic research in physiological optics and sensors. He undertook a major study in the behavior of lead sulfide as an infrared detector. He also returned to the study of the distribution of the ozone layer in the lower stratosphere, work he had begun in the 1930s in conjunction with the National Geographic U.S. Army Air Corps high-altitude balloon ascents. In fact the spectrographic apparatus and even the wicker basket to carry it into the stratosphere are still preserved at the Smithsonian Air & Space Museum. With the development of lightweight unmanned plastic balloons by General Mills, it was now possible to reach altitudes above 100,000 feet— 30,000 feet higher than before the war.

These tests were made in 1949, and although the spectrograph fell into a Minnesota lake, the film was retrieved intact, analyzed and found to have reached only the very lower reaches of the ozone layer. It was not until rocket probes were developed that the ozone layer was fully characterized. (On a philosophical note, who would have thought in 1949 that the esoteric ozone layer would prove to be such a harbinger of human impact on the environment.)

O'Brien must have enjoyed solving the unexplained riddles of human vision. One of them was the "anomalous" Sherrington effect, which related to the in-phase vs. out-of-phase binocular flicker for the two eyes of the observer. While black-and-white stimuli gave the expected results, complementary colors gave the reverse (or anomalous) results. This was cleared up when the brightness-matching of the complementary colors was more carefully done and the "anomalous" effect dropped out.

A more demanding study was required to explain the so-called Stiles and Crawford effect. Some time ago Stiles & Crawford observed that light entering the eye at the edges of the pupil produced a lower brightness sensation than light entering at the center of the pupil. This went unexplained for many years.

O'Brien postulated that because of the structure of the retina, light entering the retinal cones at the base travels down the cone by multiple total internal reflections since the cone is immersed in a transparent medium of a lower refractive index than the cone itself. Because of the shape of the cone, light entering off-axis would tend to reach critical angle and be lost sooner than light entering on-axis. Histological measurements on rabbit retinas confirmed this possibility, but any direct photometric measurements would be extremely difficult.

By scaling up the system by a factor of 6×10^4, 3 cm X-Band microwave radiation could be used and easily measured, if only a scaled-up retinal cone could be produced. A then-new material made of expanded polystyrene (now called Styrofoam) had just become available. It had the right refractive index characteristics for X-Band radiation against air. A system was set up using a surplus X-band military radar transmitter, and the results exactly matched the observed results of Stiles & Crawford.

From the work on the Stiles & Crawford effect it occurred to O'Brien that a low-refractive-index cladding on a high-index core glass would provide insulation from adjacent fibers while at the same time give extremely high efficiency reflections by total internal reflection. Thus a glass fiber could transmit light over long distances without large losses, and fibers bundled together could transmit images. Preliminary experiments with glass fibers and an ultraviolet polymerized plastic coating showed this to be the case.

This study was completed at just about the time when, on a visit from Delft in Holland, Professor A. C. S. van Heel confided to O'Brien that he had been attempting to produce light-transmitting glass fibers for a classified government project. His results from coating glass fibers with silver to enhance their transmission and prevent cross talk between fibers in a bundle had failed, and the project was in jeopardy. O'Brien pointed out to van Heel that a low-refractive-index cladding provided the right solution, which van Heel, of course, then recognized immediately. When van Heel applied this he got the results he needed and went on to other things, but not before publishing the results in the Dutch journal "de Ingenieur."

When O'Brien went from the University of Rochester to the American Optical Co. he gave the company the fiber-cladding concept and the company patent department began preparing a patent application. In their pre-application search they found van Heel's publication of the concept. However they misread the publication date (in the European sequence), and their filing date was beyond the one-year allowance under U.S. patent law—and so the most important concept of the patent was invalidated by van Heel's prior publication. At the time O'Brien was absorbed with a major technical program, the development of the Todd-AO motion picture process, which will be the subject of another essay.

On the other hand, the fiber concept became the basis for the rapid development of fiber optic technology, beginning about 1955. That led to the great contribution of fiber optics to endoscopy, night vision devices, communications, and a host of special applications, a veritable revolution in the field of optics.

After the war O'Brien was elected to the National Academy of Science and was active in the Physical Sciences Division of the National Research Council, and the Undersea Warfare Committee. Shortly thereafter General Bernard Shriever, commander of the Air Force Systems Command, asked him to set up an academy committee to advise the Systems Command on technical problems. This committee was later called the Air Force Studies Board, and consisted of scientists and engineers from a wide variety of disciplines.

James Webb, then head of NASA, requested that O'Brien set up a similar academy committee to advise NASA on future programs. This was to be called the Space Projects Advisory Council and had a similar composition as the Air Force Studies Board. This was early in the space program when orbiting objects were measured in "beer can units": It cost roughly one million dollars to put a can of beer (one pound mass) into earth orbit. One of the council's recommendations was that NASA develop a reusable shuttle, capable of orbiting objects at a much lower cost. The result, of course, was the Space Shuttle.

After retiring from American Optical, O'Brien continued consulting for various branches of the military and NASA as well as commercial concerns. When consulting for the government he always refused any compensation, considering it a patriotic contribution. He continued this until shortly before his death on 1 July 1992 at the age of ninety-four and a half.

Brian O'Brien, Jr. received his B.S. from the Institute of Optics in 1944. He is the son of Brian O'Brien. He is currently retired and living in Quinebaug, CT.

Walter P. Siegmund received his Ph.D. from the Institute of Optics in 1952. He was a member of the faculty of the University of Rochester from 1953 until 1955. He is currently retired and living in Pomfret, CT.

13. George Fraley Stories

Carlos Stroud

As a youth George Fraley lived just across the street from Brian O'Brien and his family. As World War II started George was a student at Rochester Institute of Technology when O'Brien recruited him to help with the war effort in the Institute as assistant to the director. George assisted in various ways throughout the war years and for many years afterward, working on various research projects, running the departmental stores, and being a general factotum. Through the 1980s George made regular trips to the Army Surplus Depot in Canandaigua to pick up bargain supplies. George was invaluable when you needed some rigging done, or you needed some unusual metal ordered in a hurry for a shop project. He knew the president of every local business on a first-name basis and could work miracles for those on his good side.

After more than forty years working in the Institute he had one too many disputes with the parking office and angrily resigned. He owned several acres in Mendon where he had a house and a campground. The campground was the site for many years of the annual optics fall picnic. Everyone associated with the Institute from the 1960s through the 1980s holds fond memories of the great picnics. Soon George sold his place in Mendon and moved south to Naples, N.Y., where he bought a beautiful property on a hillside, built a house and set up another campground. The picnics resumed in the grand new location and were held for several years in the 1990s.

George Fraley portrait from the Rochester Times-Union newspaper.

George's repertoire of stories is well known to generations of optics students and faculty, so that it was clear that this volume would be incomplete without inclusion of a goodly selection of these "Fraley stories." To secure an appropriate selection I drove down to Naples armed with a tape recorder and collected three hours of reminiscences, which are excerpted in a series of short articles in this section and the next under the heading of *Fraley Stories.* Of course, this sampling is just a small part of the whole collection, which is now saved in the University of Rochester archives.

14. A Story of Science in Night Warfare

Brian O'Brien

The story which I shall try to tell you tonight deals with a series of developments designed to make night warfare just a little safer. These were carried out under the general auspices of Division 16 of the National Defense Research Committee. However, this work centered at The Institute of Optics of the University of Rochester, so I am really telling you much of the war story of the Institute. You will understand that I am acting in the capacity of a reporter. This was not individual effort but was teamwork by a fairly large group, and this will be more evident to you as we go on.

In the autumn of 1938 while we were engaged very peacefully in investigating ultraviolet radiation from the sun, it became necessary to carry certain light-measuring instruments on an airplane, and to place that airplane in a direct line between the sun and similar measuring instruments located on the ground. This led to the development of a contrivance. When flying at a low altitude it is easy to see your shadow and to place that shadow anywhere you like. As you climb, the shadow vanishes and it is very difficult indeed to tell even approximately where the shadow would fall if you were close enough to cast one. This little optical contrivance merely showed the pilot where his shadow would be quite independently of the altitude at which he was flying.

In April of 1939 this work on ultraviolet radiation was scheduled for presentation at a Washington meeting of the American Physical Society, and this included a description of the contrivance, which by this time had acquired the dignified name of "sun-alignment

"Butch O'Butch" using an Icaroscope is looking the sun right in the eye and suffering no discomfort. The Icaroscope took the blindness out of daylight dive-bombing attacks in World War II.

sight." It was apparent that the sight would be equally useful in dive bombing attacks from the direction of the sun, a procedure which the Italians were already using in Ethiopia, so before presenting the material it was first discussed with Dr. Lyman Briggs, Director of the National Bureau of Standards. He asked that the instrument be shown to the then Acting Chief of the Air Corps, Brigadier General Benjamin K. Yount, who in turn asked that certain military possibilities be withheld, while presenting fully the technical nature and scientific use of the device.

In due course a brief description was published in the *Physical Review* and the French read of it and sent a French air force officer, a Captain Albert Delavigne, to see us about it. He was very charming and an experienced pilot, but in civilian clothes with no distinguishing marks except the little ribbon of the Legion of Honor. Our Navy knew of the sight as well as the Air Force and had asked for a sample. Both Services said there was no objection to showing it to the French who knew their own weakness in dive bombing and wished to do something about it. It was now very early in 1940. The war had happened but was still called a "phony war" although the French apparently realized that things might explode at any moment.

There was snow on the ground when the captain arrived, but it was a bright sunny day and one runway was open, so I took him out and flew a little demonstration for him. He was delighted with the device and immediately began arrangements for procuring a quantity for the French. Unfortunately the phony war turned into the German blitzkrieg and France fell before she was able to develop satisfactory dive bombing.

This was a first-hand example of too little and too late and made a deep impression on us. Also it was the last time we were to be concerned with sunlight or even daylight until near the end of the war, when we were again to develop an instrument concerned with dive bombing and sunlight, but from a very different point of view.

An amusing sidelight on the sun alignment sight came just a couple of weeks before Italy's entrance into the war. A letter arrived from Brigadier General Adolpho Infante, Air Attache at the Italian Embassy in Washington, stating that a daily newspaper in Italy (in Milan) had carried a popular story about our sun alignment sight, and that he was instructed by cable to find out about it. This was a poser so we stalled off the general for a few weeks. Italy's attack on France saved us from any further concern about hurting the feelings of the Italian Embassy.

By the autumn of 1940 all allied forces were out of Europe and the war had become a night war, largely defensive on the part of Great Britain. The dominant problem was defense against night bombing and the blackout was uppermost in everyone's mind. The National Defense Research Committee was just getting under way in this country, but in the meantime the National Research Council had established a committee on blackout and night combat problems, of which I was a member. Another peacetime device of ours became interesting. This was developed not as a scientific research tool but as an aid to vision in night fog conditions on inland waterways. It consisted of an optical arrangement with some of the characteristics of the common reflector buttons and reflecting road markers which you see along our highways, but there were certain important differences. As you may have noticed, the roadside reflector buttons return to your eyes the visible light from your headlights. Our arrangement received invisible radiation, ultraviolet of wavelength shorter than visible light, converted this into visible light and sent it back in the direction of the ultraviolet source wherever that source might be. An observer near that source would see the reflector unit light up brilliantly yet the whole procedure could be quite invisible to someone else only a few feet away. This had important possibilities in both military and naval operations and we were asked to speed up the development, and were provided with the necessary funds by the National Defense Research Committee early in 1941.

Although this ultraviolet system showed promise it had a serious weakness. Ultraviolet radiation of the wavelength used was generally supposed to be invisible. This was not strictly true. With sufficiently high intensity of radiation it could be seen; that is, the ultraviolet projecting sources could be seen even before the ultraviolet radiation was converted into visible light by our reflecting device of "autocollimator," as it was called. Worse, this ultraviolet was particularly visible to young people. It was amusing at a night demonstration to hear the discussion of a group of older officers, completely satisfied with the invisibility of the system, while their juniors standing by would say "But, sir, I can see that ultraviolet light."

It was recognized that if infrared radiation could be used, this difficulty of faint but definite ultraviolet visibility could be eliminated. The problem was how to turn infrared into visible radiation. Back in 1936 Dr. Zworykin, of the RCA Laboratories, had published a description of a device known as the image tube which accomplished this conversion by electronic means, but the tube and its accessories were bulky and complicated. At a meeting of the blackout illumination committee in January of 1940, Dr. Zworykin, also a member, said that he had met a European scientist in Philadelphia who mentioned having developed a phosphor capable of converting infrared radiation directly into visible light. Phosphors will be familiar to you as the common luminous paints and the fluorescent coatings on the inside of modern fluorescent lamps. We had used such phosphors in converting the ultraviolet into visible light in our autocollimators. Unfortunately phosphors for converting infrared into visible light could not act the same way. Such a conversion involves going up hill in the quantum sense, so the only way infrared could act was to trigger the release of energy previously stored in the phosphor. This principle had been described many years before, but did not look at all promising. Zworykin did not remember the name of the man nor his address, but he was nonetheless impressed and believed there might be something to even this unpromising lead. So did we, and I made inquiries everywhere but with no success.

A month or so later Lee DuBridge, the chairman of the UR Physics Department, and Victor Weisskopf, another member of the UR Physics faculty, told me that Franz Urbach was visiting our University Physics Department, and had been given a little laboratory space for some experiments which he wished to conduct. They said that Urbach had made certain developments in Vienna and wanted to see me about them. This was a most fortunate coincidence. The development was the infrared sensitive phosphor of which Zworykin had told us.

Dr. Urbach's experiments in Vienna had been interrupted by the Anschluss with Austria; he had been forced to leave Austria and finally reached this country by devious routes.

The new phosphors as Urbach described them were far superior to anything known in the literature, but reproducing them in this country from memory, to say nothing of improving upon them, appeared a long and difficult task. Nevertheless, the support of the NDRC was obtained, laboratory facilities were provided, and Dr. Urbach went to work aided by a chemist, Donald Pearlman, a Rochester alumnus, and well qualified for this undertaking.

While these things were shaping up, England was being bombed, almost into oblivion, and methods for attacking night bombers became of paramount importance. The farsighted work of a small group of English scientists in developing radar methods had made possible the defense of England by the RAF in that winter of 1940–41. The Radiation Laboratory at MIT, under the leadership of Lee DuBridge, was already making its weight felt with important new developments, but there were some serious unsolved problems. You could direct a night fighter into contact with an enemy bomber, or by airborne radar the night fighter pilot could be seen dimly silhouetted against the night sky, identification at that time was a difficult matter, and there were heartbreaking experiences of shooting down a squadron mate by mistake. Something was needed urgently to bridge the final gap between airborne radar approach and final visual identification.

This was pointed up sharply to us by a young RAF squadron leader who had been sent to this country to help out the British Air Commission and incidentally to rest up from battle fatigue. He was a red-headed boy usually known as Blood Orange Smith, and he gave us a very graphic picture of the problems of night aerial combat with which he had had intimate and prolonged experience.

We believe the problem could be solved with a variation of the common night telescope or night binocular, providing certain optical conditions could be met and the difficulty of airplane vibration could be overcome. This belief was based on some properties of the human eye, which is a truly remarkable instrument for night vision under certain conditions. Undoubtedly all of you have had the experience of walking outdoors on a very dark night when suddenly some good-sized object looms up in front of you. A horse or cow in an open field at night is a good example. At a distance nothing is visible, but near at hand the animal's silhouette is very easy to see. There is no more light, nothing is brighter, but the silhouette is bigger. It is on this principle that the night glass or night telescope operates. It does not make things brighter, only bigger, but to one unaccustomed to the use of night glasses, the first experience seems miraculous.

Conferences with Radiation Laboratory personnel gave the necessary information to permit integrating this method with newly developed short wave radar, and with the aid of a small black airplane we went to work. Both Army and Navy were interested, and by the late summer of 1941 the vibration problem had been solved, together with the necessary wide field of view, and sample instruments were ready for military flight tests.

Our equipment was undergoing tests at the Naval Air Station at Norfolk, Va. at the time of the Pearl Harbor attack [on December 7]. Several of us were with it and all through the day of December 8th we were making ready for a test to be flown that night in which we would pursue a black target airplane in simulated combat. Everyone at the station had the jitters and rumors were flying about thick and fast, but preparations were completed and the test went ahead, hampered slightly by the belts of live ammunition with which our machine guns had been loaded in spite of our protests. Sentries were challenging that evening with a new note of urgency, but everything went well, and our seaplane rolled down the ramp and into the water just at dusk. The antiaircraft defenses at Hampton Roads and on the Virginia Capes had been informed that we would be flying the mission, and instructed that no searchlights were to be turned on us to interfere with the tests. That appeared to be just too much to ask of them. Pearl Harbor had happened only yesterday! Every time we would circle over Hampton Roads preparatory to making an interception a dozen dazzling fingers of light, half a billion candlepower each, would hit us with the impact of something solid. Finally in desperation we signaled our target airplane and headed out to sea where we could have a little peace, and quiet, and darkness to complete the work.

The results of the tests were very good and I caught an early morning plane back to Washington, leaving French, Hopkins, and Stewart of our group to complete some daylight tests which the Navy also wanted. This brings up an amusing sequel which I heard about later. It was a fine day and our somewhat antiquated patrol bomber, a PBY, was flying along off Cape Henry running vibration curves, when there loomed alongside a much bigger and newer and tougher PBM just in from Atlantic patrol. It was broad daylight, but there was some mix-up in identification even though the airplane our men were using was a well-known American type with the regular American markings. Just at that crucial moment the radio transmitter went out as was a common occurrence in the early days of the war, and here was the PBM alongside, guns bristling, and no way to tell her that our airplane contained a harmless group of scientists. It looked as though the shooting would start any minute but finally Hopkins produced a flashlight, which at that short range was visible even in the daytime, the code identification of the poor old PBY was spelled out laboriously to the bristling PBM and peace finally reigned again.

By mid 1942 the success of the night telescope, now known officially as the nightsight, was assured, and the instrument was adopted as standard equipment for the new American nightfighter then known as the XP61 and later to be named the Black Widow. Doolittle had raided Tokyo, the Battle of Midway had been fought, and the war prospects looked just a little brighter than they had in the days immediately following Pearl Harbor. The submarine war in the Atlantic was going badly, however, and we were called upon to do something about the particularly annoying problem of night identification of a suspected submarine target from a patrolling airplane.

By this time the organization of the laboratory had undergone some changes, and because of the unprecedented growth in staff, laboratory sections on physical measurement, optical design, mechanical design, etc. had been set up, the heads of these respective sections constituting an operating committee. This committee contributed so much to the effectiveness of the laboratory that I would like to name its members. They are listed here alphabetically: John C. Evans, Hobert W. French, Robert E. Hopkins, Frederick W. Paul, and Harold S. Stewart. There were many others within the sections, who contributed a very great deal, but the total number was about seventy and it isn't possible to name them all.

The anti-submarine problem produced some amusing episodes but there is not time to say much of these. Perhaps the most embarrassing moment occurred one bright moonlight night over the mouth of Chesapeake Bay. Our target for that night was an obliging little English trawler equipped for submarine detection, which was supposed to be having its equipment overhauled at the Naval Base. Her captain was most cooperative but a great many things went wrong. We had an old B-188-B out of Langley Field and were short a co-pilot, so I was occupying that position and trying to maintain radio communication with the Langley Tower and the trawler. Again as so frequently occurred in those days the radio went out, and we tried every known means of signaling to the trawler directly beneath us. We ended up by almost flying down her smokestack, and again finally resorted to Morse code via pocket flashlights. After the usual difficulties we got the ideas across and the tests went off all right.

By the end of 1942 the phosphor laboratory under Franz Urbach had made important advances in the infrared sensitive phosphor, and in another section of the Institute we had developed a new and very efficient form of infrared telescope to utilize the new material. The Navy had ordered large numbers of the instruments which carried a very high security classification, and most of the components including the phosphor were designated by code. These infrared telescopes were given the dignified but meaningless name of metascope at the Navy's request, and both the Eastman Kodak Co. and Samson United Corp. were going into very substantial production on the A and B instruments, the prototypes of which

Corner cube demonstration by Evans and Hopkins.

had been built in our laboratory shops. By March of 1943 assembly of type A instruments at the Samson United Corp. was just ready to begin when we received a telephone call and a confirming telegram from Admiral Furer, Chief of Naval Office of Research and Development, asking that we do everything possible within the next eight days to complete fifty of the type A instruments. Instruments completed after eight days would be of no service in the undertaking in question. In the mail that day we received an urgent and indignant letter from a Washington civilian agency responsible for checking our expenditures, demanding to know why we had purchased twenty gross of machine screws at a cost of $26.50. The writer of the letter was indignant about such obvious extravagance on our part and immediate and detailed explanations were demanded. Fortunately President James Conant, chairman of the National Research Committee, wired us that afternoon, and on his instructions we let the gentleman in Washington wait for an explanation about the $26.50 expenditure while we got busy on the metascope.

That was a very busy week. The Samson United people extended themselves to the utmost, but there were certain essential optical parts required which were ready to be produced but which no one outside of our laboratory had yet succeeded in making. Could we make fifty sets in about six days? Our entire senior class in Optics and some of the juniors had been employed part time on some of this war work. It was good experience for

The Metascope type B was used as a naval infrared telescope.

them, they were discreet (we had Intelligence permission to use these students who were all listed and approved by name), and they went at their work with a will. The word from Admiral Furer had come near the end of the week so we called the boys together and explained the job. Those youngsters, divided into shifts, started on a day-and-night program Friday noon, and by Tuesday afternoon the optical parts and a comfortable number of spares were delivered to the Samson United factory. Who says a student can't work?

In the meantime, the laboratory staff had lined up the necessary components and for the last thirty-six hours of the assembly more than thirty physicists and engineers from our group took over the newly starting Samson United production line. The factory people pitched in with the same spirit and on the eighth day the required instruments left Rochester by plane for the Pacific Coast.

We still didn't know where these things were going. I left for California the day before the shipment and met the instruments at the San Diego Naval Base. The instruments were fine, but the spare batteries which were coming from New York had not arrived. After some frantic telephone calls to the East a new shipment of batteries was sent out by air, but did not arrive in San Diego until four o'clock the following afternoon. The task force had sailed at noon but an airplane had been assigned in case the batteries arrived later, and it delivered them to the flagship before sunset. For a time we wondered where those metascopes were to be used, but we soon figured it out from the newspapers even before we were told by the Navy. Since that occurred at the end of March in 1945, you have no doubt guessed the target too.

From this point on developments came rapidly in a variety of devices which we had conceived for the conduct of night military and naval operations. One or two of them are worth mentioning if for no other reason than for the amusing occurrences connected with them. In the summer of 1942 we had decided to bring to life an old optical principle in what is known as the triple mirror. If one has three plane mirrors mutually perpendicular to each other, as though set against the wall and floor in the corner of a room, such a combination will always reflect a beam of light back in the direction from which it came. Instead of mirrors one may use the corner sawed from a polished cube of glass, and the internal reflections between the three mutually perpendicular faces will do the same thing. If such a device is made sufficiently perfect, the accuracy with which it returns a beam of light exactly in the direction of origin is almost unbelievable. The Germans had used a few of these in World War I and the British had produced a few at a very high cost, but the accuracy was so good that the returning beam would diverge only a few inches per mile. The hours of skilled labor required to produce such a contrivance seemed to make practical utilization in quantity almost hopeless, but we were optimistic. The Mount Wilson Observatory had developed in its optical shop a very nice and rapid method for making another kind of optical device known as a roof prism in which two polished surfaces must be perpendicular to each other with a very high order of accuracy. It seemed probable that they could extend that to making three perpendicular surfaces, and could improve methods so that the production costs in man hours would be more reasonable. I initiated such a project at the Mount Wilson Observatory through our section of the NDRC, and by the end of 1942 the worst of the problem was solved and an initial sample lot of fourteen such triple reflectors had been completed.

At this time we received a telephone call from one of our associates in Washington saying that an officer from the then super-secret Office of Strategic Services had a very special problem, and would arrive with suitable credentials to discuss it. He arrived with the credentials and a very impressive beard, but he was a very effective officer as we soon learned. His problem was to land a light reconnaissance airplane in a country not at war with us but very definitely hostile, and to do it without anyone being the wiser. We were not told which country, but the terrain where the landing was to be made was described to us in detail. It was wild country and very hilly, but there was a level beach sufficient for the purpose on the shore on a small lake. One man would be sent in on foot some days in advance and could place any kind of markers we might suggest which he could carry concealed on his person. The airplane landing, however, had to be made at night, and no lights must show on the ground. Moreover, the agent who placed the markers would have to leave the area some days before the landing was to be made, so the airplane pilot would have no ground help whatever. It was agreed that the pilot could show a faint light of about one candlepower if necessary for a minute or so before the actual landing without endangering the security of the operation.

The fourteen triple mirrors had arrived from Mt. Wilson the day before and looked like a natural solution to the problem. They are so efficient that if a tiny flashlight lamp is held near one eye a triple mirror at a distance of a mile stands out as brightly luminous point of light. You can see immediately the solution, which was to line the runway with these markers and provide the pilot with a tiny light source. It took only twenty-four hours to prepare the demonstration, and with the cooperation of the Rochester Airport officials, who by this time were accustomed to our antics, we made the demonstration to the colonel. The airport was completely blacked out late at night with other airplanes warned away and nothing in the air except our small reconnaissance airplane similar to the one assigned to his mission.

Mt. Wilson triple mirror for marking night airplane landing strip.

His problem was solved and he was delighted with the result, but to this day I have not been informed where that lake was located! However, as a result of this success a very tidy production of triple mirrors was undertaken for the Office of Strategic Services by a manufacturer on the Pacific Coast, using mirror production methods developed by Mount Wilson and using accessories, system and method which we had developed here at Rochester.

By the end of 1944 conditions were rather strained in the European theater. Our airborne troops had encountered some troubles long before in the Sicilian campaign and some serious troubles at the time of the Normandy invasion. On these occasions and later in some related land operations the loss of men was distressingly high, and something had to be done about it. Unfortunately here I encounter security restrictions even at this late date. May I simply say, however, that the representative of our NDRC division at Allied Headquarters, Dr. Charles Waring, who had spent the greater part of 1945 in our laboratories and so knew our equipment well, cabled that he was returning to this country on an urgent matter involving metascopes. By this time the Army had arranged for large production of a very compact form of our metascope which we had designated the type F, and production was just getting under way. Waring arrived in this country with orders so sweeping and carrying signatures which startled us. He had only twelve days to procure the equipment and return to France, but fortunately his orders had the same effect on jaded Washington that they had had upon us, and on the eleventh day he departed from

Pilot with light-source headband for night landing.

the Atlantic Coast with four bombers carrying a sufficient quantity of our gadgets. The fact that they type F's were so compact that all could have been carried in a single airplane did not detract in any way from the wonderful pomp and ceremony of setting out in four. Four were assigned to poor Waring and four it had to be. As a result of this and sequels, an operation in which the manpower loss exceeded eighty percent was reduced on one significant occasion to a mission completed without the loss of a single man. I think this gave me more of a lift than any other single episode of the war.

As we began war work on dive bombing and sunlight, so we ended it on a different aspect of the same problem, and our last instrument to go into any substantial production was for defense against the very type of attack in which our sun alignment sight had been tried at the outset of the war. This instrument is now entirely declassified so I can tell you about it and its use. Unfortunately the Japanese had been making both bombing and torpedo attacks upon our ships in the Pacific by coming in from the direction of the sun. Search radar when functioning properly was adequate protection against most surprise attacks of this nature, but there were still limitations which caused the Navy to request some optical device immune to the dazzling effects of the sun even when looking directly at the solar disc.

No ordinary dark glass or sun goggle was satisfactory. A much improved sun goggle with a graded deposit of metal had been produced by Bausch & Lomb, using a method which I had developed some years before the war. This was very good for general eye protection of pilots and lookouts, and had been received enthusiastically by the Air Force. However, for the specific Navy problem something different was required, some device which would dim the sun without proportionately dimming the surrounding sky.

Two NDRC projects at other laboratories had been carried through in attempts to solve this problem but nothing practical had come forth. An independent solution had been developed here using a phosphor, but this was done informally and for several reasons we did not propose it in competition with the other projects. When these projects were closed the Navy asked us to undertake the problem and it was then only necessary to take the development off the shelf as it were and put it into practical form. This device was named the Icaroscope, at first as a joke after the mythical Icarus who, you will recall, flew too near the sun. Later it became a serious name, and you will find it engraved upon the instrument as they are distributed in the fleet today. It is a little thing, small enough to hold in the hand, and you use it like an ordinary telescope. It has one important and unusual property, however. When you look at the sun and a patch of surrounding sky, the sun is dimmed enormously and all out of proportion to the dimming of the sky around it. The device is thus an automatic volume limiter for light, and as far as we know, this is the first time such a result has been accomplished. No dark glass or shield has the same effect, since the Icaroscope acts selectively and only upon those objects in the field of view which are too bright for comfortable vision.

Although deliveries of the instrument in quantity to the fleet were too late to be of use in the war, there was an amusing aftermath at the atomic bomb tests at Bikini. About a hundred of the type 1 instruments were delivered by the Bureau of Ships to Joint Task Force One for use by observers in watching the air burst. These worked very well. I watched the air burst on July 1 from a front row seat, but like everyone who used the instrument was disappointed in the flash. It took all the fizz out of the bomb. Looking through the Icaroscope one saw the lagoon, the islands, and the target fleet, but the bomb flash when it came was only just comfortably brighter than the background sky. Of course, this was not the fault of the instrument since it was only doing its duty.

I am afraid I have spent quite enough time on this rambling tale, but there are a few serious lessons which we learned from this war work. The only one I want to mention is the beneficial effect, frequently overlooked, which applied science has upon so-called pure science. At the end of the war there was a great urge among physicists and others in scientific fields to get away from the kind of application and development work which had occupied them for five long years. This is understandable. We felt the same, and certainly the highly organized war-time development laboratory is not the way in which scientific talent should be used in peacetime. But there was a gain of which we may have lost sight; the tools which applied science and engineering have provided for basic research. Such tools come so gradually in peacetime that we do not realize their importance. Instead we see only the obvious, that applied science and the engineer draw basic ideas from more fundamental researches carried on by others. This is true, of course, but the process is not one way but two. The tools which the engineer provides can influence the entire progress of a pure science. Such tools came thick and fast during the war, and now we are in a position to benefit in using them. Perhaps this realization may provide us with a little closer bond between these ever disputed regions of pure and applied science.

This, I think, is enough of a rather Flong story.

This article is a draft of a speech that Brian O'Brien gave to the Rochester Rotary Club and in several other venues in the months following May 1947, when the material was finally cleared for public release.

Brian O'Brien was a member of the faculty of the University of Rochester from 1930 until 1955. He served as Director of The Institute of Optics from 1938 until 1951. He passed away in 1992.

Fraley Story: Accidental Launching

George Fraley

Already in the 1930s Brian O'Brien began launching ultraviolet spectrometers suspended in a gondola below high-altitude balloons to measure the properties of the atmospheric ozone layer. After the war the wicker gondola basket from those early flights was still stored in the attic of Bausch & Lomb. New materials had been developed to make better balloons, so O'Brien, Walter Siegmund, and Gordon Milne decided to start a new series of launches. Launches were made three summers in a row in the late 1940s from a Navy base in South Dakota just over the line from St. Cloud, Minnesota. George Fraley went along one summer, and when Parker Givens joined the faculty he also worked on the project. The balloons were filled with helium, released to rise up over one hundred thousand feet when the balloon would burst, releasing the instrumented gondola. The trailing parachute would then open at around forty thousand feet when the air was dense enough. George's job then was to chase and recover the descending gondola. It was made a particularly challenging task by the fact that successive layers of the jet stream would alternately propel the balloon at one hundred miles per hour in one direction, and then suddenly one hundred miles per hour in the opposite direction. The ten thousand lakes in the area added to the fun. The wicker basket was outfitted with kapok-filled life preserver cushions for flotation. A chase plane and a radio transmitter helped with the chase.

Preparations for accidental launching.

George described some of the adventures encountered on these summer outings:

These balloons are fairly delicate and very costly. If you got a hole in it, you threw the whole balloon away and started all over again. But those were built, made in St. Paul, by 3M. Well, there's always wind and if you didn't have any way of holding these things, the several-story-high balloon would take off and crash into a building, into a car, into a flagpole. So they always anchored the balloons with a line to a vehicle. The line was parachute line, and in between the parachute line and the vehicle was a squib which is an explosive device that had pieces of copper loose inside of it and an explosive behind it, and the other end of the squib was open so when you set the explosive off it would blow this copper through the parachute line out the other side. It was a nice way of releasing the balloon fast. Well, I can remember one day, for some reason, the military had some kind of maneuvers or something that tied up all available military vehicles. So, they decided to tie the balloon to the front end of my car—which was fine, except I had nothing to do and the instrument group had nothing to do with setting these squibs on the lines. I think that the group that was doing the squibs had spent most of the night in one of the local bars. And they forgot to put the charge into it. The balloon took off up in the air and I was thinking, well when was it going to do it. And now the wind came up and there, there I'm bouncing down the runway. Not fast, but I'm bouncing, not high, but I'm bouncing. And everybody is running around, "who's got an axe, who's got an axe?!" They finally found an axe and released it. It was interesting. And I couldn't just stop it, there was no way I could stop it.

George Fraley was a member of the staff of the University of Rochester from 1946 until 1984. He is currently retired and living south of Naples, NY.

15. Crossroads Reminiscences

Brian O'Brien Jr.

Before World War II my father had developed the first of a series of high-speed cameras to study the reciprocity effect in silver halide emulsions. The Type I was a single streak camera with an equivalent speed of eleven million frames per second.[1]

In 1946 when the military was setting up Joint Task Force One to test nuclear explosives on Bikini atoll in the Pacific (termed "Operation Crossroads"), they asked my father and The Institute of Optics to participate with his cameras. He agreed, and preparations began. It was obviously important to have some idea of the expected fireball brightness to determine exposure. The only source of this was a roll of 16-mm motion picture film taken at the original "Trinity" test at Alamogordo. Little or no information was available as to film processing conditions, but with micro densitometry and some assumptions, an approximate value was obtained.

Since the camera used a continuous loop of film, a very high-speed capping shutter would probably be required.[2] Since the light went through a single slit at one point, it was only necessary to cut off the light at this point. To do this a heavy current was run through a loop of soft aluminum wire stretched on either side of the slit. The magnetic field generated by the current attracted the two wires together shutting off the light. A closure speed of a fraction of a millisecond was attained, but the wire needed to be immersed in clear mineral oil to prevent bounce. The current from a large capacitor was dumped through the wires by a Thyrotron tube[3] on a signal from a photoelectric cell, and then a slow mechanical capping shutter finished the job.

Besides specific camera details, electrical and electronic controls had to be designed and built to be compatible with the remote control radio signals to be supplied by the task force. Since the environmental conditions to be encountered were only known generally as tropical, proper protective enclosures had to be designed to protect the cameras and controls from hot damp air, salt spray and, possibly, blowing sand. All the steel enclosures were painted white in case they had to be exposed to direct sunlight for a long time.

At this time I was stationed at the Bureau of Aeronautics in the Navy Department, and because of my familiarity with the equipment,

Weatherproof streak cameral housing for Crossroads bomb test.

my father requested me as Navy liaison officer for the project. I was reassigned to Rochester to help with the preparations.

We began getting messages from Bikini to please get out there earlier than planned. It turned out that many of the academic people arrived with equipment not quite ready. While quite extensive shop facilities were available on the scientific ship,[4] any work in the field is always many times more difficult than at home base. Realizing this from his considerable experience in scientific fieldwork, my father insisted that everything be ready to "plug and play" when it arrived. Of course this term had not been created at that time. As these messages became more urgent it was decided that I should go out in advance of my father and Gordon Milne to reassure the task force that we would be ready on time.

Eastman Kodak had built a smaller copy of the Type I camera. Because of his general pessimism,[5] my father decided we should have a shipboard backup camera in addition to the main island cameras, so he borrowed the Kodak camera. A destroyer, the USS Barton, was assigned to us, and a camera mount was designed to go on the gyro-stabilized SD gun-laying radar antenna. This antenna was on top of the optical fire director so that it could be accurately pointed toward the target area. While all the island instrumentation was to be radio controlled, I was in charge of operating the shipboard camera manually.

The island cameras were mounted on the upper level of a low tower, while the University of California Bowen camera was installed on the lower level. The Bowen camera had a very short run of film, and hence needed a fast-capping shutter. The approach was less subtle than ours. The light from the target area was reflected into the camera by an 8×10-inch, half-inch-thick plate glass mirror on a tripod outside the tower. A loop of Primacord, a clothesline-sized hollow cord filled with an extremely high-speed explosive,[6]

U.S.S. Barton scientific observation ship at Bikini Atoll.

U.S.S. Barton with camera mounted on gyro-stabilized radar antenna.

was wrapped around the edge of the mirror. This was fired by a photocell actuated blasting cap arrangement.

By this means the glass was turned into fine shrapnel and the light was cut off to the camera. During set-up and practice the University of California personnel's firing and safety procedure went something like: "Look out"—BANG!! As a result, the canvas sides to the tower eventually resembled a target for concentrated shotgun practice. Fortunately the tower was high enough so that our cameras escaped, and only the canvas around them was perforated. Their store of many rolls of Primacord was in a cardboard box on the ground in front of the tower. When a bulldozer came around to push up a protective earthworks in front of the tower an alert U of C technician managed to rescue it before the bulldozer accidentally detonated it, and the tower along with it.

A rehearsal was held two days before the "Able" test. A small TNT charge in a matching bomb case was dropped from bombing altitude. All went well. It was on target, the radio controls worked, but we had one small problem. Just as the drop happened, Admiral Ramsey's flagship steamed right between the target and our ship. The admiral commanding the task force, of course, wanted to be on the closest ship. My father immediately had words with Ralph Sawyer, who was in scientific command of the task force, and it was clearly understood that on D-day our ship, the Barton, would be the closest active ship to the blast.

One interesting sidelight relates to the protective goggles that were supplied to all personnel in the task force. From the fireball brightness calculated from that original

Alamogordo film, my father calculated that a safe value would be an optical density of 1.0. The safety officer, who was the head of radiology at a major medical school, decided to put a factor of safety of 3 on this and specified an optical density of 3.0. Logarithms were not his strong suit. While everyone's eyes were protected, they didn't see much of the shot. As a matter of fact the optical fire director crew, against orders, watched through the telescopic fire director with no protection at all, and suffered no damage.

On the bomb run there was sent an approximate minus-two-minute signal, and an audible tone was transmitted from the airplane. This tone stopped at bomb release, and automatic timers took over to operate the radio signals for the island equipment. To aid the bombardier, strobe lights were set up on the islands of the atoll along the bomber track, and the target ship, the USS Nevada, was painted bright orange with white stripes. Also, winds and temperatures were known at every thousand feet up to bombing altitude. Several hundred practice drops had been done in the Nevada desert to determine trajectory time and placement error to be expected. The three-sigma error was around 630 feet from ground zero, about the length of a capital ship.

Test tower with camera near ground zero.

On D-day all was set. I was perched on the gun director with earphones, the camera control box, and a stopwatch. At the minus two-minute signal I started the camera drum spinning, listened to the bombardier's tone and when it stopped, started the stopwatch. Five seconds before detonation I opened the capping shutter, and closed it immediately after detonation. On looking up it seemed that the mushroom cloud was leaning over toward us. Fearing radiation fogging of our film, I frantically unbolted the camera from the antenna, wrapped it in black cloth and rushed it, still spinning, down to the wardroom, hoping that the steel hull of the ship would absorb any radiation. Our fears turned out to result from only an illusion—the cloud had gone essentially straight up.

The Barton was also used by one of the radiological survey crews. It was our ship until six milliseconds after the bomb went off (the extent of our film load), and after that it belonged to them. At the direction of the radiological people, we steamed downwind all night and came back to the atoll the next day to find out what had happened.

The person on the scientific ship in charge of the remote radio control transmitter thought that he heard the audible tone from the bomber stop, but the automatic sequence timer had not started, so he started it manually. Then he heard the tone continuing. He stopped the timer and set it to use the minus-two-minute signal. Unfortunately this signal was only approximate, and the result was that all the time critical island equipment worked properly, *but some fourteen seconds after the bomb went off.* This included not only our island cameras, but the blast gauges, all the other cameras, etc.

As far as we were concerned, this turned out to be academic, since, in spite of the strobe lights, the orange target ship, and the fact that he could have made as many bomb runs as he wanted, the bombardier missed the Nevada by more than 700 *yards* on his first run and dropped it nearly down the funnel of the carrier Independence. This was outside the field of view of our island cameras, so they would have missed it anyway.

While we had no responsibility connected with the "Baker" underwater shot to be held in two weeks time, we were planning to stay to observe it. However, the Los Alamos people needed a value for the equivalent tonnage of the "Able" shot before they detonated the "Baker" shot. Since all of the blast gauge and island photographic data was lost, obtaining this value depended on what we had captured on the fourteen inches of 16-mm film from the shipboard O'Brien camera.[7] Therefore, we rapidly packed up some ten large crates of equipment, all classified "Secret," and headed back home via seaplane to Kwajalein atoll, and then a series of Army Air transport R5Ds via Hickam field, Hamilton field to Bolling field in Anacostia, Va. At each relay, as officer courier, I had to count the crates off and on the airplanes and sign for them, and in the process they managed to lose my suitcase. We spent the night in Washington, and the next day they gave us a B-25 to take us to Rochester.

Once back at the Institute preparations were started for processing the film. It was to be tray processed along with a sensitometer strip and cotton swab agitation. In order to monitor the development, a captured German "Seehund" infrared image-tube telescope was set up with a near infrared floodlight. This gave the added safety feature of being able to retrieve the film in the dark, in case it was accidentally dropped. After several rehearsal processings, the Crossroads film was developed and all went well. The result of the first few milliseconds of the "Able" shot can be seen in figure.

Streak photograph of Crossroads A-bomb test.

After appropriate micro-densitometry, the results were cabled out to JTF-1 and they went ahead with the "Baker" shot on schedule. It is interesting to note that the tonnage calculated from the radiochemical assays many weeks later agreed quite well with our results.

Brian O'Brien, Jr. received his B.S. from the Institute of Optics in 1944. He is the son of Brian O'Brien. He is currently retired and living in Quinebaug, CT.

References

1   Later, by means of an image dissector, this camera was converted to a true framing camera at the same frame speed.
2   It was possible that the fireball brightness would drop enough in the first six milliseconds that the first exposure would show through the double exposure, but a high speed shutter was advisable.
3   This was before solid-state electronics.
4   The scientific ship was a submarine tender.
5   He was a great believer in Murphy's Law, and even O'Brien's corollary, that Murphy was an optimist.
6   This explosive is pentaerythritol tetranitrate (PETN). Primacord is used to nearly simultaneously detonate dynamite charges that are physically separated by considerable distances. A modern example is the application in imploding buildings.
7   Tonnage could be calculated from the early rate of expansion of the fireball.

Fraley Story: Hunting Prairie Dogs

George Fraley

On one of the balloon launches to study the ultraviolet absorption of the ozone layer, George Fraley had a little too much time on his hands and ended up making an emergency trip to the hospital. The launches were from a naval base near Mitchell, South Dakota, in the middle of the northern prairie.

George recounts his adventure:

A lot of the time on these launches we didn't have anything to do, we were just waiting for the wind to die down. The military people, the sailors there, they had nothing to do so they would get a competition going to catch prairie dogs. Whoever got the most prairie dogs got free beer in the next weekend in St. Paul. You had to catch them alive. You can see in the picture that to fill these balloons they had plastic tubing that would go into the balloon. The tubing was about sixteen inches across when it was full, well, they had this tubing out there by the roll, miles long. They would never use it twice but it was there. How to catch the prairie dogs was . . . one guy would take a five-gallon pail of water and go out, pour the water into the prairie dog hole and the other guy would hold this clear plastic tubing over the hole. The prairie dog would come out, you grab both ends, now you got a prairie dog. This is how they did it. Well, I don't remember who it was, but somebody from the military got me to join in and I did. The problem was we didn't take a real prairie dog hole, well it was but it was old and had a yellow jackets' nest in it. So I ended up in the hospital that night and the next day there was a roll call and, I don't remember, but there was an officer from the military there and there would be no more capturing of prairie dogs going on there. Well, that did not set very nicely with the guys because some of them got pretty good at it. They got free beers. Whoever didn't catch any of them, the lowest number of prairie dogs would have to buy them all for everyone else.

Giant balloon is launched to study ozone layer in the stratosphere, but the plastic tubing had other uses.

16. Herb Graf Remembers

Carlos Stroud and Maria Schnitzler

Herb Graf joined the staff of the optics shop as an optician in 1943 and remained there doing precision optical fabrication and testing until he retired in 1987. In addition to his duties as an optician he is familiar to generations of students he helped train to grind, polish, and test their telescope mirrors in the "Fab and Testing" course. In November 2003 he visited the Institute where his recollections were taped in an interview. The audiotape is saved in the University archives.

Herb described how, after graduating from Edison Technical High School in Rochester, he worked briefly as a machinist at Delco and then at Bausch & Lomb, where he began working with optics. He described how he came to be hired at the Institute.

> I took off a couple of days from Bausch & Lomb where we were working ten-hour days putting optics in the range finders for battlewagons. I went duck hunting down in Irondequoit Bay on Stony Point. And I met a fellow down there that had a Springer Spaniel and he was duck hunting also. He asked if we could hunt together, and I said "sure," and so we hunted together a couple of times. Then, one day he said, "Herb, I've got a class that I have to tend to, but I'll be back if you're going to be here." And, I said, "Yeah, I'll be here." I didn't put anything together that he was a professor at the UR, but he was Dr. Fred Paul. One day my mother got a call from a Dr. Fred Paul at the University of Rochester. They'd like to have Herb Graf to come up and have an interview, at his convenience. They said that they were starting a research project in the optics lab, which was then underneath the right side of the library. So, I said sure I'd be happy to work here on the project. We did diamond grinding to generate all of the curves that went into Hopkins stereoscopic camera. Then we sent them over to the machine shop that was in the Biology Department in Dewey to be mounted. After that they took it out to be tested, and Bob came back into the shop and he said, "Wow, 10,000 feet and you can see a fly on a railroad track." He was real pleased.

Just after the war, Herb and Fred Paul had quite an adventure.

> I was very close to Fred because Fred got me to come up here. We really had a good time together. Before I was married Fred wanted to go back to Oregon to visit his family. And so, he took his wife, Ruth, and the three children and fixed it up so I could have a two-month leave of absence, and the whole family and I took off in their big Buick in 1946 across the country. Fred was a great outdoors person. We took along a .22 rifle and when we were out on the plains there were a few hawks sitting on telephone poles, and he said, "Herb, I bet you can't touch that hawk." So, I got out of the car and leaned over the hood with the rifle and then I fired. I can remember he hollered, "Ha, ha, I knew you'd miss them." But the hawk took off and about two wing beats later he dropped.

Herb was unusual in that he was an optician with a German surname who was not trained at Zeiss in Germany.

> I learned right here at the UR. When I first came we had a fellow whose name was Hugo Guenther who came from Bausch & Lomb, and later Bill Klinkert who took over the shop when Guenther died. Bill and Hugo were both Germans trained over there. Their

Herb Graf in the Optics shop.

background was okay and not okay. Me being of German descent though American born—why, I got along great with both of them.

He did a little fishing along with his hunting.

Mary Banning, Fred Paul and I would go up to Oatka Creek fishing together, and Bob Hopkins, Fred Paul and I would go too. Bob tried, he tried so hard to catch trout. Fred and I would catch one right after the other. Bob was just having an awful time. And then down at his place in Springwater, I guess that he got so frustrated he says, "Well, I'm going to put my own trout ponds in." So, he put his own ponds in, but he still couldn't catch fish. So, I've got some very good memories.

With the coming of the Laboratory for Laser Energetics, the optics shop became an essential part of the fabrication of the big laser systems, and was eventually transferred to control of the Laser Lab.

Bill Klinkert and I, we made all of the neodymium doped glass laser slabs for the first laser, and then the big glass rods for the next system. . . . I liked Lubin. I had lots of fun with Jay Eastman and Duncan Moore, and Jimmy Forsyth. I guess Jimmy came in as an undergraduate, then a masters, then got his doctorate. So we were associated for eight years or more. And then when he and Lubin left and started their own place over there, they called me over to assemble their first laser. . . . Yeah, if I saw Jimmy Forsyth right now I'd give him a hug.

Fraley Story: Man from Mars

George Fraley

During the Second World War an infrared viewer was developed for use in driving in the dark without headlamps. One version of the viewer was in the form of a helmet that fit over the head with viewers for each eye. George Fraley did some of the field testing in an area where Whipple Park is today. Then it was a wooded tract with a dirt road running through it. The unit was mounted in a jeep with a big vacuum tube power supply in the back and a thirty-kilovolt cable running up to power the unit on the driver's head.

Some military brass were coming to see a demonstration of the device, and the morning before the visit, Jack Evans asked George to go out and do a road test to see that everything was working well. George asked Johnny Leone to go along for company and for safety in case of any problems. The tests went well, and at noon George and Johnny decided to go over to Twelve Corners in Brighton for some lunch. Since things were working well there seemed to be no reason to take the helmet and goggles off. As they pulled into the parking lot Johnny said that there was a police car following them. George could not see in the rear view mirror, just straight ahead, but he took Johnny's word for it.

Here's how George described what happened next:

They came up and he says "Are you from Mars?" "No, I'm not from Mars, I'm from the University of Rochester." "May we ask you what is that contraption on your head? It's not something that I think you should be wearing in traffic." So, we sort of had to go through and explain to them in very broad terms what it was and what we were doing. After we got through doing it, they . . . I remember, they even came in and ate with us. Most of the afternoon there was a police car behind us. Well, that night, because there was no sense in using these things really during the day—they were night vision things. And, of course, they made everything look green during the day, and so but 9:00, 9:30 p.m. we met the military people. I think Brian went through and gave them one of his typical spiels and you know and all that kind of stuff. How easy it would be to make and everything else. We only need another $100,000 to develop it and what have you there. So they wanted a demonstration of this, so that night, Johnny had gone home, of course, at 5:30 p.m., and Jack Evans said well I'll go with you and we had my jeep at the time and we had taken red filters and put over the lights. Once you turn your lights on, the only way you could tell they are on is to get close to them and feel the heat.

I, of course, am young and oh boy these guys, Jack and two other guys and the power supply that took up half of the back of the jeep. Course the jeep had no top on. And one guy was hanging on the running board, and the other guy was opposite the power supply in the back. It was pitch black and they couldn't see anything. I mean, they walked around the jeep and got out in front of the jeep. They couldn't see any lights at all. So we went around the course there once. Well, I forgot, Jack forgot, that about two-thirds of the way through the thing there, there's a low spot there and there was a big puddle of water. So I come up over the hill, down into the water, and really . . . I couldn't really see . . . I was having a ball. I really wasn't paying much attention to the water. Well, we hit the water at a fairly good clip. The water came up over the front of us, onto the military people. Soaked them, soaked Jack, soaked me, and all of a sudden I hear "We're on fire!!" And I said I know something is wrong because I can't see any more. So, we're trying to get out of there, ripping the filters off of the lights, 'cause we didn't have any fire extinguishers, or anything else. This power supply was, of I would say, two foot square, maybe twenty inches high, something like that there, and it was fastened to the back of the seat with a big cable that came down, drooped down then came up over your back into the back of this thing here. And it was an interesting evening.

Perhaps partly as a result of this incident later units of the Metascope were developed that did not need the high-voltage source. Some used a radioactive source to sensitize the infrared phosphor.

Fraley Story: Unusual Labs on River Campus

George Fraley

During the Second World War much of the University was devoted to the war effort, with soldiers replacing students in most of the classes, and laboratories for military research projects in every available space. A lot of the work in Optics was related to night warfare. (See Brian O'Brien's essay, chapter 14, on the science of night warfare.)

Tests were carried out of cats eye reflectors with infrared phosphors. These were small plastic reflectors with infrared phosphors. They were developed for use by Australian and New Zealand spotters who were hiding on islands in the South Pacific reporting to submarines on any enemy activity in the area. The hidden spotters could easily carry a few of the small reflectors to a secret hiding place in the mountains. A submarine could then surface at night and shine an infrared search light up to the area where the spotter was hidden. The cats eye would fluoresce in the visible when illuminated by the infrared search light. The visible fluorescence would be well collimated by the cats eye so that it was visible only to the submarine. Messages could then be transmitted via code by blocking and unblocking the reflector. It was almost impossible for the enemy to detect that any of this was going on.

George Fraley described the testing of these devices:

We used the seventeenth floor of the library, cat walk around the outside of the library, that's still there, of course the stacks go all the way up there now. We had a station up there looking down to Warden Hill and there was an old wood water tower, there was a county thing there and we had instrumentation inside this but a clear view but to Rochester. You could see the cats eyes over that long distance there. We spent a lot of time driving back and forth testing them.

They did other related work.

They used the library, used the seventeenth floor again, and they would build little cities down on this flat area, just above the main library and then they would try and develop the K-21 camera, I believe it was, I think it was the K-21 camera was developed to take pictures to see whether they could see what was going on the ground. It was interesting. They were trying to decipher from camouflage to real from airplanes at night using infrared sensitive film. Kodak was producing lots of exotic film in those days. Infrared was the only way you could tell the difference. And then they moved some of that operation up to the attic in the B&L building. And they had a small town at the east end of the B&L building there. Everything was black, matte black, and the town was put onto it and then they shot down to the west side and they had a platform up there where you could set up cameras and stuff like that there.

Opposite of that we had a range, rifle range. We had a large number of different grants and contracts at the time. They had a contract to try and get rid of the flash from the guns, M-1s, that was the gun I believe at the time the military was using in the Pacific. Japanese would sit in their palm trees or coconut trees and every time they saw a flash they would just shoot at the flash, hit the guy in the head. So, we were trying to rid of . . . the department was trying to get rid of the flash. And that was really a thing . . . we were really pushing on that one. That was taking a lot of people's time and all I can remember on it is . . . we could never solve that problem because they put like silencers in front of the gun, to suppress the flash, but the kick would come back and everyone that shot the gun would have to go to the hospital to have stitches taken above his eye because its sights would come back and wallop them. So, that really . . . I don't know if they really solved that one there. That was another one of the projects there.

The Institute of Optics Faculty 1940–1949

Campbell, J. Stuart, 1935–40
Clark, Herbert A., 1938–43
Covell, William D., 1940–42
Critchfield, Charles L., 1940–41
Dray, Richard C., 1942–43
Evans, John C., 1946–49
Evans, John W., 1943–65
Fassin, Gustave, 1930–40
French, Hobert W., 1943–46
Givens, M. Parker, 1948–
Hopkins, Robert E., 1943–

Jones, Lloyd A., 1929–43
Kingslake, Rudolf, 1929–2003
Mees, C. E. Kenneth, 1929–43
Milne, Gordon G., 1948–66
O'Brien, Brian, 1930–55
Paul, Frederick W., 1948–50
Polster, Harry D., 1948–54
Staehle, Henry C., 1940–41
Stewart, Harold S., 1943–46,
    1959–62
Tuttle, Fordyce, 1940–62

The Institute of Optics
Degrees Awarded 1940–1949

Abel, Irving R., B.S., 1944

Adams, Margaret M. (née Brant), B.S., 1948

Amdursky, M. E., B.S., 1944

Beach, Robert A., B.S., 1944

Bernhardt, Myron, B.S., 1940

Blumer, James W., B.S., 1948

Brennan, Joseph S., B.S., 1943

Britton, William C., B.S., 1948

Brown, Walter R. J., M.S., 1949

Carpenter, Vance J., B.S., 1949; M.S., 1950

Cary, Donald S., B.S., 1947

Crewdson, Ernest, B.S., 1945

Davis, Jr., John R., M.S., 1940

Day, Pierce B., B.S., 1948; M.S., 1953

Delano, Erwin, B.S., 1948; M.S., 1956; Ph.D., 1966

Dianetti, Joseph C., B.S., 1944

Foster, Richard B., B.S., 1945

Frels, R. Henry, B.S., 1949

French, Hobert W., Ph.D., 1945

Gallipeau, Robert B., B.S., 1949

Gee, Alan E., M.S., 1949

German, Howard L., B.S., 1940

Gilkeson, David C., B.S., 1948

Gill, Charles L., B.S., 1949

Gray, Charles B., B.S., 1948

Gray, Robert C., B.S., 1944

Harper, David C., B.S., 1940

Hart, George G., B.S., 1948

Henty, Richard R., B.S., 1945

Hills, Jr., Robert, B.S., 1944

Hoesterey, Howard F., B.S., 1949

Hoke, Charles H., B.S., 1945

Hopkins, Robert E., M.S., 1939; Ph.D., 1945

Houck, Robert B., B.S., 1943

Howe, Dennis J., B.S., 1947

Howes, Walton L., B.S., 1948

Hudson, Jr., Richard D., B.S., 1945; M.S., 1948

Hung, Ching, M.S., 1946

Jacobs, D. H., M.S., 1942

Jaeger, Arthur. R., B.S., 1945

Jean, J. Nelson, M.S., 1949

Jones, Joy G. (née Whitney), B.S., 1945

Kadesch, Robert R., M.S., 1949

Kanwischer, John W., B.S., 1947

Kelly, Donald H., B.S., 1944

Knoll, Henry A., B.S., 1944

Koch, Donald A., B.S., 1948; M.S., 1953

Koomen, Martin J., B.S., 1940; M.S., 1944

Krolak, Leo J., B.S., 1949; M.S., 1953

Krolicki, Ted D., M.S., 1949

Langley, Jr., Frank P., B.S., 1944

Leighten, Edward H., B.S., 1943

Lipinski, A. J., B.S., 1949

Magill, Lincoln C., B.S., 1948

Marks, Jerold S., B.S., 1944

Matter, George H., B.S., 1949

Merdsoy, Urhan S., B.S., 1942

Minkler, Marcus W., B.S., 1945; M.S., 1949

Neumer, Arthur E., B.S., 1940

Newcomb, Walter C., B.S., 1940; M.S., 1942

Norton, Wayne G., B.S., 1941

O'Brien, Jr., Brian, B.S., 1944

O'Grady, Edward J., B.S., 1948

Patton, William R., B.S., 1942

Pehta, Arnold J., B.S., 1943

Phillips, Sheldon, B.S., 1948

Polster, Harry D., Ph.D., 1946

Price, Edgar E., B.S., 1940

Price, William P., M.S., 1949

Putnam, Thomas E., B.S., 1947; M.S., 1950

Reardon, J. D., B.S., 1940
Rentoumis, George M., B.S., 1943
Rogers, III, Harry L., M.S., 1948
Rosborough, Robert S., B.S., 1948
Schlauch, John E., B.S., 1949
Schnable, George K., B.S., 1944
Schottmiller, Gerard J., B.S., 1949
Sherman, Ben, M.S., 1948
Sherwood, William T., B.S., 1940
Shurkus, Albert A., B.S., 1941
Smith, Warren J., B.S., 1944
Snyder, John R., B.S., 1944
Sonderman, John B., B.S., 1940

Stateler, Jack G., M.S., 1949
Sutton, A. M., B.S., 1944
Turkay, Zahit, B.S., 1945
Waidelich, Jr., John A., B.S., 1949
Walton, Samuel F., B.S., 1948
Weil, Herschel, B.S., 1943
Weisler, Raymond H., B.S., 1941
Weiss, James P., Ph.D., 1940
Whitney, Theodore R., B.S., 1942
Wilson, Richard J., B.S., 1942
Wolff, Fred J., B.S., 1941; M.S., 1953
Wood, James L., B.S., 1943
Young, Theodore R., B.S., 1949

PART III

UNCERTAINTY: THE 1950s

III. Uncertainty: The 1950s

If Brian O'Brien can be said to have shaped the Institute in the 1940s, then Robert Hopkins can no less be said to have shaped the department in the following decade. I have used the word "uncertainty" to describe the decade because the future of the Institute and indeed of the whole field of optics was uncertain during this period. The 1940s were dominated by demands of World War II, and the Institute rose magnificently to meet those demands, but once the war was over and the large staff of the NDRC was gone, what role would optics have in the University? Nuclear and radar research were much more visible nationally than was optics research, and it was argued that they were the technologies of the future, while optics was the technology of the past. Some within the University dismissed optics as mere "gadgetry." To compound these difficulties O'Brien decided to leave the University for an industrial position where he could operate on the scale to which he had become accustomed during the war. Before leaving he did begin to implement his vision of the future of optics starting up the optical materials effort by appointing David Dexter to the faculty. Bob Hopkins carried this vision further by expanding the materials group and also hiring a bright young theorist working in the then esoteric field of optical coherence, Emil Wolf. Thus when the laser was invented the Institute was well positioned to advantage of it. Even before the laser was developed Hopkins saw and took advantage of another tool that would revolutionize optics: the computer. He led the University and the field of optical design into the computer age.

In this section we have a Hilda Kingslake essay giving an overview of Hopkins's directorship, and a comprehensive history of the early development of lens design by Robert Shannon. We also have an essay by Robert Boynton describing the founding of the Center for Visual Science, the first of the research centers to spin off from the Institute, a familiar theme in later decades. An essay by Kenneth Teegarden presents the history of optical materials research in the Institute. This is followed by an essay on the first major company to spin off from the Institute, Tropel. There is an essay on the second major professional organization in optics, SPIE, and a whole series of anecdotes about Bob Hopkins the man.

17. Robert Hopkins Sets the Course: 1954–1965

Hilda Kingslake

In 1954, Robert E. Hopkins succeeded Brian O'Brien as Director of The Institute of Optics. Hopkins graduated from M.I.T. in 1937, and received both his M.S. and Ph.D. degrees from The Institute of Optics in 1939 and 1945, respectively. Except for a few years' interruption while president of Tropel, he always has been, and still remains, associated with The Institute of Optics. His own great interest and great distinction has been in lens design, image quality, and geometrical optics in general. However, his appreciation and understanding are wide, so on being made Director, he immediately proceeded to staff the Institute for a greatly increased program of teaching, research, and cooperative efforts in a completely forward-looking approach. He was also convinced of the vital importance of good undergraduate teaching.

David Dexter, appointed by O'Brien, was made Associate Professor to develop a full program of solid state research jointly with physics. Kenneth Teegarden was appointed and at first worked in solid state associated with David Dexter; later he developed a separate section for the study of materials science. Astronomy was encouraged and Malcolm Savedoff appointed, working with physics. Again, these developments were received with considerable doubt, but time has proved the wisdom of the appointments. Between 1954 and 1965, Hopkins made some 20 appointments, many of them already well known, or soon to become so, in their field of concentration.

Robert Boynton of psychology was asked to undertake a cooperative program in vision. The Center for Visual Science was established a little later. Since the loss of O'Brien, there

Robert Hopkins in the mid-50s.

had been no professor of physiological optics. Another appointment was David B. Dutton, interested in MTF and lens testing. Emil Wolf, already distinguished for studies in theoretical optics and co-author of a now well known text, *Principles of Optics*, was an appointment of note. Yet another great appointment was Philip Baumeister, already known for his work in thin films.

It worried Hopkins, whose need was great, that he had to buy outside computer time for his studies in lens design. He probably did more than anyone to urge the University to get its own computer. In 1955, a University computer center was started, first in Taylor Hall with a desk size unit; in 1956, a larger one was installed and instruction in programming was started. Gordon H. Spencer (Ph.D. Optics, 1963) wrote the first significant program, and optics students helped man the machine. In 1961, an IBM 7070 was acquired, to be succeeded as computers and their usage developed. By this time, Cornelis de Kiewiet was president. He reported in 1959 that the computer center was finding its way more and more into research carried on in different departments of the University.

In this same 1958–59 report, de Kiewiet described "a new venture of The Institute of Optics," something he called "one of the most interesting developments in the field of sponsored research." It was called the Division of Group Research. Harold Stewart, who was associated as a research assistant with O'Brien through the war and who later took his Ph.D. at Johns Hopkins, was recalled and took charge of the new division with the status of associate professor. The Division was engaged in research projects, many of them

Robert Hopkins in the lab in 1958.

basic, for NASA (the National Aeronautical and Space Administration). Of great interest was the development of the 36-inch reflecting telescope for an orbiting satellite. The whole assembly was limited to 500 pounds in weight and presented considerable problems in optical design. The Division produced semiannual reports.

Early in 1960, Hopkins, with Emil Wolf, organized an international conference on coherence, held at the University of Rochester only weeks before the first announcement of the laser. At least seven countries were represented among chairmen of the sessions and speakers. The attendance was excellent. Not losing any time, Hopkins appointed Carroll Alley, Michael Hercher and Douglas Sinclair to initiate research on lasers. Also appointed in the early '60s were G. Baldini (Italy), A. Gold, and W. L. Hyde. Again, many of these have become known through their publications.

The year 1961 was a great landmark date in the history of The Institute of Optics. At that time engineering had been given much more prominence in the University, and a College of Engineering and Applied Science, consisting of Mechanical, Electrical, and Chemical Engineering, had recently been established under its own dean. Hitherto, engineering had been a department of the College of Arts and Science. In 1961, it was decided by the administration that The Institute of Optics should become a fourth unit of the College of Engineering, but would retain the name under which it had become widely known. It would have a director, as would the other units of the College of Engineering, and Hopkins would continue as Director. As was, of course, to be expected of any such change, there was some displeasure, but time again has proved it to have been a very sound move. Already, material science was working with other branches of engineering. Two members of the optics faculty who worked theoretically on the physics of optics were invited to join the Department of Physics, namely Emil Wolf and David Dexter, who have become well known in the field of optics.

Hopkins took a sabbatical leave in 1960–61, during which time Stewart acted as director. Late in 1961, a very large alumni meeting was held where Joseph Platt, formerly professor of physics at Rochester, then President of Harvey Mudd College, spoke after dinner on the subject, "The Future of Engineering and Optics."

When the change in status was made, The Institute of Optics remained centered on the top floor of Bausch & Lomb Hall, sharing the building with Physics. By the 1960s, both departments had outgrown their quarters, and in 1962 a wing was added to the building. It was a great improvement for optics, but some divisions still had to remain in other buildings on the Campus.

One very pleasant and useful innovation of the Hopkins years was the publication of an illustrated, very attractive news sheet called *Institute of Optics News*, but popularly known as I.O.N. It came out several times a year with news of people, projects, and alumni

Robert Hopkins in 1971.

achievement. Usually a list of theses, publications, and papers read at meetings was included and gave an excellent idea of the variety of interests of the faculty.

Theses:

"Rotational Shearing Interferometers" (M.S.)
"Continuous Second Harmonic Generation" (Ph.D.)
"Testing of Optical Surfaces" (Ph.D. student from Mexico)
"Losses in ruby lasers due to crystal deviation from an ideal medium" (Ph.D.)
"Temporal summation of positive and negative flashes and related problems" (Ph.D. student from Japan)

Publications or papers read:

"Contributions of threshold measurements to color discrimination theory" (J.O.S.A., 1962)
"Time resolved spectroscopy of the emission from a ruby laser" (International Conference on Spectroscopy)
"Use of convergent and divergent illuminations on plane gratings" (J.O.S.A., faculty member from India)
"Theory of multiphoton ionization" (Phys. Rev. Letters)
"Methods of altering the characteristics of a multi-layer stack" (J.O.S.A.)

Summer schools became an important feature of the Hopkins years, and have continued to this day. Subjects varied, and sometimes two courses ran parallel or in sequence. With rare exceptions, they have been extremely well attended. Attendees have come from industry, government departments, a few from education, and one or two "just for a vacation." In addition, they serve to bring industry and government into contact with the faculty.

An extraordinary educational venture of the Hopkins years was known as the "Road Show." Hopkins and Givens received in 1963 a grant from the National Science Foundation to develop new teaching experiments and demonstrations using the optical laser. Hopkins, Blakney, Dutton, and Givens equipped a traveling unit and, by prearrangement, gave lecture demonstrations to seven colleges in the Northeast on existing uses of gas lasers, as well as of more conventional geometrical and physical optical experiments. These were followed by further demonstrations to an interested company and to the National Science Foundation Institute for High School Teachers in Mississippi, the University of Maryland, and of course to the summer school in Rochester. It was a demanding and interesting episode. Teaching was always a real concern of Hopkins'.

By 1965, sponsored research and related projects amounted to $500,000, so that most of the faculty could not visualize the very limited financing and opportunities of the early years, not only for the infant Institute of Optics but also everywhere in research.

Hopkins, in 1964, asked to be relieved of his directorship in order to give his whole time to teaching and research at The Institute of Optics. He has since been appointed Professor Emeritus.

Fraley Story: Let Sleeping Cows Lie

George Fraley

The high-speed cameras were used for dramatic things other than photographing atomic bomb explosions. Some of those experiments were better carried out off campus. George Fraley and Gordon Milne bought some property in Mendon adjacent to Mendon Ponds Park.

George describes the setup

So, we took the barn with really no funds except our salaries and took the bottom part of the barn and turned it into a fairly decent research center which was officially known as the "Off-Campus Test Site." We put a john, we put septic tanks in. Gordon took the silo which was not wood, it was tile. He put stairs up the middle and put his telescope up on top of that and we buried two large underground concrete septic tanks, which were not used as septic tanks, but were to run this high-speed photography. Well, see the problem was, we were spinning stainless steel chunks of metal that was polished on all four sides, I mean as a mirror. And I think they weighed sixteen pounds and we were spinning them at 3000 rps, which was quite fast. [Editor's note: That is revolutions per second, equivalently 180,000 revolutions per minute.]

Los Alamos taped one of these things, 'cause they wanted to see what was going to happen if they went faster than 3000 rps and I guess they found out that it would destroy one of the labs from kinetic energy and all this type of stuff. So, the University sort of frowned on our trying to spin mirrors that fast on the fourth floor of the B&L building because we could blow the end of the building off and then whoever was walking on the sidewalk, we would take them out too. So, they gave us a small stipend, a small amount of money to help develop the spinning mirrors for the high-speed photography out at our place. We spun the turbines and the mirror in the bunker, bounced the signal back to the cameras and then they would use the side of my hill for the blast. The military came up two or three times and would set off, I think the biggest charge was three or four pounds. We were using TNT and stuff like that. They came up with C4 plastic explosive once. That made a shock wave that really . . . the neighbors didn't appreciate. The cows stopped giving milk. And all the pictures were falling off the walls.

18. Lens Design at The Institute of Optics: Three Influential Decades at Mid-Century

Robert Shannon

The Origins

The tradition of lens design at The Institute of Optics began in about 1930 when Rudolf Kingslake took up the activity. Lens design at the Institute was of course a manual activity from this beginning up to the mid-1950s. The approaches to ray tracing and third-order-aberration calculation evolved from the base developed by designers in the early part of the twentieth century. By the 1940s, mechanical calculators had been developed that would permit accurate calculation of arithmetic operations, and were rapid enough to supersede the use of hand calculations using logarithmic tables.

Lens design at that time was based upon experience more than anything else. The successful lens designer was a somewhat lonely soul, who would be immersed in a single problem for months on end. The basis for the work was an understanding of thin lens theory, paraxial optics, and third-order aberrations based upon the computation of Seidel coefficients. Adjustments were made until the third-order aberrations were within a reasonable level to balance the expected higher-order aberrations. The design was then evaluated using ray tracing. The designer then manually adjusted the lens parameters and redid the calculations until he could declare the design completed. The principal reference book on the subject was published by A. E. Conrady in 1929. This book provided a useful manual for self-learning as well as a text for academic instruction.

Robert Hopkins and mechanical calculator.

Classical forms of lenses that had previously been found successful were the basis for understanding how to develop a lens design that would meet a certain need. Ray tracing by hand was exhausting, with meridonal rays constituting the core of the work. An understanding of the effect of close skew rays and occasionally the tracing of a few general skew rays was used to determine whether a lens had any chance of meeting the specifications for a particular application.

Image evaluation was a subjective and comparative process. Ray intercept curves were hand-calculated and hand-plotted and used to estimate the energy concentration. This estimate was used in empirical models to suggest the resolution that could be attained with a lens.

The understanding of diffraction images had progressed to some level of practicality, with diffraction integral evaluation for simple apertures and some basic aberrations, such as defocus, available by the 1940s. The Optical Transfer Function, now a common image evaluation criterion, had been defined in the 1940s, but it was not until late in that decade that the basic theory of the computation for the diffraction-based transfer function was developed.

Lens design at the Institute was a major activity during the World War II period. The need was for practical photographic and visual systems, in which the aberrations were generally necessarily larger than the diffraction-limited range. This required significant practical experience to evaluate the imagery that could be expected from a specific design. A variety of problems were worked on at the Institute during that time, with rapidity of solution and construction being of prime importance. Approaches to understanding this range of problems underlay most of the Institute's design activities at the time. This experience formed the basis for the practical approach to lens design that was exhibited at the Institute following the war.

At The Institute of Optics the basic knowledge for understanding lens design was provided by the course taught by Rudolf Kingslake, who had left the Institute in 1940 to join the design department at Eastman Kodak. The continuity behind the development of design approaches and programs within the Institute was due to Bob Hopkins. He had developed an approach to design in the early 1940s and had been responsible for several designs during that time.

Robert Hopkins shows a camera lens.

In the late 1940s and early 1950s, the U.S. optical industry was moving into a peace-time basis and toward the production of volumes of camera lenses. The Institute provided a natural focus of the efforts in developing new approaches to design. During the 1940s Hopkins and Jack Evans, along with Don Feder, devised a projector unit that was integrated with an approach to ray tracing using a Marchant calculator. This allowed a human calculator to read a number from the register of a Marchant calculator, turn a dial on the display to slide the trigonometric tables projected conveniently just above the calculator, and locate and interpolate the appropriate required sine or cosine without having to turn the pages in a table of trigonometric functions. This innovation increased the speed of manual ray tracing and probably represented a step in the state of the art. The ray trace speed even with that innovation remained the order of a minute or more per surface for a meridonal ray.

There were some significant lenses developed by Hopkins and others at The Institute of Optics in the 1950s. One of the most outstanding was the optics for the Todd-AO cinema system. This was developed as a result of Michael Todd approaching Brian O'Brien of The Institute of Optics about devising a wide-screen projection system like the multi-projector Cinerama, but in which it "all comes out of one hole." O'Brien and Walt Siegmund of The Institute of Optics looked at Cinerama and devised a system which used wide film to provide sufficient image quality and illumination for the purpose. One of the key parts of the system devised by Siegmund was the use of a very wide-angle lens which, when used for taking the picture, would provide a very strong sense of viewer participation by providing a useful peripheral image to the audience. This lens was a new state-of-the-art type of system which was designed at the Institute by Bob Hopkins. This "bugeye" lens was an important part of the overall Todd-AO system. The design was carried out largely by hand but with assistance in ray tracing on computers at American Optical, with construction and testing of some of the lenses by the Institute. This bugeye lens was used in the initial production of *Oklahoma* but never became popular for successive productions, probably because it was a concept not well understood by directors and cameramen.

Appearance of Computers

Electronic digital computers began to appear in the late 1940s. The primary use for these machines was to support the financial operations of companies, and most were rather unsuited for such activities as ray tracing. There had been some developments in scientific computing that had resulted in computers such as ENIAC, a large-scale vacuum tube machine located at Harvard. Such machines were marvels of the period but were very limited in terms of computational capability and speed.

At that time there was a large amount of activity for technical computation purposes in analog computers which allowed the very rapid, almost real-time solution of differential and other equations. The output speed of an analog computer was far greater than that of the day's digital computers for the types of problems to which it was applicable. The accuracy required in ray tracing indicated that digital computers were required for any useful computing on lenses.

There was one analog computer for lens design that briefly resided at the Institute in the 1950s. This was engineered at American Optical—it was an electrical analog computer that could be used to obtain the power distribution for a thin lens triplet to obtain the desired chromatic residual and Petzval sum, and included the glass data and separations of the elements. The information on each piece of data was dialed in and the output was the required powers of the three elements. (At least, that is how I remember it. There does not seem to be any existing description of the device. Chuck Rimmer remembers being given the task of "calibrating" the computer, a concept alien to today's digital computers.)

It was obvious that digital computers were the only type of machine suited for the accuracy required in ray tracing and aberration calculation; thus interest moved onto using computers first for simple ray tracing and later into applications for "Automated Optical Design." As for the application of digital computers to "automatic" design at mid-century, there were two different philosophies expressed in the 1950s. In a 1963 paper Gordon Spencer took note of these two points of view. In summary:

> Philosophy A: Lens design can be completely stated in explicit mathematical terms and hence a computer can be expected to carry out the total activity.

> Philosophy B: Lens design inevitably requires qualitative judgments and compromises to be made and hence the computer should be regarded as a tool capable of presenting the designer with possible solutions.

This was a hot topic for debate back then. Today, even with digital computers more than a million times faster than those of the 1960s, the role of the lens designer seems secure. The answer seems obvious now, but in the 1960s the promise of even better and faster computers left the option of replacing the designer with a complete piece of software a possible option. The course of software development by each group of designers through the 1950s and 1960s would follow the choice of philosophy chosen by that group.

Teaching Lens Design at the Institute

A sample of the lens design teaching at the Institute at mid-century can be obtained by examining one year. The example chosen is 1953–54. The lens design course was generally taken in the senior undergraduate or second year graduate period. Design was taught both by Rudolf Kingslake and Bob Hopkins. Kingslake taught his course on Wednesday nights for about two hours with a short break during the lectures. Hopkins offered a lens design computation laboratory on Saturday Mornings.

The Kingslake course content was contained in an extensive set of course notes which covered topics that eventually appeared in an expanded form in his book *Lens Design Fundamentals*. The Kingslake course consisted of a very intensive series of lectures with some question-and-answer sessions and provided the classical basis for understanding lens design. The course provided a very thorough grounding in the fundamental concepts of design, with a moderate amount of guidance on practical aspects of carrying out the designs.

Hopkins's laboratory session complemented this with the practical design of some specific lenses. At that time all of the computation was done on Marchant calculators, with the students each carrying out their own ray traces. There was heavy use of third-order aberration calculation with manual variation of the design parameters. The designer would identify key parameters and develop change tables for the variation of the third-order aberrations with these parameters. Verification of the design was accomplished using meridonal ray tracing done by hand. Examination of ray fans and reference to the change tables on third-order aberrations was used to adjust the lens to a final design. It is notable that only a few of these designer-driven iterations were usually required to approach a reasonable design.

The types of lenses designed in the course were some doublets, a landscape-type lens, and a triplet. The approach toward these designs was more or less described in the well known Mil-Handbook 141 sections on lens design.

Beginning about 1954, Bob Hopkins was convinced of the importance of applying computers to lens design in some way. There had been some application of computers of the time to ray tracing, and some early work on correction of lenses. There was a bit of a problem in that he did not have access to a computer. In fact, the University of Rochester was devoid of any scientific computing capability. The first course in computer programming was taught in the absence of a computer by a professor in the Mathematics Department. In order to touch any reality, the professor invented a generic computer and computer language called, as I remember, HYPAC for "hypothetical computer." The course was basically on how machine language and assembly coding operated, using some examples of simple solving and search algorithms. FORTRAN was still a few years away.

In the absence of other resources, Hopkins arranged for the students to have access to an IBM 604 calculating punch at Bausch & Lomb that did permit very awkward ray tracing at several seconds per ray surface, but was a very welcome innovation. By 1955 he had arranged for access to an IBM CPC, or Card Programmed Calculator, located at the Cornell University Computer Center. Input was through punched cards, and the program to calculate third-order aberrations or to trace rays was stacked on cards between the surface data cards. Output was through an IBM vertical bar printer, a remarkable mechanical monster of which very few people have any recollection. There was a difficulty in that the cards had to be delivered ninety miles to Ithaca, and one of the vivid memories students of that time carried with them was of high-speed drives with Hopkins in a wood-sided station wagon to and from the computer center at Cornell University.

The first stored program computer that became available at the University of Rochester was the Burroughs E101. This machine seemed to have been obtained by the urging of the Institute, because I do not recall significant use by any other department. Nevertheless, this constituted the beginning of one of the first university-associated digital computer centers in the country, and Tom Keenan was hired to head and develop the center.

The stored program on the Burroughs machine was about 144 steps that were programmed by inserting metal pegs into a set of pegboards that were then set into the machine. Data in and out was through a Burroughs Accounting Machine set on top of the computer. This computer was used for third-order calculation and ray tracing, and some limited attempts at aberration mapping versus lens parameters. This was a computer of limited application and interest, but did indicate the possibilities inherent in stored program machines. There was, of course, very great relief at not having to carry out hand calculations for ray tracing on a desk calculator.

The Burroughs was soon replaced by an IBM 650 which permitted a thousand stored program steps on a magnetic drum that could be programmed using symbolic assembly language (which occupied the other thousand words of memory on the drum). This machine was the first that permitted any attempt at automatic correction, and a third-order aberration correction program was written by Charles McCarthy. The machine also carried out ray tracing and did geometrical image analysis using radial energy distribution and geometrical modulation transfer function.

Once real stored program computers were available, a sequence of programs began to be developed at The Institute of Optics for optical design. These started with ray tracing, included third-order calculation and automatic correction to defined targets of these aberrations, and eventually led to programs capable of using ray aberration targets for automated design. Subsidiary programs to permit calculation of image evaluation functions were eventually incorporated into these programs, and the way was paved toward the general automatic lens design programs. The practicality of this at the University of Rochester was enhanced with the replacement of the IBM 650 with an IBM 7070 computer in 1961. This was a sort of advanced version of the drum-based 650 that permitted scientific computing such as lens design, along with character-based data manipulation required by other departments at the University. It, in turn, was eventually replaced by a faster transistorized 7074 in 1963.

The practical approach of linking the designer to the design program was a fundamental part of the Institute's developments under Bob Hopkins. He was a strong believer in integrating the designer into the process, rather than treating design as a mathematical exercise. The programs developed in the late 1950s and early 1960s eventually included high-order Buchdahl Aberration coefficients which permitted better control of the aberration targets. Ray trace targets were eventually added, but the speed of computation of these, especially on the IBM 650 computer, tended to be used as finishing rather than in-process design aberrations.

The ALEC (Automatic Lens Correction) program was written by Gordon Spencer in support of his Ph.D. dissertation. This program used aberration coefficients plus a small set of rays and differential rays to construct the merit function.

Once the IBM 7070 had been acquired, a true large-scale stored-program computer was available for optical design programming. This enabled the development and use of the ORDEALS program—the acronym stood for Optical Routines for Design and Analysis of Optical Systems. ORDEALS was initially based on the set of IBM 650 programs converted to machine language to operate at higher speed. This program eventually was ported to the 7070/7074. The ORDEALS program incorporated third- and fifth-order aberration correction as well as a full set of ray trace analysis capabilities. The fifth-order aberration coefficients were based upon Buchdahl's coefficients, as translated into Rochester language by Chuck Rimmer. ORDEALS was the core of The Institute of Optics teaching and design activities during the 1960s.

Gordon Spencer, Chuck Rimmer, and Pat Hennesey formed Scientific Calculations Inc. in 1963. At the beginning, they worked on variants of ALEC. Spencer took on a task to develop a program for Bob Potter at IBM Research on the 7094 computer which contained extensions beyond ALEC. This became the FLAIR program, which was distributed by IBM and eventually became a staple of the Institute's program package. (It is not known what FLAIR is an acronym for.) The FLAIR program was further developed at the Institute in the 1970s by Peter Sands, who wrote an extensive manual for the program. The major independent optical design program development to arise from Scientific Calculations was the ACCOS program (Automatic Correction of Centered Optical Systems) developed by Spencer and Hennesey, which became a standard in the optical industry in the 1970s. This program was expanded to include many features as several versions were developed. The core of the program retained the practical approach to lens design which was characteristic of The Institute of Optics during the 1960s.

Development of the Field

The developments at the Institute were limited by the available computing gear, which did not always keep up with the state of the art of the time. Others did, however, move forward with larger and possibly better machines. Donald Feder at Eastman Kodak had access to an IBM 704 machine that ran Kodak's financial software, and while slower than the leading 7090 class machine, did permit reasonably large and fast programs to be written. Feder had developed a program called LEAD (acronym unknown, but likely Lens Evaluation And Design). This program was directed toward the philosophy of leaving all the design work to the computer program with minimal human designer guidance.

This development stimulated Hopkins to hold an informal symposium in 1962 at The Institute of Optics at which a dozen or so lens designers were invited to discuss the state of the art. At that symposium, Feder issued a challenge for the assembled designers to set specifications of a lens which he would design totally automatically. The specifications called for an F1.2, six-degree lens using four elements, and remaining within some minimal set of boundary conditions. Feder went off and overnight came up with a design that was reasonable, but in subsequent discussion did not totally impress the assembled designers. This symposium lens became a sort of de facto standard for studying the capabilities of various computer programs being developed at the time. Several papers in the 1960s resulted from attempts to improve the original design obtained from the Feder program. The importance of careful selection of appropriate boundary conditions in carrying out automatic design was an important feature of these discussions.

The activity at the Institute in lens design was supported by a number of visitors in the 1960s. Charles Wynne visited and discussed his work on the high-speed Atlas computer in developing the SLAMS program for lens optimization. This program was one of the first that incorporated all of the major features into a ray-trace-based optimization program. His description of the course of design roaming through solution space intrigued those at the Institute.

Hans Buchdahl also spent a period at the Institute. This led to the aforementioned development of computer algorithms based upon the Buchdahl Coefficients by Chuck Rimmer. These coefficients are a part of all the major lens design programs today.

The status of automatic lens design programs was summarized in a landmark meeting at the Institute in 1966, the first Conference on Lens Design with Large Computers. This conference, organized by Lem Hyde and sponsored by the Institute, brought together most of those involved in lens design software at the time. The timing was right, and this conference was perhaps the single most important landmark in the history of the field of automatic optical design.

The conference began with Charles Wynne summarizing his work using the Damped Least Squares approach to design. The importance of appropriate selection of the damping factor as a driver in finding solutions had been recognized and served in part as the subject for some other papers at the conference. Dave Grey, then of Aerospace Corp., introduced his concept of linearizing the design problem by orthonormalization of variables in design space. Other programs described other approaches, including adaptive setting of aberration targets as devised by Glatzel at Zeiss.

Gordon Spencer described in some detail the status of the ORDEALS program on the Rochester 7074 computer. It is interesting to note that this program took up some 27,000 36-bit words when compiled onto an IBM 7090 computer. In today's language this equates to about 135 kilobytes or so, a fraction of what is carried on one floppy disc today. The efficiency of programming of that time versus today's profligate use of storage space is remarkable. This discussion was supplemented by a discussion by John Buzawa on the design of a specific lens using this program. He noted that the total computer time for this design was about one-half hour on the 7074 at a cost of about $150.

Several papers discussed experience with other programs of the day, and provoked much discussion. There was consideration as to whether the computer would really become the total designer, or whether the ultimate use is as an adjunct to a human designer. One notable recorded remark from an unnamed participant in the audience: "This lens designer is almost ready to believe that the computer, even though it is less intelligent than the human being, is more intelligent than a lens designer."

By this time the approach to automatic design had progressed to the point where much of the discussion was directed to the establishment of a useful and functional merit function to set the direction of the program when iterating through the design.

The late 1960s and early 1970s saw a change in the momentum regarding the activity in lens design programming at the Institute. Part of this can be attributed to Bob Hopkins leaving the Institute to concentrate on developing Tropel in 1968. By this time much of the program development was being done in industry, where there was better access to the latest high-speed computing equipment. In addition, several groups, such as Scientific Calculations and Optical Research Associates, had been formed and began to develop the major commercial optical design programs that form the core of the industry today.

Automatic lens design programs had developed by 1970 to the point where they were commercially viable, and several organization developed programs that became universal standards. The momentum passed to these organizations, and the Institute concentrated on other aspects of the lens design and manufacturing problem.

Lens design software development at the Institute did not entirely stop. The FLAIR program was maintained and documented by Peter Sands, but not significantly expanded. Doug Sinclair became interested in the use of small computers to provide a personal link between the computation and the designer. He started first with the HP65 programmable calculator in about 1970 and moved on to various other expanded desktop calculators such as the HP 9845 and other machines in the early 1970s. These saw considerable use in teaching at the Institute. Sinclair also saw an opportunity to pioneer the rapidly emerging technology of applications of small computers, and left the Institute in 1975 to form Sinclair Optics and market the expanded set of OSLO optical design programs for the then-new personal computer.

The final major expansion of Automatic Optical Design into a universal tool occurred with the introduction of the personal computer in the early 1980s. Today the designer has on the desk his or her own machine with orders of magnitude more capability than even the 650 and 7044 computers. The personal computer also is optimized to communicate graphically with the designer, leading to the observation that the ultimate development of the lens design program is to integrate and extend the capabilities of the individual designer. Now, instead of a few optimizations against estimated image quality targets, the lens designer, including the lens design student, can carry out hundreds of iterations on a single design and obtain a thorough evaluation of the lens performance. Certainly the lens designers and design students at the Institute at mid century would have been understandably elated by the ability to have such tools at that time.

The 1950s and 1960s were an exciting time in the field of optical design. The traditional intuitive understanding of how complex lenses operated was being melded into the new age of computers. The work done at The Institute of Optics during that time formed a basis for most of the computer program developments that followed.

Chuck Rimmer, Gordon Spencer, and Doug Sinclair provided valuable information regarding their recollections of the period and activities discussed in this essay.

Robert Shannon received his B.S. and M.S. from the Institute of Optics in 1954 and 1957, respectively. He was Director, Optical Sciences Center, University of Arizona, Tucson, AZ from 1984 until 1992. He is currently Professor Emeritus at the University of Arizona.

19. Hoppy Stories

Employees of Corning-Tropel Inc.

There is probably no one in the history of the Institute who is more beloved by his students, colleagues, and everyone who knows him than Bob Hopkins. A number of his friends and former students formalized their affection by endowing the Robert E. Hopkins Chair of Optical Engineering in his name. James Fienup is the first holder of this chair. A celebration was held on October 9, 2001, in honor of his joining the faculty. As a part of the festivities John Bruning, the CEO of Corning-Tropel, the company that Bob co-founded, gave a speech. Dr. Bruning described Hopkins:

> Hopkins, who directed the Institute of Optics from 1954 to 1965, stands out as one of the Institute's most influential figures, as an optics entrepreneur, an innovator in the field of lens and optical-system design, and as a teacher and mentor for hundreds of students. "Bob Hopkins could look at a lens and tell if it would work," according to Professor Duncan Moore '74 (Ph.D.), one of Hopkins's former graduate students. "He shaped assignments to encourage a hands-on approach."
>
> Bob Hopkins was a strong contributor to the success of many individuals and companies that have become important names in the optical industry. The recently endowed Hopkins Chair at the Institute was founded in his honor to carry forward the tradition of excellence in applied optics and optical engineering that he started at the Institute and at Tropel.

In his speech Bruning also recounted a series of humorous anecdotes that he had collected from current and past employees of Tropel.

The "Hoppy stories" that he collected are familiar to anyone who passed through the Institute in the period from the 1930s to the 1980s. Hoppy was the stereotypical absent-minded professor, even when he was in industry. He was brilliant in his intellectual endeavors, kind to a fault, but a little detached from the details of life around him.

Scattered throughout this section and the next one are a series of these Hoppy stories contributed by various Tropel employees.

Hoppy lecturing on lens design.

Hoppy Story: Neanderthals

Vance Carpenter

During the era of Brian O'Brien when Hoppy was a graduate student, several students (minus Bob) were examining a binocular type instrument that had a particularly large interocular separation. One of the young physicists suggested that "anyone with such a large interocular spacing must be a Neanderthal". Being inquisitive and scientific, the young physicists further conjectured that there might indeed be a correlation between a person's intelligence and their interocular distance. The physicists gathered data, fit a curve, and discovered a surprisingly strong correlation between their own test scores and inter-ocular distances. They showed the data to Hoppy who thought the study was both compelling and fascinating. When they measured his interocular distance, which fell way below the line, Bob immediately dismissed the study as unscientific and ridiculous.

Vance Carpenter received his B.S. and M.S. from the Institute of Optics in 1949 and 1950, respectively. He was a member of the faculty of the University of Rochester from 1956 until 1962. He is currently retired and living in Fairport, NY.

20. Psychology, Optics, and the Center for Visual Science

Robert Boynton

More than fifty years ago, during my final year as a graduate student in experimental psychology at Brown University, my mentor, Lorrin Riggs, assisted me in applying successfully for a National Research Council postdoctoral fellowship to work under the supervision of Brian O'Brien, director of The Institute of Optics. By the sheerest coincidence I was offered and accepted instead an assistant professorship in the Department of Psychology, located in Morey Hall directly across the quadrangle from the Bausch & Lomb Hall, which housed the Institute.

At age twenty-seven, I arrived at the University in the fall of 1952. Unbeknownst to me, and perhaps also to O'Brien, 1952–53 turned out to be his final academic year at the University. My first meeting with him was in his office, where I recall very little except that he had a Dictaphone with a speaker horn that recorded on a cylindrical disk resembling the one that Thomas Edison had invented. Later I recall overhearing O'Brien refer to me as "that psychologist who comes to optics colloquia," which in fact I did. Had I known that he was teaching physiological optics for the last time, I would have audited his course that year. As matters turned out, I had very little interaction with him.

I had been hired at the starvation wage, after deductions, of $293 per month. To make ends meet, I was unhappily forced to teach a night-school course in introductory psychology on the University's Prince Street Campus, where women undergraduates would be confined until 1955. Meanwhile, Bob Hopkins, who was seeking someone to teach O'Brien's physiological optics course, reacted to the suggestion of at least one consultant that he might want to look in his own backyard. To assess my competency, Hopkins and George Higgins of the Eastman Kodak Co. took me to lunch at the airport one day, where more than the meat was grilled.

Subsequently I received the following letter, dated June 10, 1954, written by Edward Hoffmeister, dean of the College of Arts and Science:

> Dear Dr. Boynton:
> Upon recommendation of Dr. Robert E. Hopkins, Acting Director of The Institute of Optics, supported by Dr. G. Richard Wendt, Chairman of the Department of Psychology, and with the endorsement of President de Kiewiet, I am happy to appoint you to teach a course physiological optics in The Institute of Optics during the year 1954–1955, with a stipend of $1000. It is my understanding that this stipend is an "extra," not affecting your base salary, and that this agreement is for one year only.

I eagerly accepted and, as it turned out, I would teach the course (which initially paid fifty percent more than night school) for many years. Eventually this led to a faculty appointment, and eventually I became professor of psychology and optics. My joint appointment resulted in the dubious honor of attending the faculty meetings of both departments. At one of the optics gatherings in the fall of 1960, Jack Graham, dean of the new

Robert Boynton.

School of Engineering, breezed into our meeting. With no warning he announced that, henceforth, although The Institute of Optics could keeps its name, it had lost its independent status. From then on, Graham told us, the Institute would be a department in the School of Engineering, and Hopkins would report instead to him.

I supervised masters theses in optics written by students who had been sent to the Institute by the U.S. Coast Guard. These were Guy Clark, Charles Glass, David Naus, Ernest Tindle, William Wetherell. Although I had many Ph.D. students in psychology, I had only one in optics, namely Mitsuo Ikeda, who later became a leading vision researcher in Japan.

From the start, Bob Hopkins was The Institute of Optics faculty member with whom I maintained the closest association. In those days, Hilda Kingslake served as a kind of informal social secretary for the Institute and hosted gatherings at the home she shared with Rudolf. I recall that on those occasions Bob Hopkins would inevitably be found in a corner somewhere, involved in an animated conversation about computers. There was good reason for this: Bob desperately needed a programmable digital computer to trace his rays, because—as he told me—he was spending about four hours daily pounding on the keys of a Monroe calculator and he was getting sick of it.

And so it was not surprising that Bob Hopkins played a leading role in getting a computer center launched on campus. In 1955, he and I were members of a small group who learned to program the Burroughs E-101, the first computer on campus. Like a slide rule, the machine couldn't even keep track of decimal points, and to program the thing you had to stick pins into holes. We had time to go out for coffee while the computer did a job that might take a couple of seconds today. Nevertheless, it seemed miraculous at the time.

Bob Hopkins and I both bowled in the U of R Engineers' League. One season, when we were co-secretaries, we developed what may well have been the first computer program anywhere for keeping track of bowling-league data. The memory of the IBM 650, which by then had replaced the Burroughs, was insufficient to list the bowling averages in descending order. We had to do this afterward by card sorting before taking the cards from the sorter to the chain printer, a ponderous device that hammered its digits and capital letters through a typewriter ribbon onto huge sheets of paper.

On November 26, 1962, Hopkins was the first person to whom I sent a rough draft of a proposal describing the possibility of a Center for Visual Science (CVS). I cautioned him that "you are the only person to receive this yet, since I wish to discuss the idea with Peskin, Cohen, and Doty before distributing the document to the full group." I asked him to keep the matter confidential because "I do not want people to learn indirectly that their names have been used in a proposal about which they have no knowledge." As it turned out, whereas Jim Peskin would make only a modest contribution to CVS, Gerald Cohen in Electrical Engineering and Bob Doty in the Center for Brain Research would become two of the most important faculty participants in the center, which was approved by the board of trustees on September 11, 1963, ten months after the idea had first occurred to me. Very modest start-up funds were provided by Jack Graham and the arts college dean, Kenneth Clark. Clark was always very helpful to me, both in my role as founding director of CVS and later (1971–74) when I concluded my twenty-two years at Rochester as chair of the Department of Psychology.

As originally conceived, the Center for Visual Science was oriented principally toward graduate education. I taught a course called "Introduction to Visual Science," populated by students from psychology, engineering, physiology, and optics, many of whom went on to do visually relevant dissertations under the direction of professors in their home disciplines. I tried to encourage the idea that we all have our strengths and weaknesses which should be respected so that we can learn from one another's perspectives. Another seminar involved the participation of CVS faculty (all of whom with appointments in one of the regular departments) who lectured on their special interests.

We also staged a series of colloquia featuring well-known outside speakers including, during the first year, Mathew Alpern, W. S. Stiles, Lorrin Riggs, Jacob Nachmias, and William Rushton. In 1964 we held the first of what became a series of June meetings, still going today, forty years later. That first one, which was concerned with "Vision With Stabilized Images," was inspired by Robert Ditchburn, who had been visiting The Institute of Optics on an NSF fellowship.

With vision now being taught in the Center for Visual Science, the need for a course in physiological optics in the Institute disappeared, and many of the optics faculty were happy to have it "over there." For the next decade, until I left the University for California in 1974, my association with The Institute of Optics lessened, although I was responsible

William Wetherell (B.S. '58, M.S. '61) and Howard Smith (B.S. '60, Ph.D. '65) in the physiological optics laboratory.

for temporary appointments to the Institute's faculty of Frank J. J. Clarke and Donald H. Kelly. Where my research was concerned, I never took advantage of the Institute to the extent that David Williams would later.

After I attended the fiftieth anniversary of The Institute of Optics a quarter-century ago, I returned home to Del Mar with the official memento, a plastic positive lens of about two diopters, inscribed on its perimeter with the words "100 Years—Eastman Kodak, 50 Years—The Institute of Optics." I look forward to the seventy-fifth anniversary celebration, which I expect to attend as a newly minted octogenarian.

Robert Boynton was a member of the faculty of the University of Rochester from 1955 until 1972. He is currently a member of the faculty of the University of California, San Diego, CA.

Hoppy Story: Car Wash

Anthony R. Phillips

One morning Hoppy came in to work, dressed in a suit, which was normal. One side of his body was dripping wet. When asked what happened, he simply responded that he went through the car wash with the driver's window down.

Hoppy Story: The Price of Lenses

Anthony R. Phillips

Bob was once asked by a longtime customer why the prices of Tropel's lenses had gone up so much recently. Bob's answer was, "Well, you have to understand that we now have all these high-speed computers to do the design, and they are expensive."

Anthony R. Phillips is currently a senior engineer/scientist at Corning-Tropel Corporation, Rochester, NY.

21. Research and Education in the Field of Optical Materials

Kenneth J. Teegarden

This is a brief history of the field of optical materials at the University of Rochester covering the period from 1940 to the present. I have undoubtedly left out some of the people who were important to the history. I apologize beforehand for those omissions. Also, I have not gone into the details of the research carried out during the period covered—including a comprehensive list of publications could have done this, but such a list would probably have been too long for inclusion in this book. I encourage those who are interested in sampling the breadth and significance of the research areas mentioned below to generate a partial list themselves.

Prior to 1940, Frederick Seitz, a solid state theorist who later played a major role in the development of his field, occupied a faculty position in the Department of Physics but that department was almost exclusively devoted to nuclear physics. Work on optical materials began in earnest in The Institute of Optics during the World War II and was expanded in subsequent years by Brian O'Brien, director of the Institute during the war and shortly thereafter. In the late 1950s, research in solid state physics spread to the Physics Department, initially through joint appointments with the Institute. In a sense, therefore, current programs in condensed matter physics in the University can be said to have their roots in this earlier program in optical materials in the Institute.

Kenneth Teegarden with apparatus to be launched in early Aerobee rocket.

Initial work on optical materials started in The Institute of Optics in the form of an extensive program to develop stable infrared sensitive phosphors. Wartime work on these materials was carried out under the direction of Franz Urbach with support from the U.S. Air Force. The infrared sensitivity of the phosphors was due to the presence of shallow electron traps, which could be ionized by low-energy photons. Recombination of these electrons with conduction band holes then produced radiation in the visible region of the spectrum. To prevent complete bleaching of the traps and consequent disappearance of infrared sensitivity, the traps needed to be continuously repopulated. This was accomplished by the incorporation of radioactive beta emitters into the materials. Although this approach was apparently successful, it led to considerable radioactive contamination of the fourth floor of the old wing of Bausch & Lomb Hall. One of my first assignments after arriving at the University was to help clean up radioactive waste left over from the phosphor program. This program was phased out shortly after the war ended, and Urbach took a position at Eastman Kodak Co.

M. Parker Givens was appointed to the position of assistant professor of optics in 1947. Professor Givens, coming directly from his studies at Cornell University, began a fundamental study of the optical constants of metals and insulators in the vacuum ultraviolet. The decision to add Professor Givens to the faculty was made in part by the need to continue earlier work on the properties of materials in the soft x-ray region of the spectrum, and in part to initiate a more basic approach to optical materials. This appointment was a radical departure from the established applied direction of the Institute and was apparently met with considerable skepticism by several members of its faculty. The basic work by Professor Givens did have practical consequences, however. The measurements had to be carried out in high vacuum both to preserve surface purity and to permit the use of soft x-ray radiation. At that time little of the equipment needed for this work was obtainable commercially and had to be constructed in-house. Thus the research resulted not only in original measurements on the optical constants of a variety of solids but also in unique technology and methods. In addition, Professor Givens's activities expanded beyond the bounds of pure solid state physics. For example, he became involved with a project to produce aspheric lenses more rapidly and more cheaply then had been possible previously. One of these was the movie projectors for the large screen Todd-AO system. Lenses that produced a high-quality image over the wide projection angle needed were too complicated or even impossible to construct using only spherical surfaces. This problem was solved by using the sagged aspheres. Several aspheric lenses were also sold to the emerging Xerox Corp. for use in prototype copying machines.

Professor Robert E. Hopkins, who became director of the Institute after the departure of Brian O'Brien, expanded fundamental studies of the optical materials through several new appointments. In 1952 David L. Dexter, a solid state theorist who had been working at the University of Illinois (Urbana) as a research associate, was hired as a research associate in the Institute. Dexter was joined in 1953 by David B. Dutton and in 1954 by myself; our appointments were also in The Institute of Optics as research associates. Both Dutton and I were recent graduates of the Physics Department at Illinois, where our theses involved studies of the optical and electronic properties of point defects in the alkali halides. One might ask why such a tightly knit group working in a field apparently devoid of practicality was transported to the Institute. Was the choice based on some master plan, or were there other reasons for the decision? It is true that the work I began required the use of vacuum ultraviolet equipment and in a sense complemented the work of Parker Givens. However, David Dutton turned his attention to a study of large bandgap semiconductors,

Professor Dexter has graduate student Albert Gold up to the board in solid state physics class.

and theoretical work by David Dexter ranged over a wide variety of topics. It is worthy of note that Frederick Seitz was also at Illinois during the time of our appointments and by then had become a major figure in the field of solid state physics. It is also interesting that my and Dutton's thesis advisor, Robert Maurer, had relatives living in Rochester and frequently visited the University. At any rate, the connection between the solid state physics group at Illinois and The Institute of Optics seems to have been strong and may have played a role in the decision to make these appointments. This group of four people (Givens, Dexter, Dutton and Teegarden) continued as a unit in the Institute until 1961, when the College of Engineering was formed. It was then decided that the Institute become part of the new college and that the Department of Physics, which had been devoted entirely to the field of nuclear physics, would be allowed to offer faculty appointments to some Institute members.

The Physics Department began broadening its base to include solid state physics, choosing to make an offer to Dexter, which he accepted. Despite these administrative changes, collaboration between the original members of this group in both departments continued to be strong. In 1959 David Dexter published a paper in which he described the group as "the solid state physics program at the University of Rochester." Also, additions to the faculty continued to be made. Robert S. Knox, who received a Ph.D. in optics and physics in 1958, was appointed assistant professor of physics in 1960, and Albert Gold was appointed assistant professor of optics in 1962. Both were students of Dave Dexter and both had spent postdoctoral time in Urbana. Professor Gold later became associate dean of the College of Engineering, and Professor Knox became chairman of the Department of Physics and Astronomy at Rochester in 1969.

David Dutton in the laboratory.

Professor Dexter and graduate student Robert S. Knox in 1957 study an avoided crossing. Note that pipe smoking seemed to be common among the solid state group.

This group carried out a research program of well integrated theoretical and experimental studies that led to:

1. Seminal studies of the absorption spectra of ionic solids, solid rare gases and large band gap semiconductors which laid the foundation for theories of excitons and interband transitions in these materials,
2. Contributions to our understanding of the interaction between excited electronic states and the phonon structure of these solids,
3. Major contributions to the theory of energy transfer between electronic states in solids, and
4. Pioneering work on multiple photon absorption in solids.

This group had considerable success in securing grants and contracts to support the research. The Air Force Office of Scientific Research and the National Research Foundation were the main sources of this support, which was used in part to expand the research effort through the addition of postdoctoral fellows. These included Simpei Tutihasi from Japan, Giancarlo Baldini from Italy, Robert Illingsworth from England, V. Vaydonovitch from the USSR, N. Kristianpoller from Israel, and Martin Creutzburg from Germany, among others. The diversity of these appointments attests to the international reputation attained by this program in optical materials.

The program also, of course, supported graduate students. Many of these students went on to faculty positions in other universities or to major positions in industry. Among them are a few who were destined to continue important roles at the University of Rochester and at other universities. Robert S. Knox and Albert Gold are mentioned above. Beall Fowler, a student of Knox's and extensive co-author with Dexter, went on to become the chairman of the Physics Department at Lehigh University. Robert Knox's son, Wayne Knox, was one of my students and is currently director of The Institute of Optics. Another of my students, Stephen Jacobs, has played a major role in the development of optical materials for laser applications and the construction of several generations of the fusion laser at the Laboratory for Laser Energetics. He also was instrumental in the development of magnetorheological finishing of optical surface and was the thesis advisor for Donald Golini, founder and president of QED Technologies, an extremely successful business here in Rochester.

It is clear that the program in optical materials (or condensed matter physics) initially begun in the Institute seeded this important field in other departments in the University. Its graduates have gone on to play important roles in the other universities as well. The scientific contributions to the field of condensed matter physics have been distinguished. It is a pleasure look back on the accomplishments of the people involved, and a continuing honor to be associated with them.

Kenneth J. Teegarden has been a member of the faculty of the University of Rochester since 1954. He served as Director of the Institute of Optics from 1981 until 1987.

Hoppy Story: The Trip to Corning

Robert Maier

Tropel had been consulting for Corning for several years, on a number of fronts. Hoppy and Charles Munnerlyn had spent the day in Corning on such a mission, returning to Fairport in Hoppy's VW Beetle. As they passed thru Naples, New York, they failed to notice the gas tank was near empty. Selecting the "high" road, they headed north out of Naples. Well up the mountain, the car chugged to a stop. They pushed it a bit, managing a "K" turn in the middle of route 64. Following this, they "coasted" over hill and dale covering a distance of nearly five miles, back into Naples, to a gas station that was miraculously still open at 11:30 p.m. on a Tuesday night. Bob's stories didn't always end that well.

Robert Maier received his B.S. and M.S. from the Institute of Optics in 1964 and 1966, respectively. He is currently a technical manager at Corning-Tropel Corporation, Rochester, NY.

Hoppy Story: To Catch a Thief

Vance Carpenter

At an illumination conference in Boulder Colorado in the late 1970s, Hoppy joined a group dinner at a local restaurant. After splitting the bill and lingering for conversation, they all got up and left the table. Moments later, an irate maitre'd ran out protesting that the bill was not paid. Bob had collected all the money and put it in his pocket.

Vance Carpenter received his B.S. and M.S. from the Institute of Optics in 1949 and 1950, respectively. He was a member of the faculty of the University of Rochester from 1956 until 1962. He is currently retired and living in Fairport, NY.

22. On Tropel and The Institute of Optics

John Bruning and Douglas Goodman

The influence of The Institute of Optics on Corning-Tropel Corp. can be summarized simply: Without the Institute, Tropel would not exist.

During World War II, the Institute worked for the Department of Defense on image-stabilized binoculars. Some years later, interest in this project grew, but the Institute no longer wanted to participate. In 1953, Robert Hopkins proposed to Jim Anderson and Jack Evans that the three of them start a company to do this work. Thus Tropel was born. The name was first ROPEL—Rochester Optics and Electronics—but this was found lacking, and a T was added.

The first full-time Tropel employee was John Buzawa, also of The Institute of Optics. Buzawa was so valuable to the company that the three founders made him a fourth partner, and he eventually became the president.

Prior to joining Tropel, Jack Evans '39, '49 (MAs) taught at the Institute for fifteen years. Later, Evans left to found Velmex, a company that specializes in precision mechanical motions and slides. Anderson left Tropel in 1989 to start Optics Technology, specializing in small precision lenses and mechanical parts.

Seminar in Optical Design including Tropel pioneers: (left to right beginning in back) Matt Rimmer, Bill Mimmack, Tom Harris, Bob Hopkins, John Buzawa, Jim Shane, and Jan Hoogland.

In the years that followed, the Institute provided most of Tropel's optical designers and engineers, mostly masters or bachelors graduates. Some of these employees did stints at other optical companies before working at Tropel. Hopkins, connected to both the Institute and Tropel, was among the first to exploit the computer as a tool for handling problems in lens and optical-system design.

During the 1960s and 1970s, Tropel became involved in the design and fabrication of optics used in the microelectronics industry. Hopkins, in his zeal to improve the performance of lenses used for microcircuit fabrication, realized that better optics required better glass and more precisely fabricated lens elements; thus he placed a great emphasis on measurement technology and laser interferometry in particular. From this period forward, Tropel became a leader in precision optics for the semiconductor industry and a leader in metrology instrumentation.

Hopkins was officially associated with Tropel until 1972, when the company was purchased by Coherent, which moved the medical operation to Palo Alto, Calif. in 1975.

Charles Munnerlyn, one of Hopkins's many Ph.D. students, stayed in the Rochester area after graduation to head research and development for Tropel in the early 1970s. Munnerlyn worked on laser metrology and also led an effort to develop the first automated digital device to measure refractive errors in the eye. Called the Dioptron, the instrument directs a light source into the eye of a patient as he peers through an eyepiece. Light from the pattern reflected by the retina produces an analog signal, which is converted to a digital signal and fed into a computer. The computer in turn fits a sine wave to the selected signal, then calculates the refractive error of the eye from the sine wave signal. The Dioptron was one of the first devices to incorporate an Intel microprocessor.

A significant gift from Munnerlyn is kicking off the biggest expansion of the Institute's facilities since it was created seventy-five years ago. Playing to the University of Rochester's strengths, a new one hundred thousand-square-foot building will house scientists studying both optics and biomedical engineering, with plenty of overlap in

Some recent connections between Tropel and the Institute, Bryan Stone, Greg Forbes, John Bruning, and Duncan Moore.

areas such as optical medical diagnosis and Munnerlyn's own specialty, laser vision correction.

The synergy between the Institute and Tropel continues: Tropel is always in need of the best students trained at The Institute of Optics, and Tropel employees give back through the teaching of core courses with industry relevance. Tropel currently employs twenty-five University of Rochester graduates.

John Bruning is currently President and CEO of Corning-Tropel Corporation, Rochester, NY.
Douglas Goodman is currently a senior scientist at Corning-Tropel Corporation, Rochester, NY.

Hoppy Story: Show Me the Light

Mark Wescott

During the mid-1970s, Tropel developed a 1× lens for a wafer lithography system, and Bob was in the thick of it. He could be frequently found in the lab, shooting images, developing and evaluating tests on silicon wafers. The performance of the lens was very sensitive to the polarization state of the imaging beam, and images viewed through a microscope gave colorful clues to subtle aberrations. One day, while engrossed with a particularly elusive problem, Bob burst out of the lab and exclaimed to no one in particular, "Who the hell around here knows anything about polarized light?!!"

Mark Westcott received his B.S. from the Institute of Optics in 1970. He is currently an optical engineer at Corning-Tropel Corporation, Rochester, NY.

Hoppy Story: The Pete Backer Story

Robert Maier

Pete Backer was a marketing guy. He'd been with Tropel for a couple of years. Hoppy decided he wasn't working out, and went to his office about 3:30 p.m. on a Friday afternoon to "let him go." Pete was just leaving as Hoppy arrived. The conversation went like this:

Hoppy: "Are you going someplace?"
Pete: "Well, yes. Remember? I'm just leaving for two week's vacation."
Hoppy: "Oh. Well listen, I think we're going to have to let you go, but we'll talk about it when you get back. Have a nice vacation."

Robert Maier received his B.S. and M.S. from the Institute of Optics in 1964 and 1966, respectively. He is currently a technical manager at Corning-Tropel Corporation, Rochester, NY.

23. The Institute and SPIE: The International Society for Optical Engineering

Brian J. Thompson

The Society of Photographic Instrumentation Engineers (SPIE) was founded on July 1, 1955 to support the applications of photo-optical instrumentation. The initial core of this effort was really range instrumentation, but it quickly broadened out to cover more and more important technologies and engineering endeavors. It was clear in these early days that SPIE was not a traditional technical society, i.e., one that is inclined to be run by and for the members. Instead SPIE was dedicated to technology transfer and to the support of the users of the science, technology and instrumentation that its fields of interest encompassed.

The first award by the society was the "Karl Fairbanks Memorial Award" established in 1958. It is worthy of significant note that our own Rudolf Kingslake received that award in 1971 for service to industry. However, the involvement of the Institute and its members goes back further both directly and indirectly. My own personal involvement goes back to my days at Technical Operations, Inc. and started in 1963—the year that the society held its first technical seminar-type conference and published its first official proceedings. The subject was image enhancement.

Naturally the society needed a journal, and the first formal one was established in 1962 under the official title *Society of Photographic Engineers Journal,* or *SPIE Journal.* It came out as a bimonthly, and the December/January 1963/64 issue contained the first of the *Physical Optics Notebook* articles that George Parrent and I were invited to prepare. We continued that endeavor for sixteen consecutive issues. Later, SPIE reproduced those sixteen articles as a tutorial text. By the time this occurred I was already in place at the Institute as its director. Hence, the forward was written from my Institute address in October 1968. After several reprints of this book, a new and much-expanded version, with George Reynolds and John DeVelis as our lead co-authors, was co-published with the American Institute of Physics under the title, *The New Physical Optics Notebook: Tutorials in Fourier Optics* (1989).

The society's journal has gone through a series of changes from *Society of Photographic Instrumentation Engineers Journal* to *Society of Photo-Optical Instrumentation Engineers Journal* to *Journal of SPIE* in 1971. A major and very significant change took place in the journal in 1972 when Douglas Sinclair of the Institute accepted the editorship with a mandate to re-think the journal, including its name, the format, the process, etc. With great insight Doug suggested that the journal should be called *Optical Engineering,* and so it is to this day. His vision for it has certainly been realized as successive editors have built on those solid foundations set in 1972.

Not long after *Optical Engineering* was launched, the society established the Kingslake Medal and Prize for the most noteworthy paper to appear in the journal. The long list of recipients contains many distinguished scientists and engineers with a strong association with the Institute—and we are very proud of their accomplishments.

Because The Institute of Optics was part of the College of Engineering and Applied Sciences and because its mission was to cover the discipline of optical science and engineering, it was important for the leadership of the Institute to play significant roles in a number of professional societies. The Optical Society of America clearly was of central importance to us and to Rochester in general, since the society owes its beginnings to The Association for the Advancement of Applied Optics founded in Rochester in 1915. Certainly SPIE was also of importance to us. The list of officers, directors, fellows and committee members over the years shows a record of our commitment and the commitment of our graduates. I did my share, including being elected president in 1975 and 1976, with indentured servitude both before and after those years. With most societies, being president for a year ends up being in office for five or six years depending on the succession rules!

Nineteen seventy-seven was an important year. SPIE moved its headquarters to Bellingham, Washington, its income reached one million dollars, the one-hundredth proceedings was published, and its two-thousandth member enrolled. (It is hard to believe it was ever that small when you look at today's numbers!) It was natural at this point in its history to establish the Gold Medal Award. Rudolf Kingslake was the fourth recipient in 1980, Robert E. Hopkins in 1983, and myself in 1986, plus a number of distinguished alumni, including most recently Robert Fischer (2000) and James Wyant (2003).

Over many years there was a constant discussion about the name of the society that almost from its launch was simply referred to as SPIE. Everyone realized that this name did not provide any information to the outside world. Many colleagues in other disciplines looked at you quizzically when they heard you say that you were going to a "spy" (SPIE) conference! But the name SPIE had a very special place in many people's hearts. Emotional attachments of this kind should not be ignored. So, the great compromise was "SPIE—The International Society for Optical Engineering." Success! Former (and long-term and very effective) executive director Joe Yaver will tell you who to blame (or applaud) for this new and now lasting name.

Successive annual meetings and other specialized programs became larger and larger as the engineering aspect of optics in general continued to evolve. The programs and the published proceedings show a significant involvement from faculty and students in the Institute and major commitments from our alumni. Many alumni held various positions in the society, up to the highest level of president (e.g. presidents Robert Shannon, 1979, 1980; Barry Johnson, 1987; Robert Sprague, 1991; Roland Jacobsson, 1998).

The society always stayed connected to its roots while expanding its horizons to encompass the rapidly expanding fields involving the application of optical science and technology in the service of the nation and the world commercial economy. Thus, it is not surprising that in 1982 SPIE was appointed the international Secretariat for the Fifteenth International Congress on High-Speed Photography and Photonics. SPIE had been responsible for publishing earlier proceedings.

It is interesting from the Institute's point of view that SPIE had from its early days an involvement with high-speed photography in the broadest sense. Gordon Milne was an early pioneer in this field, and the Institute's war effort made many important contributions to bomb test photography and streak photography that extended into the post-war era. Elsewhere in this volume, George Fraley recounts great stories from that immediate post-war era and tales of experiments conducted on his campsite as well as in and on top of the Institute in Bausch & Lomb Hall.

Personally I had a particular interest in this high-speed technology and in the commercial equipment developed from it. In part this arose because of the period I spent as technical director of Beckman and Whitley (B&W), a division of Technical Operations Inc. "B&W," as it was often called, was one of the leading manufacturers of high-speed cameras, both frame and streak.

During this short essay I have spent some time on the background that led to "SPIE—The International Society for Optical Engineering" taking an important role in the spectrum of professional technical and scientific societies. We in the Institute are pleased to have supported that activity, and it has supported us in our educational and research mission. For many years SPIE has had a significant program of short courses at its meetings and its Optical Engineering Press has published some excellent tutorial texts. The Institute's involvement in these teaching and tutorial texts can be seen by scanning the list of authors of Optical Engineering Press volumes, and the topics and teachers of short courses at any meeting.

To end this essay—three other things of note that connect The Institute with SPIE. The first is again personal. Little did I know that when Joe Yaver, executive director of SPIE, and I discussed the need for a series of volumes of collected reprints of various sub-topics of optical science and engineering, that I would still be involved as series editor, some 170-plus Milestone Volumes later!

Emil Wolf is understandably not a major participant in SPIE; his tremendous strength is in the fundamental theory of our field and is thus aligned primarily with the field of physics. Nevertheless the impact of his work on many of us (both colleagues and students) has been profound as we pursue the implications and applications of his insights. His work has always had a theme of "optics in terms of observables." As I write this paragraph, I have just returned from a two-day seminar at the annual meeting of SPIE. The seminar title was "Tribute to Emil Wolf: Engineering Legacy of Physical Optics." A monograph

Robert Sprague (Ph.D. '71), SPIE President, presents the Conrady award to Rudolf Kingslake.

will be published on the papers presented at the meeting; I was proud to give the opening address.

The last of the three topics brings us back to Rudolf Kingslake, one of our first two faculty members in our Institute and to whom this volume is dedicated—in part, that is, as the other "part" is dedicated to his long-time partner, Hilda Kingslake. Both Hilda and Rudolf were both students of A. E. Conrady at Imperial College; Hilda, of course, was Conrady's daughter. The Conrady name and tradition lives on through them. In 1990 SPIE presented the first Conrady Award to Rudolf and Hilda Kingslake. The presentation was made by the president of SPIE, Robert Sprague, a distinguished Institute alumnus, at the annual meeting in San Diego. Congratulations to all three of you, and to all the many others who have contributed to the well being of the Institute and SPIE.

Brian J. Thompson has been a member of the faculty of the University of Rochester since 1968. He served as Director of the Institute of Optics from 1968 until 1975. He is currently Provost Emeritus of the University of Rochester, Rochester, NY.

Hoppy Story: Computer Lab

Robert Maier

The teaching lab was just down the hall from Hoppy's office—3 doors. He came in one morning to illustrate a point to the class, but soon realized he'd left his computer output in his office. So, he excused himself and went to his office to retrieve the output. Returning with the output, he inadvertently left his reading glasses in his office. So, back he went for his glasses, returning with his glasses, but no computer output. This process repeated itself about four times before he came back with both the output and his glasses.

Robert Maier received his B.S. and M.S. from the Institute of Optics in 1964 and 1966, respectively. He is currently a technical manager at Corning-Tropel Corporation, Rochester, NY.

The Institute of Optics
Faculty 1950–1959

Baumeister, Philip W., 1959–79
Blakney, Robert M., 1959–66
Boynton, Robert M., 1955–72
Carpenter, Vance J., 1956–62
Dexter, David, 1953–61
Di Francia, Giuliano T., 1953–54
Dunham, Theodore, 1953–57
Dutton, David B., 1954–63, 1975–78
Evans, John W., 1943–65
Ewald, William P., 1956–65
Eyer, James A., 1959–66
Finkelstein, Nisson, 1958–59
Fox, David, 1958–59
Fumi, Fausto, 1957–58
Givens, M. Parker, 1948–
Hopkins, Robert E., 1943–

Kapany, N. S., 1956–57
Kingslake, Rudolf, 1929–2003
Milne, Gordon G., 1948–66
Murty, Mantravado V. R. K., 1959–64
Nakai, Yoshio, 1959–61
O'Brien, Brian, 1930–55
Paul, Frederick W., 1948–50
Perrin, Fred, 1958–61
Peskin, James C., 1959–77
Polster, Harry D., 1948–54
Savedoff, Malcolm P., 1958–59
Siegmund, Walter P., 1953–55
Stewart, Harold S., 1943–46, 1959–62
Teegarden, Kenneth J., 1955–
Tutihasi, Simpei, 1956–58
Tuttle, Fordyce, 1940–62

The Institute of Optics
Degrees Awarded 1950–1959

Altman, Richard M., B.S., 1950; M.S., 1958

Axelrod, Norman N., Ph.D., 1959

Baker, William L., B.S., 1956

Bebb, William H., M.S., 1958

Becker, Alex, B.S., 1954

Becker, Eleanor A. (née Witulski), B.S., 1954

Blakney, Robert M., Ph.D. 1955

Buchanan, William B., B.S., 1957

Buzawa, M. John, B.S., 1952; M.S., 1954

Caley Jr., Wendell J., M.S., 1959

Campbell, Charles J., M.S., 1952

Carlough, Jr., Warren. A., B.S., 1958

Carman, P. Douglas, M.S., 1951

Carpenter, Vance J., B.S., 1949; M.S., 1950

Carter, Daniel E., Ph.D., 1954

Coelho, Roland, M.S., 1955

Davis, Nancy (née Hutchinson), M.S., 1952

Day, Pierce B., B.S., 1948; M.S., 1953

Delano, Erwin, B.S., 1948; M.S., 1956; Ph.D., 1966

DePalma, James J., M.S., 1957

Discher, Wendell V., M.S., 1951

Doane, Marshall G., B.S., 1959; M.S., 1961

Eyer, James A., Ph.D., 1957

Feldman, Paul, B.S., 1957

Forman, Paul F., B.S., 1956

Fujimura, William S., B.S., 1959

Gardner, Leland V., B.S., 1952

Ginsberg, Robert H., M.S., 1951

Glass, Charles J., M.S., 1956

Goetz, William E., M.S., 1953

Granger, Edward M., B.S., 1957; M.S., 1969; Ph.D., 1975

Grant, Duane E., M.S., 1958

Griffin, Gordon R., B.S., 1953

Haines, Jesse H., M.S., 1957

Harris, Thomas I., M.S., 1958

Hay, Bryan S., B.S., 1958

Heimer, Richard J., B.S., 1956

Hercher, Michael M., B.S., 1956; Ph.D., 1964

Hochheimer, Bernard F., M.S., 1953

Hoffman, J. Nelson, B.S., 1955

Howe, Jr., Harlan G., B.S., 1957

Hutchinson, Nancy, M.S., 1951

Jackson, Frederic H., B.S., 1954

Jarvis, James G., M.S., 1953

Jensen, Peter A., B.S., 1953

Keim, Robert E., M.S., 1957

Kendall, Don L., M.S., 1958

Kerr, Howard S., M.S., 1952

Kiner, Manuel L., B.S., 1953

King, T. A., B.S., 1951; M.S., 1955

Klemm, Robert E., B.S., 1951

Knox, Robert S., Ph.D., 1958

Koch, Donald A., B.S., 1948; M.S., 1953

Koester, Charles J., Ph.D., 1955

Krolak, Leo J., B.S., 1949; M.S., 1953

Kunz, Joseph F., B.S., 1950

Laikin, Milton, M.S., 1957

Lambert, William E., B.S., 1950

Landau, George J., B.S., 1955

Last, Jay T., B.S., 1951

Lauroesch, Thomas J., M.S., 1951

Lidfeldt, Alfred L., B.S., 1950

McKinley, Harry R., B.S., 1959

McSwain, Berah D., B.S., 1956; M.S., 1962

Meiron, Joseph, Ph.D., 1955

Milne, Gordon G., Ph.D., 1950

Murty, Mantravado V. R. K., Ph.D., 1959

Newell, Raymond F., B.S., 1951

O'Connell, John M., M.S., 1957

O'Neill, Patrick K., M.S., 1957

Pappert, Richard A., B.S., 1952

Parker Donald J., B.S., 1950
Peistrup, Clifford F., M.S., 1954
Perry, Stanford, M.S., 1959
Pike, John N., Ph.D., 1958
Pilston, Robert G., B.S., 1951
Price, William H., M.S., 1955
Prister, Jr., Charles, B.S., 1953
Putnam, Thomas E., B.S., 1947; M.S., 1950
Rabedeau, Melbourne E., M.S., 1959
Rees, Jr., James D., B.S., 1957; M.S., 1965
Rimmer, Matthew P., B.S., 1956; M.S., 1963
Rippel Jr., Charles W., B.S., 1950
Robinson, Theodore, B.S., 1958
Ruben, Paul L., B.S., 1959; M.S., 1963
Schuma, Richard F., M.S., 1959
Sexton, John W., B.S., 1952
Shannon, Robert R., B.S., 1954
Siegmund, Walter P, Ph.D., 1952
Simpson, George R., B.S., 1953
Smith, Abbott M., B.S., 1955; M.S., 1957; Ph.D., 1961
Smith, F. Dowswell, Ph.D., 1951

Smoyer, Claude B., B.S., 1959; M.S., 1965
Spencer, Gordon H., B.S., 1957; Ph.D., 1963
Staudenmaier, W., B.S., 1952
Sutherland, D. R., B.S., 1954
Tatian, Berge, B.S., 1951
Temple, Russell A., B.S., 1951
Thomas, Jr., Woodlief, M.S., 1958
Thorburn, Eugene K., B.S., 1950
Tindle, Ernest R., M.S., 1959
Toohig, Timothy E., M.S., 1953
Ullom, James R., M.S., 1952
Urbach, John C., B.S., 1955; Ph.D., 1962
Voggenthaler, John A., B.S., 1956
Warzak, Jr., Frank J., M.S., 1957
Weeks, Richard F., Ph.D., 1959
Wesler, John E., M.S., 1954
Wetherell, William B., B.S., 1958; M.S., 1961
Wieder, Harold, B.S., 1950; M.S., 1958
Wing, Albert B., M.S., 1952
Wolff, Fred J., B.S., 1941; M.S., 1953
Woodruff, Robert W., Ph.D., 1954

PART IV

THE LASER: THE 1960S

IV. The Laser: The 1960s

The big development in optics in the 1960s was without question the invention of the laser. It would completely revolutionize the field and make optics an enabler for dramatic break-throughs in a whole range of disciplines. The Institute was well positioned to take advantage of the explosion of optics research. Emil Wolf had just joined the faculty. Just weeks before the announcement of the invention of the laser, professors Wolf and Hopkins organized an international meeting on optical coherence that placed the University at the center of the emerging new field of quantum optics. This conference was the first of a series, the Rochester Conferences on Coherence and Quantum Optics. The Optics Road Show was launched, and some very bright young students got the Institute into the ground floor of laser development.

At the beginning of this decade the position of The Institute of Optics within the University was changed as it became an academic department in the newly formed College of Engineering and Applied Science.

In this section we explore these themes and also review the history of transmission thin films research in the Institute from its beginnings in the 1930s up through the transfer of the facilities to the Laboratory for Laser Energetics in support of the development of the Omega laser system. We review the directorships of Lewis Hyde and Brian Thompson, and the early days of laser development in the Institute. Finally, Jim Wyant describes the relationship of the Institute with its sister department, the Optical Sciences Center of the University of Arizona established some four decades after the Institute began.

24. Lewis Hyde and The River Campus: 1965–1968

Hilda Kingslake

In 1965 W. Lewis Hyde, a man of wide human interest, was appointed as the third Director of the Institute. He was a graduate of Harvard and had been on the faculty of The Institute of Optics for two years. Previously he had been the Director of Development of the American Optical Company's J. W. Fecker Division at Pittsburgh. Here at the University he had been serving as Associate Dean of the College of Engineering, and was a member of two subcommittees of the University Senate: The Library Advisory Committee, and the Subcommittee on Graduate Studies. The university community as a whole began to hear of The Institute of Optics as never before.

Hyde's own professional interest was in high-precision instrument design, an interest not represented on the faculty since the time of Gustave Fassin in the early days of the Institute. Hyde gave a very popular course with a great array of specimens for discussion.

While he was Director, Hyde made a number of appointments to the faculty, including P. J. Sands of Tasmania; J. M. Forsyth who later won the Lomb Medal of the Optical Society awarded to a young scientist under 30; and M. Creuzburg from Germany. He also made the first appointment of a new kind of Administrative Assistant, a member of the staff who would relieve the Director and other faculty members of much organizational

Lewis Hyde.

work. Mrs. Susan Raup was the first such appointment; she was followed in due course by Karen Strand, and the present incumbent David Child.

In 1966 Hyde organized the first International Lens Design Conference for which Mrs. Raup was able to do much of the detail work and later assembled a major publication on the proceedings of the conference. A large number attended the conference from foreign countries. Stimulated by its success, this conference has been followed by three others at five-year intervals, organized by the Optical Society of America.

In 1968 Hyde resigned to become Provost of the Bronx campus of New York University.

Hoppy Story: Mike Hercher's New Jacket

Robert Maier

Hopkins had a summer place up in the hills around Wayland, New York. He periodically invited people down for an outing. On one such occasion Institute of Optics folks, including some grad students, were invited down there. Mike Hercher was an instructor at the Institute, and a consultant to Tropel. Mike removed his new sports jacket, and laid it on the grass in order to pitch horse shoes. Meanwhile, Hoppy set about giving others a demonstration of his new riding lawn mower. You can guess what happened next.

Robert Maier received his B.S. and M.S. from the Institute of Optics in 1964 and 1966, respectively. He is currently a technical manager at Corning-Tropel Corporation, Rochester, NY.

25. Optical Thin Films at The Institute of Optics: A Brief History

Stanley Refermat

This brief history of optical thin films at The Institute of Optics reports some of the activities from the late 1930s to present. The history of optical thin films at the Institute can be organized into three periods, each with a laboratory designed for specific purposes. The earliest lab organized by Mary Banning supported the World War II effort. Philip Baumeister sparked an energetic research and teaching program. The third lab supported construction of the Omega Laser at the Laboratory for Laser Energetics.

The material for this brief history was gathered from library archives, from personal communications, and from my recollections as a student and as a member of the professional staff at the Institute.

The Early Years: Late 1930s–Early 1950s

The earliest mention of optical coatings at the Institute is by Hilda Kingslake. "In the late 1930s (Brian) O'Brien set up an evaporating unit for metallizing mirrors, and when later the thin-film antireflection coatings were introduced, he adapted his machine for this purpose."[1]

Institute of Optics faculty, students and staff focused on helping the war effort. "Dr. O'Brien (Institute of Optics Director) initiated an active program in response to the National Defense Research Council effort on behalf of the war (WWII). Mary Banning established the Thin Film Laboratory equipped with vacuum coating chambers to carry out a research program."[2]

A recent communication from Brian O'Brien Jr. describes some of the activities at The Institute of Optics during World War II. "I did work for Mary Banning, as did several other undergraduates. I don't remember just when she set up the evaporator lab but we did a lot of coating work during the war. This included multi-layer low-reflecting coatings, nickel neutral density filters, partial reflecting coatings, etc. I remember one job we did producing 50% coatings on 45/90 prisms for our entire fleet of submarine periscope cameras. These were actually not done by vacuum evaporation but by heat decomposition of titanium tetrachloride into titanium dioxide coating on glass."[3]

"In 1947 Mary Banning wrote a classic paper[4] explaining how to deposit multilayer filters and how to control their thickness."[5] She also described the 1943 development of the polarizing beamsplitter in this paper as well. During the late 1940s Alan Gee developed a film thickness monitoring system of sufficient accuracy to enable Harry Polster to produce a frustrated total reflection filter.

Air Force Post Books Talk By U. of R. Woman Scientist

There's nothing dull about science and atomic energy —not when Dr. Mary Banning of the University of Rochester talks about them.

Dr. Banning, petite, friendly daughter of the author, Margaret Culkin Banning, will speak on "Atomic Energy and Air Power" at the Air Force Day meeting in the 40 and 8 Chateau at 8 p. m. tomorrow. The meeting is being sponsored by Air Force Post, American Legion.

The scientist, a native of Duluth, won her bachelor of arts degree at Vassar and her doctor of philosophy degree at Johns Hopkins in 1941. When the ink was barely dry on her diploma she stepped from the comparative seclusion of campus life into hectic wartime research which made ultimate victory possible.

She is a pilot in her own right and her favorite avocations in addition to flying are canoeing, fly fishing and photography. Her travels have taken her to Europe and South America and she plans trips to the Orient and Europe for re-

Dr. Mary Banning of the University of Roches-

Dr. Mary Banning from 1946 Rochester Times Union.

Dr. Polster also developed the fifteen-layer all-dielectric narrow band interference filter while at The Institute of Optics.[6]

The Baumeister Era: 1959–1979

Philip Baumeister was the premier academic researcher, teacher, and student advisor working in the discipline of optical coatings. Philip drove the use of digital computers to design and analyze multilayer thin films, and led research across a broad range of optical coating application areas including synthesis and design, metrology and instrumentation and fabrication, especially UV filters and materials. Philip facilitated dissemination of optical thin film technology by organizing professional meetings attended by international audiences.

George Dobrowolski of the National Research Council (Ottawa) recently told me a story that illustrates Phillip's low-key, substantial influence. George established an international reputation developing mathematical techniques for thin film synthesis. George frequently traveled from Canada to the University Computing Center in the early 1960s to use Philip's thin film analysis code. George recalls the computer as an IBM 650 that required input and

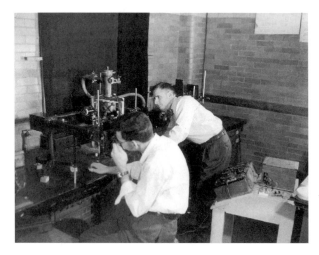

John Urbach and Phillip Baumeister.

Barry Dame and Big Berthe.

output via punched cards. A card reader interpreted the output deck, and the information was sent to a printer. Philip's unselfish cooperation enabled George to achieve his early theoretical successes. Dobrowolski concluded, "I owe Philip a large debt of gratitude."[7]

Philip established his lab with his coating machine, "Berthe," as the star. Berthe arrived in 1962.[8] Berthe was equipped with electron beam and resistive evaporation systems enabling deposition of a wide range of thin film materials. Berthe and associated metrology instrumentation enabled the pioneering fabrication of induced transmission ultra-violet interference filters.

During a period when optical coating designs and fabrication techniques were often closely held, Philip made substantial contributions to the dissemination of technology by means of international symposia he organized. Two symposia are worth noting. In June 1966 he coordinated a three-day series, "Design and Fabrication of Multilayer Optical Filters." Principal speakers included recent Baumeister Ph.D. students V. R. Costich and E. Delano, J. A. Dobrowolski (National Research Council, Canada), O. S. Heavens (University of York, England), R. J. Pegis (St. John Fisher) and D. L. Perry (Bell Telephone Laboratories, New Jersey).[9]

Philip followed up with another three-day series in June 1967 titled "Optical Thin Films and Multilayers." Philip was assisted by visiting professor J. Roland Jacobsson of the Institute for Optical Research (Stockholm, Sweden). Roland was the leading authority on inhomogeneous optical thin films. He spent one year teaching at The Institute of Optics. Other lecturers included William R. Hunter (U. S. Naval Research Laboratories, Washington, D. C.) a leading authority on the properties of ultra-violet materials; Michael Smith (Xerox Research Laboratories, Webster); and A. Francis Turner (Bausch & Lomb, Rochester).[10] Turner was a pioneer in optical thin film development and applications from the 1930s onward.

Optical Coating and the Laboratory for Laser Energetics (LLE): 1975–1980

The Laboratory for Laser Energetics started in the late 1960s with collaboration between faculty members Michael Herscher, Institute of Optics, and Moshe Lubin, Mechanical and Aerospace Sciences. By the mid 1970s LLE was funded by a consortium of private firms, the University, and state and federal agencies to establish the National Laser Users Facility (NLUF). The objective was to investigate the interaction of intense light with matter, to study basic physics and laser fusion.[11] The path forward included building the twenty-four-beam-line Omega laser system, constructing a facility on the East River Road campus, and assembling the professional staff to build and operate Omega and conduct the research. The funding was associated with an aggressive schedule for development and construction of Omega. The technical basis for Omega was demonstrated with the successful four-beam-line Delta system located in the Gavett Hall lab. Omega's scaled-up requirements for radiant energy densities, laser power, pulse repetition rates and the coherent nature of light posed new challenges. Substantial scaling of design concepts and some invention associated with optical materials and processes were required to build Omega.

In 1975, after discussions with Moshe Lubin (director of LLE) and Brian Thompson (dean of engineering), I accepted an offer to establish and operate an optical coating lab at

The Institute of Optics to support the thin film development and production requirements for LLE. The motivation for establishing the coating lab on campus was straightforward. Coating requirements for the Omega system limited the number of reliable commercial suppliers, and schedule was a critical factor in the LLE plan. Some of the critical optical coating specifications included state-of-the-art film thickness uniformity over large substrates and in large quantities. The resultant thin films had to withstand intense laser irradiation with production rates sufficient to satisfy a demanding schedule. In addition, some of the substrates such as the laser rods were very expensive and had lead times measured in months. One or two commercial firms demonstrated the ability to meet most technical requirements. They were both located in California and they committed their capacity to supporting a similar program at Lawrence Livermore National Laboratory (LLNL). The risks for LLE were associated with schedule reliability and the probability of damage to precision optical components due to shipping across the country. Moshe Lubin decided a dedicated, reliable optical coating lab was essential to the successful development and operation of Omega.

I started planning the coating lab in the summer of 1975. I developed a schedule consistent with LLE milestones, submitted a budget and developed requirements for the lab. About this time, Jay Eastman joined LLE as Omega program manager. As program manager, he also was manager of the coating lab. That was fortunate for me because Jay became a valued colleague. During the planning stage, we had to make decisions that broke new ground and relied solely on our professional judgment. I am grateful for Jay Eastman's counsel, which enabled our lab's success.

We were assigned space in the recently vacated Gavett Hall engineering machine shop (the shop moved to a better facility in a stand-alone building). When I first entered the empty shop and noticed the aroma of cutting oil, I wondered how we would clean it up so our coatings would not suffer organic contamination. The University had a very competent contractor, and proper application of epoxy paint accomplished the objective of sealing the contaminants. While the facility was prepared, we ordered two coating machines, one forty-eight-inch and one seventy-two-inch box coater. We also ordered metrology equipment and components for the substrate cleaning facility. We worked long hours for six months integrating and shaking down the equipment to make up schedule slips due to late delivery of equipment. An additional three months was needed to establish and stabilize processes for inspection, pre-coat cleaning, and thin film performance verification.

The LLE plan called for building the first six of twenty-four beam lines as an engineering model. The six beams, called Zeta, were to be operational in 1978. The coating lab was up and running by the end of 1976. We spent 1977 developing and producing coatings for the Zeta optics on schedule. Steve Jacobs, chief optical scientist for LLE, provided substantial support materials and special metrology support for the lab. Steve also led the development of improved laser glass at Hoya. Ken Walsh directed the optical metrology team that supported the coating effort.

The most challenging coatings were large thin film polarizers. Polarizers made of crystals or other materials would not withstand the laser power and could not be made in the aperture sizes needed. The thin film polarizers were up to seven inches by

Jay Eastman on the bank of the Genesee.

fourteen inches and required thickness variations less than 1 percent. Other coatings included anti-reflection coatings on the ends of 90 mm laser rods, large forty-five-degree reflectors with differential phase change upon reflection for "p" and "s" components of less than one and two degrees, and coatings effective at 1.053 microns and 0.351 microns for frequency-tripling applications.

Zeta was very successful, and we started work on the balance of the twenty-four beams. The schedule called for Omega to be operational during 1981. The coatings had to be completed in about eighteen months. We ramped up to two full-time coating technicians and relied on our metrology and materials support teams to help us complete the coatings on schedule. In all we coated about three thousand optical elements.[12]

Optical Coating and LLE: 1980–Present

When the coating assignment for Omega was complete, I decided to make a career change and joined Eastman Kodak Co. in 1980. Doug Smith joined LLE shortly thereafter. He managed the move of the coating lab to LLE and expanded the facility for greater coating capacity. Doug operated the lab to successfully coat optics to convert Omega to a UV system.

Today the coating lab continues to thrive and contribute, providing coating services to LLE and LLNL. The Institute of Optics/LLE coating lab provides more than half the critical polarizer and large turning mirror coated optics for LLNL. The tradition of thin film optics contributions to major programs started during World War II and continues today in support of laser fusion research.

Stanley Refermat received his M.S. from the Institute of Optics in 1967. He is currently employed at Eastman Kodak Company, Rochester, NY.

References

1   H. G. Kingslake, "The Institute of Optics, 1929–1987," University of Rochester.
2   *The Institute of Optics Image* 2:1 (fall 1970): 6.
3   Brian O'Brien Jr., private communication, October 25, 2003.
4   M. Banning, "Practical methods of making and using multiplayer filters," *J. Opt. Soc. Am.* 37 (1947): 792.
5   A. Macleod, "The early days of optical coatings," *J. Opt. A: Pure Appl. Opt.* 1 (1999): 779–783. UK.
6   *The Institute of Optics Image* 2:1 (fall 1970): 7.
7   Dr. George Dobrowolski, NRC, private communication, November 4, 2003.
8   *Institute of Optics ION*, November 1962.
9   University of Rochester Press Release, June 10, 1966.
10 University of Rochester Press Release, June 8, 1967.
11 Dr. John Soures, private communication, November 4, 2003.
12 Steve Kumpan, private communication, November 4, 2003.

26. Rochester Pinafore

David MacAdam

There have always been Christmas parties in the Institute, but in some years they are much more elaborate than others. In the early 1960s there some rather remarkable ones. One was the subject of an editorial by David MacAdam in the *Journal of the Optical Society of America.*[1]

The "very model physics doctor of philosophy" on the editor's page for March brought out of hiding the following parody on Gilbert and Sullivan's "When I was a Lad" from *H. M. S. Pinafore.* It arrived anonymously, but discreet inquiries established the facts that it was 1) composed by the faculty of The Institute of Optics at the University of Rochester, 2) presented at a student-faculty Christmas party at the Institute in the early 1960s, and 3) a response to a student-presented skit roasting the faculty. A significant research and thesis might be done by some Ph.D. candidate who would undertake to bridge the "two cultures" by studying the devotion of physicists (especially optical physicists?) to Gilbert and Sullivan and their propensities and skills in writing parodies on the patter songs.

1. When I was a lad I sought my degree
   At the Optics school on the Genesee.
   I studied hard and I studied long
   And I even learned some Optics as I went along.
     CHORUS: He even learned some optics as he went along.

   I learned my Optics so cleverly
   That now I am the holder of a P-H-D.
     CHORUS: He learned his optics so cleverly
       That now he is the holder of a P-H-D.

2. When I studied as a freshman, I never did stop.
   And soon my grades reached the very, very top.
   As an honor student I acquired some fame
   Copies of my papers earned a special name.
     CHORUS: Copies of his paper earned a special name.

   I copied all my papers with hand so free
   That now I am the holder of a P-H-D.
     CHORUS: He copied all his papers with a hand so free
       That now he is the holder of a P-H-D.

3. In my sophomore year I did excel.
   I took my courses and passed them well.
   In math and physics I became quite skilled.
   And my thirst—for knowledge—could never be filled
     CHORUS: And his thirst—for knowledge—could never be filled.

   But I curbed my thirst so effectively
   That now I am the holder of a P-H-D.
     CHORUS: But he curbed his thirst so effectively
       That now he is the holder of a P-H-D.

4. In my junior year I studied every night
    While Maxwell's equations I did recite.
    The paths through lenses I computed and drew
    And Diffraction Theory I did pursue.
       CHORUS: And Diffraction Theory he did pursue

    I pursued my course so cleverly
    That now I am the holder of a P-H-D.
       CHORUS: He pursued his course so cleverly
                   That now he is the holder of a P-H-D.

5. In my senior year I reached my goal
    And I was given my parchment scroll.
    I stood in line for my Bach. degree
    I dangled at my side my Phi Beta Key.
       CHORUS: He dangled at his side his Phi Beta key.

    I flaunted that key so conspicuously
    That I was rewarded with a P-H-D.
       CHORUS: He flaunted that key so conspicuously
                   That he was rewarded with a P-H-D.

6. When I got my degree my folks were mad
    'Cause instead of earning money I became a grad.
    Of optical knowledge I'd acquired such a grip
    I managed to acquire an assistantship.
       CHORUS: He managed to acquire an assistantship.

    That assistantship did so well by me
    I'm almost sorry I've a P-H-D.
       CHORUS: That assistantship did so well by him
                   He's almost sorry he's a P-H-D.

7. As a lab instructor we had light to diffract
    And lenses and prisms to refract.
    I counseled my students with advice of sorts
    I made up the grades for their lab reports.
       CHORUS: He made up the grades for their lab reports.

    I guessed at the grades so cleverly
    That now I am the holder of a P-H-D.
       CHORUS: He guessed at the grades so cleverly
                   That now he is the holder of a P-H-D.

8. I studied so hard I never did sleep.
    Soon my grades were at the top of the heap.
    I did so well on every quiz
    I took my quals and was quite a whiz.
       CHORUS: He took his quals and was quite a whiz.

    I took them each time so cleverly
    That eventually I got my P-H-D.
       CHORUS: He took them each time so cleverly
                   That eventually he got his P-H-D.

9. Now students all, wherever you may be
    If you want to rise to the top of the tree
    If your soul isn't fettered to a light-lab stool
    Be careful to be guided by this golden rule—
       CHORUS: Be careful to be guided by this golden rule—

If you have to learn your subject, learn it cleverly
And you all may be holders of a P-H-D.
   CHORUS: If you have to learn your subject, learn it cleverly
            And you all may be holders of a P-H-D.

While Dr. MacAdam did not divulge the author of the lyrics of the song in his editorial, rumor has it that such parodies were just one of the many talents of faculty member Phillip Baumeister.

David MacAdam was a member of the faculty of the University of Rochester from 1977 until 1996. He died in 1997.

Reference

1   *J. Opt. Soc. Amer* 56 (1966): 848.

Hoppy Story: Who's Driving?

Mark Westcott

When Bob was still teaching at the Institute, he was car-pooling with another professor. One day after classes, the two of them were returning home and Bob was driving. When he drove past the exit which led to the other professor's home, his passenger remarked, "Bob, you missed my exit." Bob replied: "Oh, I thought you were driving."

[*Editor's note:* I must come to Hoppy's defense on this one. He was not the only absent-minded person in the Rochester optics scene. I have it on good authority that a variant of this story actually occurred when Erich Marchand and Max Herzberger were car-pooling to work at the Kodak Hawkeye plant. Both were inveterate chess players who played mental chess matches as they drove back and forth. One morning a checkmate was perilously close when the plant gate passed by unnoted, leading to the exchange reported above. There is no question that both Hopkins and Marchand were capable of concentrating on the problem at hand to the exclusion of all else.

Erich was a lifemaster chess player who was New York State champion four years. After he retired from Kodak he taught classes part-time at the University and coached the student chess club. He even had a major tournament named for him. He often played exhibitions in which he took on the entire club in simultaneous matches. He also amused himself at playing Blackjack at casinos in Las Vegas and Reno. He could easily remember all the cards played in a seven-deck game, but the casinos quickly learned of his skills, and after they found that hostesses offering free drinks were not enough distraction, they began using a new deck for each deal or simply closing the table down when he arrived.]

Mark Westcott received his B.S. from the Institute of Optics in 1970. He is currently an optical engineer at Corning-Tropel Corporation, Rochester, NY.

27. The Institute and the College of Engineering and Applied Science

Carlos Stroud

The location of The Institute of Optics within the administrative structure of the University has evolved over the years. At present the Institute is an academic department within the School of Engineering and Applied Sciences which is itself a subdivision of the College of Arts, Sciences and Engineering—but as the word "Institute" suggests, The Institute of Optics has a history and a current role that is somewhat different from that of the standard academic department in the University. We will briefly review that history and role, particularly in relation to the formation of the College of Engineering and Applied Science in the late 1950s.

When the Institute of Applied Optics was founded in 1929, it was not given the same status as other academic departments reporting to the dean. Instead it reported directly to the president of the University, Rush Rhees. President Rhees was directly involved. As recounted in earlier essays, he actually traveled to England to personally interview the first two faculty members to join the Institute from outside the University. The new Institute had some special resources available to it, and some special obligations that made it unique within the University structure. Generous corporate support by Eastman Kodak and Bausch & Lomb, including $20,000 in equipment funds and $20,000 per year for five years for operating costs, provided some opportunities for research that were not common in a relatively small teaching college that was just beginning to aspire to become a national research university. The impetus for this support was a perceived national need for scientists and engineers trained in optics and optical instrumentation. There was no other academic department specializing in optics in the United States at the time, so the new department had a special obligation to provide the engineers and scientists for the optics industry, particularly the large fraction of it which was based in Rochester. There was also a special obligation to provide leadership for national organizations in the field of optics, in particular the newly formed Optical Society of America. Simply by being the only department specializing in this field, it took on these responsibilities. In return for the funds, the University agreed that "to a reasonable extent the employees of the companies should be allowed to attend lectures and share other benefits of the existence of an institute of optics."

The new institute did enjoy a close relationship with the physics department from the beginning. After a first year on the old Prince Street Campus, the Institute was housed on River Campus in the fourth floor of the new Bausch & Lomb building; the other floors were occupied by physics. The first Acting Director, T. Russell Wilkins, was a junior physics professor, and the students took a range of physics courses as a part of the regular curriculum. In the first years most of the research students working in optics were formally graduate students in physics.

The Institute's unique status was even further enhanced during World War II, as a large fraction of the military optics research in the country was centered in the department, and the branch of the National Defense Research Council was located here. The faculty and staff grew to approximately fifty.

Following the war the situation changed rather dramatically. The size of the Institute was quickly reduced as the NDRC programs ended, physicists and chemists returned to campus after the war with the prestige of their disciplines greatly enhanced by important contributions to the war effort, and the University began to remake itself into the Ivy League mold of a research university. A research university is generally made up of a series of colleges and professional schools, so the University began to consider how to reorganize itself along these lines. Engineering had been a department in the College of Arts and Sciences; in 1958 it was decided to establish a new College of Engineering and Applied Science including the departments of chemical, electrical and mechanical engineering.

Initially, the Institute maintained its unique status and was not part of the new college; however, a number of events occurred that pushed it in that direction. First, the stature of the new college would be considerably enhanced by adding another department with national and international visibility. Second, the University was gifted with several very talented and ambitious leaders on campus. In addition to Brian O'Brien, there were William Noyes in chemistry and Robert Marshak in physics, both with ideas that required considerable resources. When O'Brien left the Institute in 1954 to go to industry, the Institute lost many of the resources that it had enjoyed. O'Brien had directed the Institute in a very personal fashion. Most of the funds supporting the program had been raised through his personal contacts in industry and government. He had been involved in essentially every aspect of the Institute's existence for the previous twenty years. Furthermore, a lot of the equipment in the Institute belonged to him personally so that on his departure the program lost a great leader, an extremely able fundraiser, and a goodly fraction of its research facilities. Although the Institute was fortunate to have the very able Robert Hopkins to take over the reins, there were soon rather severe financial pressures. The problems were exacerbated by the administration's ruling that the income from a small endowment as well as a reserve fund derived from contract overhead charges were committed to O'Brien personally so that they reverted to the University on his departure, and were not available to the Institute.[1]

There were extensive studies and discussions concerning how the Institute could be put into a more stable and conventional way of operating within the University. President De Kiewiet decided to make the Institute an academic department within the College of Engineering and Applied Science while maintaining its historical designation as The Institute of Optics. A regular departmental budget was set up similar to that of other departments. During the 1950s the Institute had established a substantial program in solid state physics with David Dexter, Kenneth Teegarden, and David Dutton. Emil Wolf had joined the faculty in physical optics and coherence theory, Malcolm Savedoff had joined the faculty in astronomy, and Robert Boynton had a joint appointment in physiological optics. When the Institute was moved into the engineering college, Dexter, Savedoff, and Wolf were offered appointments in physics in the College of Arts and Science, Parker Givens was given his choice of an appointment in physics or in optics, and the rest of the faculty were offered the chance to continue their appointments in The Institute of Optics. Boynton's primary appointment was in psychology so that only his secondary appointment was changed.

The Institute's temporary financial problems were alleviated and, as can be seen in the essays in this volume describing the events of the past forty years, the Institute prospered in the new college. In fact, faculty members of the Institute have served important leadership roles in the College of Engineering and Applied Science. Rudolf Kingslake served briefly as acting dean and was followed by Brian Thompson, who served as Dean from 1974 until 1984, when he was became Provost of the University. In January 1995 the College of Arts and Science and the College of Engineering and Applied Science were combined into the College, with Engineering remaining as an entity called the School of Engineering and Applied Sciences within the College. Duncan Moore served as the first dean in this new School from 1995 to 1997. In 2003 the College was renamed the College of Arts, Science, and Engineering. The Institute of Optics remains a department in the School of Engineering and Applied Sciences within this college.

Of course, The Institute of Optics is no more an engineering department than it is a physics department; rather it is an optics department that ranges over all subfields of optics from fundamental quantum optics to applied instrumental design and fabrication, from optical properties of materials to medical optics. It is not unusual to have a wide range of sub-fields within a department, any physics or electrical engineering department has a similarly wide range. All of the sub-groups in a physics department generally agree however that the primary goal of their discipline is to develop new fundamental understanding of physical processes. All electrical engineers can similarly agree that their goal is to apply accepted physical principles to develop new technologies that have practical applications. Optics faculty members have no such common criterion for judging the significance of their work. Some are scientists concerned with fundamental knowledge while others are engineers focused on practical applications, inventions and entrepreneurship. Perhaps more remarkable is the fact that many, perhaps most, of the faculty alternate between the two publishing in *Physical Review Letters* and applying for a patent, occasionally even in the same month!

The current situation is probably ideal with the Institute within the School of Engineering and Applied Science but with six faculty members holding joint appointments in the Institute and the Department of Physics and Astronomy. Students benefit from the breadth of training that this provides and generally are free to decide even after they complete a doctorate in Optics whether they wish to pursue an academic career, perhaps in a physics or electrical engineering department, or pursue an industrial career. They are well prepared for any of these possibilities.

Reference

1   Letter from Raymond L. Thompson to President DeKiewiet, November 30, 1954.

28. A Personal Reminiscence

Murty V. Mantravadi

My name is Mantravadi Venkata Radha Krishna Murty (M. V. R. K. Murty for short). While I was in the Institute I used M. V. R. K. Murty as the name on most of my publications. Since Mantravadi is my surname (family name), I decided to change my name when I became a US citizen in 1989 to the style of Murty V. Mantravadi.

I finished my undergraduate degrees in Mathematics and Instrument technology in India by the end of 1952 and worked as a lecturer in Instrument Technology at the Madras Institute of Technology for about 3 years till the end of 1955. I came under the influence of a German Professor by the name of Richard Walauschek who taught us Optics at Madras Institute of Technology and since that time, I had great ambition to pursue graduate study in Optics. So, I applied to Rochester and the Imperial College in England for admission. I got the letter of admission from Institute of Optics during the last part of 1955. I did not want to lose any more time, so I decided to join the Institute of Optics as a graduate student for the spring semester in February 1956. In those days there was no GRE or TOEFL and apparently I was admitted on the strength of Professor Walauschek's recommendation and my own record in my previous studies.

The travel from India to USA was also great once-in-a life-time experience for me. I booked the lowest possible fare passage from India taking a boat from the Port City of Cochin on the west coast of India to Boston. It was a cargo ship stopping at odd ports like Zibuti on the horn of Africa, Port Said in Egypt and Halifax in Canada. It cost me $375 including food for almost 30 days. I left India some time in the first week of January and arrived at Boston in the first week of February. I took a Greyhound bus from Boston to Rochester and my first few days were in the local YMCA. I came to the Institute of Optics immediately and met Dr. Robert Hopkins in his office to discuss about my course work. By the way I was offered a stipend of $600 for a semester to act as a teaching assistant. Surprisingly that amount was quite sufficient for me and in fact I was able to save some. I got a room on Genesee Street just across the river, so I could easily walk to the campus. I came from a tropical country with summers of 120 degrees and here I am in Rochester right in the middle of winter and huge mounds of snow. That was a quite a change of scenery and climate for me.

I took courses from Prof. Hopkins, Prof. Givens and the once weekly (3 hour) class of Dr. Kingslake. I also took courses from Prof. Jack Evans and Prof. Boynton. I remember distinctly the classes taken by Prof. Hopkins. While deriving some equations and then substituting numerical values, he used to say "upstairs" and "downstairs" instead of numerator and denominator. Also instead of substituting, he would say "plugging in". I used to have very good discussions with Prof. Givens in his office about diffraction, interference and some little experiments I was thinking about. Professor Givens was the most versatile in that he was handling the regular optics courses but also was handling other areas like optical constants of metals, vacuum UV spectroscopy and its use for absorption measurements of extremely thin metal films. The n and k of the complex refractive index $n + ik$ were determined by using ellipsometry immediately after the deposition of the metal in the vacuum chamber. This was needed because the surfaces would be oxidized if they are taken out of the vacuum. I remember Larry Emons, Hal Weider and Norman Axelrod were in this activity. I also remember Prof. Bipin Agarwal from Allahabad University, India spent a year (1956) with Professor Givens to do experiments on the absorption of the metal films in the vacuum UV region using the large vacuum spectrograph.

There used to be a large Twyman-Green interferometer at the Institute of Optics and I was always fascinated with it. It provided for me the basic instrument on which I made additions and modifications to my thesis work. I was really happy when I got my Ph.D. in June 1959 almost $3\frac{1}{2}$ years after starting my graduate studies. Prof. Jack Evans was especially helpful to me to provide summer jobs at Tropel which enabled me to bring my family to the country in 1958. I assisted Prof. Hopkins as an assistant during my entire graduate study. I can recall some of my contemporary graduate students: Robert Shannon, Richard Weeks, Robert Knox, Robert Keim, Donald Kendal, Robert Potter, Norman Axelrod, Larry Emons, Pat O'Neil, Hal Weider and many others. I remember we used to have a soup club during lunch time and most of the above were members. We used to heat the soup in a sauce pan on a bunsen burner. There were also one or two regular graduate students deputed by the Coast Guard every year, but I can not recall the names now.

After my graduation Prof. Hopkins offered me a research associateship to work on some of the projects then being funded by the newly formed NASA. We designed and built objective spectrometers to be flown on unguided rockets. NASA obtained some useful data of stellar UV spectra of some bright stars. I recall some of my colleagues on this project: Neil Hochgraf, Robert Blakney, Bill Staudenmeir, Gordon Milne, Harold Stewart. On the technical side, we had help from Bill Klinkert (optics shop) Paul and Hamburger (precision machining) Horner and Kucil for drafting. If I remember correctly, this activity was done under a small group formed in the Institute of Optics called the Division for Group Research. It was disbanded afterwards.

In 1961 I was given a 3 year appointment as an assistant professor. I used to teach geometrical and physical optics (classes and lab) for undergraduates and graduate students. As I mentioned before, I used the Twyman-Green interferometer extensively in my lab course. It was at that time, the He-Ne laser became commercially available. Because of the extreme temporal and spatial coherence of the laser, we tried to replace the Hg lamp source with the laser source. In addition to the conventional Twyman-Green (Fizeau) fringes, there was a confusing background of other fringes. I was able to locate the source of these fringes. These were due to the thick beam splitter acting as a shearing interferometer. Then I realized that a separate shearing device could be made to test optics and verify the collimation of light beams, Bill Klinkert, our master optician provided me with a very good parallel plate and another one with small wedge angle and I was able to get very clean shear fringes with and without tilt. I published this in Applied Optics in 1962. This collimation test is now used by many in the original form or modified form in many labs where collimation is very critical. This was the begining period of laser research and I remember Mike Hercher, Doug Sinclair working on their laser related theses. One of the active faculty members at that time on lasers was Prof. Carol Alley. I had 4 M.S. thesis students during my faculty years and I recall their names: Frank Grum, M. M. Rao, Edward Hagerrott and Art Shoemaker. Since I was playing with interferometers and especially white light interferometers, it came to me as second nature to locate and obtain the white light fringes in a quick and simple way.

During my faculty years, I came across some people at the Institute of Optics who are leaders in their fields. Daniel Malacara and I encountered each other in the Bausch and Lomb building and initially we each thought the other was from his country because we had both brown skins. Then he told me he was from Mexico and I told him I was from India. I showed him my parallel plate shearing interferometer and he decided to take it up for further work as his Ph.D. thesis. It was not the end of our association when I left Rochester in 1964. I spent 3 months (1973) as a visiting scientist at INAOE, Puebla, Mexico at Malacara's invitatation. It was at that time that I, Alejandro Carnejo (another U of R optics alumnus) and Malacara collaborated on several publications and also started on the now widely known book *Optical Shop Testing* edited by Malacara. I also spent two years (1982–83) at Centro de Investigacion en Optica in Leon, Mexico where Malacara was the Director. I enjoyed my stays in Mexico and they were also productive in research and publications.

Roy Freiden was a graduate student in the early '60s and worked for a while as my teaching assistant. He is now a Professor at OSC, U of Arizona, Tucson. David Shafer was an undergraduate student who took some of my courses. I remember him coming into my office once with a paper (either home work or test answer paper) and asking me why I gave him such a high grade. Most people came to me complaining about the low grades I gave. He had other interests such as study of classical languages, Sanskrit, Latin and Greek. Now he is one of the leading and innovative optical designers in the country. Robert Hilbert was another undergraduate student who continued on to do the M.S. He was interested in my work on testing optics and I was interested in his thesis on concentric optics. He used to recall his experiences with Frank Cooke with whom he worked during summers.

During the period of my stay as a graduate student and as a faculty member, there were quite a number of visiting scientists from abroad and also from USA. Some names I recall were N. S. Kapany and Bipin Agarwal from India, Kubota and Yamada from Japan, Boivin and Deslile from Quebec, Buchdahl from Australia, Ingelstam from Sweden, and Hanau from Lexington, KY. My interaction was mainly with Ingelstam, Deslile and Boivin. Ingelstam was especially interested in the modified Michelson interferometer I devised for producing Newton-like fringes at infinity in one direction only. These are straight fringes with a linearly variable frequency. This system was used by Frank Grum for his MS thesis to determine the OTF of various photographic materials. I got the required parallel plates of BK7 made by Bill Klinkert and gave them to Ingelstam who wanted to investigate extensively the OTF properties of various recording materials. There were also many foreign students during this period. Some of the names I recall were Ikeda and Ozawa from Japan, Swami, Chirra and Thomas from India, Malacara from Mexico. I can recall some of my colleagues on the faculty during this period were Hopkins (Director), Givens, Evans, Baumeister, Eyer, Alley, Dexter, Fox, Knox, Teagarden, Stewert, Blakney, Hyde. I was also in touch with Baumeister and his students especially, Frank Mulligan and Verne Costich.

By the end of 1964 I decided to go back to India after nearly 9 years of stay in Rochester. But I have not lost my connection to Rochester and was in touch from time to time. It was during 1964–66 that I was Professor of Instrument technology at Madras Institute of Technology, India (the MIT of India) that I came across Bala S. Manian and Vasant Kumar as my students who were very bright in their classes. I was in a way responsible to recommending them for admission to the Institute of Optics as graduate students. They did their MS in Rochester and their Ph.D's elsewhere. Bala is now a leading innovator/venture capitalist in the San Jose area in California. Vasant Kumar was a senior scientist/manager at Northrop in Los Angeles area and it so happened that in 1987 after I left

Mexico and couple of other jobs, I joined Northrop as a Senior Research Scientist/ Engineer in his department. I retired from Northrop in 1994.

We were very active off campus as well as on. The monthly meeting of the local Optical Society was attended by scientists and engineers from local industry such as Bausch and Lomb, Kodak, Xerox and others. It was at these meetings I used to meet the people from the local optical industry. Max Herzberger, both Kingslakes were regular attendees at these meetings. Then there were people like Miss Crowley who were organizing receptions and fun meetings for foreign students and faculty. There was Dr. Devadut, Professor at Colgate Divinity School whose home was open to many Indian and other foreign students. Of course, the Kingslakes were always inviting us for dinners at their home. We felt very welcome in Rochester in those days and I am sure it is still a very hospitable city. We were also connected to Rochester in a sentimental way because two of our children were born there in Strong Memorial Hospital.

Murty V. Mantravadi received his Ph.D. from the Institute in 1959 and served on the faculty from 1959–1963.

29. Early Days of Coherence Theory and the First Rochester Conference on Coherence[1]

Emil Wolf

The terms *coherence* and *correlations* seem to have entered the optics vocabulary about the beginning of the twentieth century, many years after Maxwell discovered that light was an electromagnetic phenomenon. Prior to that time there were only a few investigations, which have a bearing on this subject. The first one was made by a distinguished French optical scientist E. Verdet who around 1865 asked a question which is equivalent to the following: If sunlight illuminates directly two pinholes in an opaque screen, how close must the pinholes be, so that the light which emerges from them can form interference fringes on superposition? He estimated the distance to be about 1/50 millimeter. In modern language this small distance is the diameter of the area of coherence formed by sunlight on the surface of the earth.

Little, if anything, concerning coherence was done after that for more than forty years, until 1907, when Max von Laue published two papers concerning the entropy of partially coherent ray bundles. In the first of these papers von Laue introduced a quantitative measure of correlation between two light beams. This was probably the first definition of a degree of coherence of light, but von Laue's investigations did not attract much attention and they have been largely forgotten. In fact, until about the middle of the 1940s hardly

Emil Wolf at first Coherence Conference in 1960.

anything more was written on this subject. Nor did two papers by Erwin Schrödinger receive much attention. One of Schrödinger's papers, published in 1920, dealt with coherence and interference. The other, published in 1926, was a precursor of important work done several decades later by Roy Glauber on the subject of coherent states. Earlier, around 1890, Michelson introduced two interferometric techniques, one for measuring energy distribution in spectral lines, the other for measuring stellar diameters. It was not until very much later that it was realized that the first of these methods implicitly uses the concept and the properties of *temporal* coherence, the other those of *spatial* coherence.

A turning point in the development of coherence theory was the publication of a paper by Fritz Zernike in 1939 in which he introduced a precise measure of spatial coherence in light fluctuations at two points in an optical field, the so-called *mutual intensity* and also its normalized version, the *degree of coherence*. He showed that these quantities could be determined from simple experiments, namely, from measurements of the sharpness of interference fringes formed in a Young's interference pattern. He established a number of interesting properties of the mutual intensity and of the degree of coherence and he also formulated a basic law of optical coherence theory, known today as the *van Cittert-Zernike theorem* (P. H. van Cittert derived it, in 1934, under somewhat more restricted conditions). It explains, in quantitative terms, how a completely incoherent source may give rise to partially coherent light, and in some cases even very highly coherent light in some region of space on free propagation.

Thus until about 1940 there were only a few publications dealing with or closely related to coherence; but it is of interest to note that among the authors of these publications were some very distinguished scientists, including four Nobel Prize winners, namely A. A. Michelson, Max von Laue, E. Schrödinger and F. Zernike.

Following the publication of Zernike's paper, his theory was applied to a number of problems of instrumental optics, notably by H. H. Hopkins and his students in England. Many of the results obtained by this group showed that coherence concepts are very relevant for the design of optical systems and for the understanding of their performance.

Around that time, in the early 1950s, I was working at Edinburgh University, collaborating with Max Born in the writing of a book, *Principles of Optics*. When I came to writing the chapter on interference of light and I examined the various better-known books on optics, I was very disappointed with them; all of them discussed interference only in connection with monochromatic waves. Not a single textbook that I examined took into account fluctuations in realistic sources and in realistic light fields. As I pondered upon how to treat interference in the book we were writing, I gradually realized that a satisfactory treatment of interference requires a generalization of Zernike's mutual intensity and of his degree of coherence. The quantities Zernike introduced were functions which characterized correlations between light vibrations at two points in an optical field, at the *same* instants of time. I soon found that to formulate a broader and more rigorous theory one must generalize Zernike's concept of the mutual intensity. Namely, one needs to take as a measure of coherence the correlation of the field fluctuations not only at two points in space, but also at two instances of time. The correlation function which I introduced for this purpose in 1955 is known as the *mutual coherence function*, and this function satisfies rigorously two wave equations in free space. It turned out that all the results relating to propagation of the mutual intensity and of the degree of coherence derived previously, in particular the van Cittert-Zernike theorem, are approximate solutions of these two wave equations.

When I discovered these two equations (which are now almost obvious but they were not so in the 1950s), I phoned Born from my Edinburgh home and told him that I found some rather exciting new results which I would like to discuss with him. Born suggested we meet for lunch. I came to his office at lunch time, and as he was putting on his coat he asked me what the excitement was all about. I said, "Professor Born I have discovered that not only the optical field propagates as a wave, but so do its coherence properties." Born looked at me rather sadly, put his arm on my shoulder as if to comfort me, and said, "Wolf, you have always been such a sensible fellow but now you have gone completely crazy."

There is another amusing story relating to my interaction with Born about coherence. In 1956 Born was already in retirement and I was on a visiting appointment at New York University, still working on our book. One day I received a letter from Born in which he asked me why the manuscript was not yet finished. I wrote back saying that the manuscript is almost completed, except for a chapter on partial coherence on which I was still working. Born replied at once saying, "Wolf, who apart from you is interested in coherence? Leave the chapter out and send the manuscript to the printers."

I finished the chapter anyway and our book was published in 1959, only a few months before the invention of the laser, and many of the reviews of our book which were then appearing stressed that *Principles of Optics* contained an account of coherence theory, which had become of crucial importance to the understanding of some features of laser light. Born was then as happy as I was that the chapter was included. It was not a foresight on my part to include the chapter on coherence at what in retrospect was undoubtedly the right time; rather it was the consequence of my desire to treat an important phenomenon, namely interference of light, on a more realistic basis than was done previously.

Incidentally, soon after our book was published I received a very nice letter from Born in which he praised our collaboration and said, "Wolf, I cannot recall a single occasion when we disagreed about anything."

I should add that I hope that you will not regard the two stories which I just told you about my interaction with Born as indicating any disrespect for him. Like most scientists who were fortunate to have had the opportunity to interact with Born, I had the greatest respect for him, not only as a scientist but also as a kind and warm human being. The stories I told you just illustrate that his first reaction to new ideas was frequently rather critical, but if he was wrong he usually quickly realized it and would then apologize.[16]

Born retired in 1953 from the Tait Chair of Natural Philosophy which he held at the University of Edinburgh for seventeen years, and a year later I left Edinburgh to take up a post-doctoral appointment at Manchester University in England. Some time after I arrived in Manchester, I received a phone call from Professor Henry Lipson, a distinguished crystallographer who was then the head of the physics department at the Manchester College of Technology. He said, "We are doing some optical experiments here, using Fourier optics, to get a better interpretation of X-ray diffraction data, utilizing the analogue between diffraction of X-rays and diffraction of light. We seem to be getting some spurious effects which we do not understand. We have a Ph.D. student whose name is Brian Thompson. He thinks that this problem has something to do with partial coherence. We do not know anything about partial coherence but Brian tells me that you might be able to help us."

I went to look at the experiments Professor Lipson spoke about. After Brian and I talked for a while I felt that he may well be right and we decided to do some joint work to clarify this. Brian was to do some controlled experiments and I was to do the theory. After a few weeks we met and compared our results which were essentially concerned with Young's interference experiments with light of different degrees of coherence. When we compared our results, there were some serious discrepancies between them. I thought, of course, that Brian's experiments were not right and he thought that my theory was wrong. We could not get to the bottom of it. A few weeks later Brian phoned me and said, "I checked the masks with the pinholes which have been used here for many years and I found that they were wrongly calibrated. When I corrected my results taking this into account, yours and my results agree completely." That was the beginning of a long friendship!

Our results, which we soon published, were the first experimental verifications of some of the predictions of Zernike's theory of partial coherence. Incidentally, fairly recently, about forty years after our paper was published, the experiments were repeated by a group of Italian scientists using more modern techniques. They obtained essentially the same results as we did, with higher accuracy.

Whilst in Manchester an important development took place that had a profound influence on the future evolution of the field of optical coherence, namely the discovery by Hanbury Brown and Twiss around 1956 of the possibility of determining the degree of coherence of thermal light by means of photoelectric experiments; and they suggested that by the use of this technique one could measure stellar diameters in a novel way. The experiments were carried out at the Jodrell Bank Radio Station, close to and part of the University of Manchester. Having been at Manchester at that time I was fortunate of being able to learn first hand about these experiments just as they were being performed and I witnessed a very great deal of controversy that surrounded them.

The Hanbury Brown-Twiss experiments were the first ones to draw attention to higher order correlations between light fluctuations at two space-time points. Such correlations are not encountered in ordinary interference experiments. There were many misunderstandings and controversies surrounding the experiments. It was claimed, for example—by some quite distinguished physicists—that the existence of this effect would contradict the basic principles of quantum mechanics. Faulty experimental evidence was provided for this claim. When these "negative experiments" were carefully analyzed, it turned out that those who performed them greatly misjudged the value of signal-to-noise ratio. It was later found that in some of these experiments the signal-to-noise ratio was exceedingly small because of the very low photon degeneracy of the only kind of light, which was then available, namely thermal light. It was later estimated that in one of the experiments, 10^{11} years (which is somewhat longer than the age of the Earth) would have been needed to observe the Hanbury Brown-Twiss effect!

The controversy was resolved by a beautiful short paper published in *Nature* in 1956 by Edward Purcell whose credentials were not questioned because of his fame, especially in the field of nuclear magnetic resonance for which he was awarded the Physics Nobel Prize four years earlier, in 1952.

Purcell's considerations were the starting point of the analysis presented in two papers by Leonard Mandel in 1958 and 1959; in one he derived what today is known in the theory of photo-count statistics as "Mandel's formula." It is the basic formula relating to the photoelectric detection of light fluctuations.

Robert Hopkins and Emil Wolf organized the first Coherence Conference in 1960.

R. Hanbury Brown leads blackboard discussion at the first Coherence Conference.

Around the time when Hanbury Brown and Twiss performed their experiments, another group of scientists, Forrester, Gudmundsen and Johnson, performed another important experiment which involved photoelectric detection of light. They succeeded in generating *beats* from the superposition of mutually incoherent light beams—an effect they called *photo-electric mixing*. These experiments attracted much attention when it was realized that they threw some light on the controversy surrounding the Hanbury Brown effect.

Let me now return to my stay in Manchester during the time when these developments were taking place. My appointment at the University of Manchester was ending in 1958 and I was looking for a more permanent academic employment. It was not easy in those days to find such an appointment and I worried a great deal about it. During the Easter vacation in 1958 I was away from Manchester, correcting proofs of *Principles of Optics,* and I asked a secretary in the physics department to forward to me the proofs which were being sent to me to Manchester in batches by the printers. However, a batch of them did not reach me. When I returned to Manchester, I asked the secretary whether she forwarded to me everything which arrived for me and she said, "Of course!" I was not convinced, and the next day when she went to lunch I had a good look around her office. In one of the cupboards I found not only the missing batch of proofs but also a letter from the University of Rochester addressed to me. I opened it and found that it was from Professor Robert Hopkins, then the director of The Institute of Optics, asking me whether I would be interested to join the faculty. He mentioned that he would be in England in about two weeks' time and if I was interested we could meet and talk about it. Those were the days when faxes and email were not available, but I managed to get a message to him just in time and we met in Manchester in early July 1958.

Hopkins told me that he was approached by William Rodney of the Air Force Office of Scientific Research, who told him that the U.S. Air Force was very much interested in the possibility of generating optical radiation whose coherence properties would be similar to those attainable with microwaves. He encouraged Hopkins to organize a conference on that subject. Hopkins was interested. He knew of my work on coherence and when we met in Manchester, he said that if I joined the faculty of the Institute, that he would like me to take charge of organizing a conference on coherence, which the Air Force Office of Scientific Research had already offered to fund. I accepted his invitation and I came to Rochester a few months later. I have often thought since then how much easier the life of directors and of department chairmen must have been in those days. For Hopkins was able to offer me an academic appointment at The Institute of Optics without needing the consent of the tenured faculty of the Institute or the approval of the dean and the provost. Maybe I was just lucky! I also often wondered what my future would have been had I not found his letter in the cupboard of the secretary at Manchester University.

I arrived in Rochester in early July 1959, and Hopkins and I immediately started putting together an organizing committee. By today's standards it was a small conference—there were twenty-six papers and participants from seven countries. However, it was attended by about two hundred scientists from many countries. The program was divided into six sessions: basic experiments, properties of partially coherent fields, coherent scattering, stimulated emission, interferometric techniques in optics and in radio astronomy, and coherence problems of instrumental optics. Although it was a small conference, the participants included practically all the pioneers.

I.R. Senitzky and E.T. Jaynes argue at CQOII.

George Sudarshan, and early collaborator with Wolf and Mandel on coherence theory.

Among the highlights: C. H. Townes was co-author of a paper presented by one of his collaborators about coherence and stimulated emission devices, A. T. Forrester discussed mixing of incoherent light, and I. R. Sentzky talked about quantum-mechanical treatment of coupled molecular systems. There was also a paper by S. Pancharatnam, whose work was the forerunner of the concept of the Berry phase. R. H. Dicke spoke about coherence and the concept of transition spin, and H. Gamo presented a matrix formulation of theory of partial coherence. Eli Snitzer gave a paper titled "Coherence Properties of Visible Light Propagation in Dielectric Wave Guides." His presentation included a mosaic of photographs, which were precursors to the sort of figures which most of you have probably seen many times since then—namely those of laser modes.

The conference turned out to be very timely indeed. It took place June 27–29, 1960. Less than two weeks later, on July 7, 1960, the *New York Times* reported that Theodore Maiman succeeded in obtaining inversion of population and laser emission. Maiman's brief note on the subject was published the following month, on August 6, 1960, in *Nature*.

In retrospect there seems to be no doubt that the conference achieved what Rodney and the Air Force Office of Scientific Research was hoping for when they offered to provide funding for it. It certainly stimulated interest in the field of optical coherence and led to many new developments. An excellent and a fuller account of this aspect of the conference is given in a book, *The Laser in America, 1950–1970*, by Joan Bromberg, a historian of science.

Participants of the first conference included many famous scientists, and in almost every conference in this series some physics Nobel Prize winners participated. In addition to Edward Purcell who participated in the first meeting and Charles Townes who co-authored a paper presented there, later meetings were attended by Nobel Prize winners Willis Lamb, Nicholas Blombergen, Arthur Schalow, and Claude Cohen-Tannoudji.

Encouraged by the success of the 1960 Rochester Conference, more such conferences followed. By the time the second conference took place in 1966, Leonard Mandel had become my colleague after coming to Rochester in 1964 from England. He took a very active role in the organization of the second and the successive conferences. By then the field of *quantum optics* began to emerge, and many significant contributions to it were reported at these meetings. The name of the conferences was then appropriately changed to *Conference on Coherence and Quantum Optics*. The number of participants and of the contributed papers rapidly increased from each conference to the next.

The second conference included papers which closely reflect the birth and the development of quantum optics, in which Mandel played a leading role. There was a paper by Roy Glauber, who presented an outline of quantum optics. Willis Lamb and Marlan Scully presented the first detailed quantum theoretical treatment of the laser—then called the optical maser. Mandel and Davidson

Melvin Lax at CQOII.

Emil Wolf in 2004.

described experiments or measurements of triple photon correlations, which could be used to study sixth-order correlations in electromagnetic fields.

Later conferences covered topics such as the generation of squeezed states, manipulation of atomic velocities using lasers, optical cavity QED, laser dynamics and many other subjects which are now central in quantum optics. Just like the first one, all the subsequent conferences in this series were supported by the Air Force Office of Scientific Research, largely due to the initiative of Dr. Schlossberg.

I would like to pay a tribute to someone who has contributed so much to quantum optics in general and to these conferences in particular, namely Leonard Mandel. I take great pride in having been responsible for him coming to Rochester, for having had the privilege of collaborating with him on many papers and on a book, and for having been close friends with him for about forty-five years. I mentioned earlier that after *Principles of Optics* was published, Born wrote to me and said that he did not recall a single occasion when we disagreed on anything. Well, as I indicated, this was not entirely true. But it is true to say that during my much longer association with Len Mandel which extended over several decades, there was not a single occasion, as far as I can remember, when we had any disagreement, neither about science, nor about much trickier subjects such as departmental and national politics. Those of you who knew Len must be aware that apart from being a great scientist, he was a very kind, gentle and compassionate person. I salute the memory of a very dear friend whom I greatly miss.

Emil Wolf has been a member of the faculty of the University of Rochester since 1959. He is the Wilson Professor of Optical Physics.

References

1   This essay is an abbreviated version of a lecture given after the banquet at the Eighth Rochester Conference on Coherence and Quantum Optics, Rochester, New York, June 21, 2001. For an account of the historical development of coherence theory see my article in *Selected Works of Emil Wolf with Commentary* (Singapore: World Scientific, 2001), 620–33.

2   Fuller recollections of Max Born and of our collaboration is given in my article published in *Optics News* 9 (1983): 10–16.

30. The Jaynes-Franken Bet

Carlos Stroud

One of the central concerns of quantum optics, particularly the Rochester variety, has been the range of validity of semiclassical treatments of the interaction between light and matter. In the semiclassical theory the electromagnetic field is treated classically according to Maxwell's equations, while the matter is treated quantum mechanically according to Schrödinger's equation. Particularly intriguing was the question of whether spontaneous emission and the associated Lamb shift could be properly treated using classical fields.

This question was the subject of three lectures given at successive Rochester Coherence and Quantum Optics conferences in the 1960s and 1970s by Edwin T. Jaynes.[1] Jaynes, who moved from Stanford to Washington University in 1962, supervised a number of students whose theses bore on the question. These students included Joseph Eberly and Carlos Stroud, current faculty members of The Institute of Optics. In 1967, at the second conference, Jaynes gave a lecture in which he outlined a semiclassical approach, which he called "neoclassical theory," in which the classical radiation reaction field of an emitting atom was allowed to act back on the atom. This theory led to nonlinear equations of motion for the atomic variables. Although he did not provide detailed solutions of the equations, Jaynes claimed that they should be adequate to treat spontaneous emission and the Lamb shift, two of the most notable successes of the fully quantized theory.

During the question period, Peter Franken of the University of Arizona stood to challenge Jaynes to actually carry out the detailed calculation of the Lamb shift using the theory that he had outlined. The challenge took the form of a bet: Franken offered to bet one hundred dollars whether Jaynes could carry out the Lamb shift calculation during following ten years. Willis Lamb, who was in the audience, would be asked to hold the stakes and

Peter Franken challenges Ed Jaynes with a bet that he cannot derive the Lamb shift without quantizing the electromagnetic field.

decide the winner. Furthermore, Franken was willing to take either side of the bet: Jaynes could bet that he could, or that he could not, do the calculation! Not too surprisingly, Jaynes accepted the bet that he could indeed do the calculation. Lamb agreed to hold the stakes and to invest it in Xerox stock—a very wise choice at the time. The bet was reported with accompanying photographs by David MacAdam in the October 1966 issue of the *Journal of the Optical Society of America*.[2]

The bet and surrounding controversy stimulated a great deal of work by Jaynes and his students and by others exploring the limits of semiclassical theory, and testing the predictions of neoclassical and related theories in various experiments. This work represented a large fraction of the work reported at the third conference in June 1972, when Jaynes made a progress report but did not either claim or concede the stake. The next coherence conference was held in 1977. By that time, Jaynes and his students had carried out calculations exploring most of the predictions of neoclassical theory.[3] They found that indeed the theory predicted that an excited atom would spontaneously emit radiation with the proper decay constant, and that there was a radiative frequency shift which agreed at least semi-quantitatively with the Lamb shift of quantum electrodynamics. However, the dynamics of the theory was quite different from that of conventional theory. The decay of the atomic inversion was a hyperbolic tangent rather than exponential function of time, and the radiative frequency shift was also a time-dependent function, proportional to the inversion. Experimental tests of this dynamics by Hyatt Gibbs[4] and Stroud's group in Rochester[5] did not support the new theory. Still, the theory had predicted a form of spontaneous emission and Lamb shift without field quantization, so that it was not clear which way Willis Lamb would decide the bet.

The session in which Jaynes reported his progress and Lamb announced the results was packed. Lamb expressed appreciation for Jaynes's progress on the problem but decided to award the stakes to Franken on the basis that Jaynes had not produced an accurate numerical value of the shift using semiclassical theory. Unfortunately, Lamb had forgotten to invest the stakes in Xerox stock so that Franken did not become a rich man on the basis of winning the bet.

It is interesting to note that in his article in the proceedings of the conference, Jaynes cited the experiment of Clauser[6] on Bell's inequalities, and said that if the results reported there were correct, that all his work on alternatives to quantum electrodynamics would "go down in flames." Indeed those results have been verified and extended, but the bet and the research that it stimulated played an important role in the history of the Rochester conferences and of quantum optics in general.

Ed Jaynes gives Willis Lamb the $100 for his stake in the bet.

Willis Lamb agrees to decide the winner of the bet.

References

1   E. T. Jaynes, "Survey of the Present Status of Neoclassical Radiation Theory," *Coherence and Quantum Optics*, ed. L. Mandel and E. Wolf (New York: Plenum, 1973), 35; and "Electrodynamics Today," in *Coherence and Quantum Optics IV*, ed. L. Mandel and E. Wolf (New York: Plenum, 1978), 495.

2   David MacAdam, *J. Opt. Soc. Amer* 56 (1966): 1148.

3   E. T. Jaynes and F. W. Cummings, "Comparison of Quantum and Semiclassical Theories with Application to the Beam Maser," *Proc. IEEE* 51 (1963): 89; M. D. Crisp and E. T. Jaynes, "Radiative Effects in Semiclassical Theory," *Phys. Rev* 179 (1969): 1253; C. R. Stroud, Jr. and E. T. Jaynes, "Long-Term Solutions in Semiclassical Theory," *Phys. Rev* A 1 (1970): 106.

4   H. M. Gibbs, G. G. Churchill, and G. J. Salamo, "Contradictions with the Neoclassical Theory of Radiation in Weakly Excited Multilevel Systems," *Phys. Rev* A 7 (1973): 1766–70; H. M. Gibbs, "Test of Neoclassical Radiation Theory: Incoherent Resonance Fluorescence from a Coherently Excited State," *Phys. Rev* A 8 (1973): 456–64; H. M. Gibbs, G. G. Churchill, and G. J. Salamo, "Erratum: Contradictions with the Neoclassical Theory of Radiation in Weakly Excited Multilevel Systems," *Phys. Rev* A 10 (1974): 458.

5   F. Schuda, C. R. Stroud, Jr., and M. Hercher, "Observation of the Resonant Stark Effect at Optical Frequencies," *J. Phys* B 7 (1974): L198; M. L. Citron, H. R. Gray, C. W. Gabel, and C. R. Stroud, Jr., "Experimental Study of Power Broadening in a Two-Level Atom," *Phys. Rev* A 16 (1977): 1507–12.

6   J. Clauser, "Experimental Limitations to the Validity of Semiclassical Radiation Theories," *Phys. Rev Lett.* 23 (1972): 1348.

Hoppy Story: Damn Computers!

Vance Carpenter

One time in class (late 1960s), Bob was scribbling some numbers on the blackboard and came to a point where he couldn't proceed until he subtracted two numbers—he stopped, hesitated, turned around to the class and said, "Will someone please subtract for me, I've used the calculator so long I can't subtract any more."

Vance Carpenter received his B.S. and M.S. from the Institute of Optics in 1949 and 1950, respectively. He was a member of the faculty of the University of Rochester from 1956 until 1962. He is currently retired and living in Fairport, NY.

31. Brian Thompson Forges Ahead: 1968–1975

Hilda Kingslake

Brian J. Thompson succeeded W. Lewis Hyde, inheriting an Institute of Optics which had grown unbelievably in the last 15 or 20 years, from a faculty of four or five to one of about 20. A visitor's first impression could be deceiving, however, for several units of the Institute were in other buildings.

Thompson graduated from Manchester University in 1955, taught for a while at both Manchester and Leeds, and came to this country in 1963. Since then, he has had experience both in industry and university. He taught at Northeastern University in Boston as adjunct professor and held senior scientific positions at Tech Ops Inc. and at Beckman and Whitley. While his basic research field is physical optics, he has also done special studies in holograms, particle sizing, and hybrid opto-electronic processors.

In his unique, direct, and easy way, Thompson familiarized himself with the whole situation, including the Institute's history and its alumni. The news sheet was to continue but under a new name: instead of *I.O.N.*, it would be called *IMAGE*. In the summer 1969 issue of *IMAGE*, Thompson published a report of a survey of the alumni: income figures reported showed no relation between income and the level of degree. The four men with the highest incomes had only B.S. degrees. However, these people quali-

fied early in the history of the Institute and this relationship is expected to change. Nearly all the alumni felt the importance of specializing in optics. In 1969, the demand for personnel trained in optics still, as throughout the history of the Institute, exceeded the supply.

Thompson continued the summer courses, which date back to the 1950s. Subjects varied; for several years it was always contemporary optics. Recently, two separate courses have been given either in parallel or in sequence, one on modern optics and one on optical systems design. Four or five of the faculty take part, and company visits and social occasions are included.

Thompson made a considerable number of appointments to the faculty in the course of his seven years as Director, including a number of foreign visitors. The following is a typical list of faculty in the 1970s: Professors—

Brian J. Thompson becomes the Director.

B. J. Thompson, R. N. Boynton (shared with psychology), M. Parker Givens, R. E. Hopkins (part-time), R. Kingslake (part-time), K. Teegarden, A. Boettner (visiting from University of Michigan Department of Industrial Hygiene for a study using pulsed laser holography), J. M. Burch (visiting from the National Physical Laboratory, England); Associate Professors— P. W. Baumeister, M. Hercher, J. C. Heurtley, Moshe Lubin (mechanical and aerospace sciences), J. C. Peskin, D. C. Sinclair, B. B. Snavely (part-time); also, Assistant Professors—M. Creuzburg (visiting from Germany), J. M. Forsyth, G. C. Sherman, C. R. Stroud, J. M. Brady, and Research Scientist, D. B. Dutton; also, J. H. Altman and J. F. Hamilton, lecturers from Eastman Kodak Company; 23 altogether.

From 1971 to 1977, the following have been added as others resigned or a need arose: N. Balasubramanian, D. T. Moore, J. L. Brown, C. W. Gabel, P. T. Gough (New Zealand), D. L. MacAdam (part-time), and N. George. Many of these faculty are well known in their fields, and their names will immediately be recognized by the informed reader.

In 1971, the student registration was as follows: 50 doing graduate work for M.S. and Ph.D., as well as 25 in the part-time program which had been introduced recently. Twenty-two students were in the undergraduate full-time program. All the graduates were finding jobs, and some had several offers. In the same year, there were three Ph.D. theses, seven M.S. theses, 43 articles in scientific journals, three books published, and 18 papers presented at scientific meetings.

The Laboratory for Laser Energetics had very recently been established as an inter-disciplinary laboratory in the College of Engineering and Applied Science, of which The Institute of Optics is a unit. The Institute is playing a major role in the establishment of this unique university research center. As time goes on, specialists in The Institute of Optics are being called in for advice and cooperation. Several of the faculty have been lost to L.L.E. Moshe Lubin directed the Laboratory, and about six or eight of the faculty have been involved. Actually the Laboratory for Laser Energetics is providing excellent research opportunities for graduate students.

The Institute received a valuable gift in 1970: a set of three high-precision optical flats made of the non-expanding Cervit glass-ceramic material was presented by Owens-Illinois, one of the industrial friends of the Institute. It was accepted with due ceremony by the President of the University, following a program of speakers from The Institute of Optics in the morning. The Institute of Optics through the years owes so much—even its very existence in the beginning—to its friends in industry who through material gifts, scholarships, and advice in some way assist the Institute from time to time. A supporting group from industry, known as the Industrial Associates, meets at least annually for two days to hear papers from the faculty and senior research students, to tour the Institute, and to talk over developments and mutual problems in relation to the Institute.

Thompson, in the early part of his administration, began to collect books for an Institute of Optics library. Recently, he became interested in the possibility of assembling a collection of ancient and valuable books which the Rush Rhees Library would add to its collection of rare books. This thought occurred in 1971 when Mrs. William P. Price donated her alumnus husband's collection to the Institute. Mrs. Franz Urbach also donated some books.

A very fine innovation of the Thompson years has been the colloquia for the benefit of graduate students: a series of speakers through the year are invited to address the students in late afternoon. A coffee hour for socializing and scientific discussion is a pleasant beginning or ending to the meeting. Subjects of the talks are reports of most recent developments. Speakers are traveling scientists known to be passing near Rochester, research workers from local industry, our own faculty, or a student who has something to report; there is an unlimited variety of interesting information and intimate contact with the speaker. They are well attended and planned by a faculty member who takes the responsibility for the year.

Summer-school lectures are normally given at the University, but sometimes speakers are invited to repeat a course elsewhere. In 1973 such a large number of optically interested people in Israel wished to attend the course that Professor Emanuel Marom of the University of Tel Aviv invited Thompson and Kingslake to give a two-week course in Israel; modern optics one week and optical systems design and geometrical optics the other week. About 50 attended, and the expedition was a great mutual pleasure.

M. Parker Givens becomes acting Director when Thompson becomes Dean of Engineering.

Since 1950, 21 Coast Guard officers have come to Rochester, at first for training in optics only; then they took the acoustics at M.I.T. Since the establishment of the College of Engineering and Applied Science, they have taken both courses here in a three-year program, many ending with an M.S. in both optics and electrical engineering. The officers are experienced men with three to five years of active duty behind them. This additional training fits them for interesting scientific assignments in the Service.

In 1975, it became clear that Thompson had done too well, for he was appointed Dean of the College of Engineering and Applied Science, and once again The Institute of Optics had to find a new Director. However, Thompson was not quite lost to the Institute, for he remains Professor of Optics, lectures regularly, and is still publishing optical papers.

In an interview article, published in *Optics News*, summer 1979, Brian Thompson expressed his thinking with regard to The Institute of Optics:

President Sproull has often referred to the Institute as a "jewel in the crown of the University." A university of Rochester's size must select its areas of excellence carefully, since it cannot hope to cover all fields in depth and breadth. The international reputation of the Institute brings the College and the University to the attention of a wide spectrum of scientific, engineering, and technological workers. Perhaps the greatest impact that the Institute has had is in interdisciplinary research and the role it has played in the spawning of new ventures and programs on campus. The first of these was the Center for Visual Science, a more recent example being the Laboratory for Laser Energetics. At the present time there is a rather significant effort going on in medical optics. Faculty and students in the Institute are collaborating with faculty and students in electrical engineering, mechanical engineering, and radiation biology, in a number of projects. In the last few years the Institute has been coupled closely with a group in the chemistry department in a program researching the field of laser chemistry. I can only be delighted with the impact that the Institute has had on both the College and the University. These interactions only come about, of course, because the Institute remains strong and in the forefront of all phases of today's optical science and engineering.

Brian Thompson's resignation was, of course quite unforeseen. Professor Parker Givens was appointed Acting Director and eventually served for almost two years.

32. Early Work in Lasers at The Institute of Optics

Michael Hercher

The first work on lasers at The Institute of Optics closely followed Maiman's publication of the first successful operation of the ruby optical maser—as it was called at the time (Microwave Amplification by Stimulated Emission of Radiation). Of course the idea of stimulated emission had been around since Einstein's paper on A and B coefficients in 1917. I had always thought that the advent of the laser had been delayed by decades because Einstein's concept of stimulated emission generally appeared in the very last chapter of textbooks—and most courses never got to the end of the book! In any event, shortly after Maiman's account of his ruby laser success, plans were made to repeat his experiments and to learn everything we could about optical masers at The Institute of Optics. I was lucky to be just at the point of selecting a Ph.D. thesis topic when the ruby optical maser hit the scene, and within a few months we too had an operating source of brilliant red light—a laser.

Nowadays, when you can buy a two-milliwatt red diode laser pointer at Staples for ten dollars, it is hard to convey the sense of awe that was created when we saw the first laser light. The laser didn't gradually develop from a very weak source of light into an intensely brilliant beam. When it happened, it happened all at once—and it was spectacular!

Mike Hercher clowning with the photographer.

We had started out by purchasing a number of short linear xenon flashlamps and a power supply from EG&G, and then arranging them around a two-inch-long ruby laser rod, and wrapping the whole package in aluminum foil to reflect more light into the ruby. The flashlamps "optically pumped" the chromium ions in the ruby (without the chromium ions the ruby would have been clear sapphire) to create optical amplification at a wavelength of 694.3 nm, and mirrors were applied to the ends of the ruby rod to provide optical feedback. Our early efforts failed because of the poor quality of the ruby rod, so we developed an interferometric technique for assessing the optical quality of laser rods, and were then able to polish the shape of the end surfaces of the rod to compensate for refractive index inhomogeneities, which in turn eventually resulted in our first observation of laser light: a beam of unprecedented intensity and spectral purity that seemed like a stroke of red lightning.

I continued working on my ruby laser thesis for another year or so, modeling and exploring mode structure, operation at low temperatures, Q-switching, coherence properties, and generally having a great time. Meanwhile, Doug Sinclair started his thesis work on the helium neon gas laser. Soon after, Jim Forsyth, working on argon ion lasers, and Howard Smith, working on the frequency-doubling of a HeNe laser, added to the growing volume of work on lasers and laser applications at the Institute.

One of the interesting and early fallouts of the early laser work at the Institute was a growing link between the geometrical and physical optics group in Bausch & Lomb Hall, and the solid state group led by Ken Teegarden in Gavett. Lasers represented an inescapable mating of radiation and materials. Another result was the acceptance of coherent radiation as the normal and readily understood state of affairs, with incoherent radiation eventually becoming viewed as the more complex form of light.

Of course lasers were an instant public relations hit. On one occasion I was asked to do a laser demonstration for a group from the Rochester Chamber of Commerce. One of

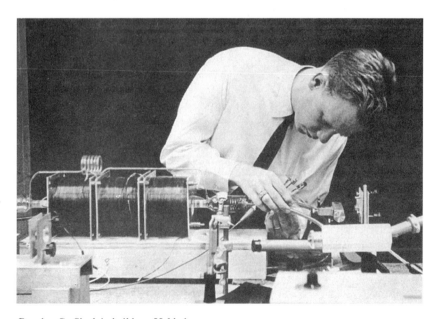

Douglas C. Sinclair builds a HeNe laser.

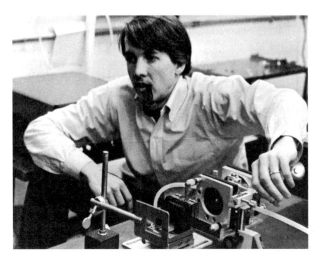

H. Alan Pike with the first tunable cw dye laser.

our cheap tricks was to burst a distant balloon (i.e., across the stage) with a pulse of light from a ruby laser. We used dark blue balloons to maximize the absorption of red light. Just before I was due on stage, I decided to improve my chances for success by painting the balloon with flat black paint. Unfortunately, the paint solvent dissolved the balloon, which immediately burst, covering me with wet, black pieces of balloon! I somehow found a clean white shirt and the show went on.

Laser work at the Institute continued to diversify in many directions. Alan Pike did his thesis work on broad-band tunable organic dye lasers, and John Gallagher worked on neodymium YAG lasers pumped by quartz halogen lamps, and on methods for generating green light by frequency doubling in lithium niobate. Meanwhile, Barry Bebb worked with Al Gold and Ken Teegarden to develop a theory of the multiple-photon ionization processes that became a reality using intense laser radiation. Matt Young explored the means by which a focused Q-switched laser could create an intense spark in air and other gases, and Gadi Neumann studied laser-pumped dye lasers and was able to turn fluorescent swizzle sticks, toothbrush handles, and even theatrical gelatin filters into lasers.

In the early days of lasers, water-cooling was needed for the continuous operation of both high-power ion lasers and YAG lasers. Water cooling invariably leads to water leaks, and in our case, to the realization that there might be a better site for a laser lab than immediately above the physics library. I once tried to seize the initiative by phoning down to the physics library to report that there was apparently water coming up through our floor from the library below.

On another front, Moshe Lubin set his sights high and established what was to become the Laboratory for Laser Energetics. His goal was to develop a means for generating electrical power from nuclear fusion produced by focusing multiple Q-switched and amplified laser beams onto a small particle containing deuterium and/or tritium. This was a huge project and continues to this day. Moshe Lubin's energy and vision inspired a generation of laser scientists at the University.

The laser resources at The Institute of Optics led to collaborations with a number of other departments at the University. On one occasion, Bill Bassett from the geology department wanted to explore the possibility of converting carbon to diamond by focusing intense laser light onto a small particle of carbon suspended in a saline solution under very high pressure. The pressure was applied by compressing a small amount of saline solution, containing carbon particles, between diamond windows through which the laser beam could be focused. A focused beam from a ruby laser was duly fired at the carbon particle. We almost succeeded: a significant portion of the diamond entrance window was converted to carbon!

Lasers have totally changed the field of optical engineering. When I was an undergraduate at The Institute of Optics, it was the only institution in the nation that granted a degree in optics—and there were only five or six people in my class! The laser provides a far more powerful and controllable source of light than thermal sources (like the Sun); all the power from a single mode laser can be focused to a spot with an area equal to the square of its wavelength. This makes possible non-linear effects such as frequency conversion, as well as making laser light a very practical and efficient carrier for information, whether in the form of optical fiber networks or DVDs.

Michael Hercher was a member of the faculty of The Institute of Optics from 1963 until 1975. He received his B.S. from the Institute in 1956 and returned to the Institute in 1960, finishing his Ph.D. work in 1963. In 1980 he was a founder of Optra Inc. in Topsfield, Massachusetts, where he is currently chief technical officer.

33. Service to Industry: Summer Schools and Industrial Associates Program

Brian J. Thompson

The Institute of Optics was born out of an academic need to provide a scientific and technological educational program in support of industrial research, development, and product design. The academic program would, of course, have its own internal strong research and development activity as an integral part of its degree programs to stay on the cutting edge of developments in optical science and engineering. It was this overall concept that led both Kodak and Bausch & Lomb to support financially the founding of "The Institute of Applied Optics" and to guarantee the funding for the first five years. This guarantee on their part would ensure a supply of well-educated graduates for the local and national work force. In addition, the companies in the greater Rochester area would be able to send their employees to part-time programs and special evening courses to upgrade their skills, or to retrain graduates from other disciplines so that they could work effectively on optical component and systems design.

Summer Schools

One special technique to fulfill the particular educational role that th᾽ University had accepted was the early invention and introduction of summer courses that would be available on a residential basis to participants from any geographic location. A flyer in 1931 announced the "Summer Course in Optics for Industrial Laboratory Engineers" July 6–August 1. The brochure contained the leading statement that "The Institute of Applied Optics at the University of Rochester was founded in 1929 . . . to meet a demand from the

Rudolf Kingslake's Summer School class of 1976.

optical industry for men properly trained in the underlying principles involved in the design, construction, and use of optical instruments and appliances."

Interestingly the brochure listed the following administrative officers of the Institute: Rush Rhees, president of the University; T. Russell Wilkins, acting director; Lloyd A. Jones, Eastman Kodak Co.; and Wilbur B. Rayton, Bausch & Lomb Optical Co. The faculty of the Institute were also listed, in addition to the acting director, as Brian O'Brien, professor of physiological optics; Rudolf Kingslake, assistant professor of geometrical optics; A. Maurice Taylor, assistant professor of physical optics; Gustave Fassin, instructor in mechanical design; Ernest Petry, lecturer in optometry; Herbert E. Wilder, instructor in optical-shop work; and Jobe Sedwick, instructor in anatomy of the eye.[1]

It is interesting to note that, except for the optometry program, the structure of the Institute was very similar to the model used at Imperial College in London. The presence of the optometry program had a lasting effect in that vision remained an important area for the Institute and led eventually to the now separate Center for Visual Science at the University. Early graduates of the optometry program (which was only in effect from 1930–36) had outstanding careers, in particular William G. Allyn (class of 1934) led the Welch Allyn Co. to great success in medical instrumentation that all started with its ophthalmoscope. It is a great pleasure to record that William G. was the second generation of Allyns in the company, and today the fourth generation is assuming leadership positions. There is still a strong relationship with the University.

To return to our formal summer school offerings, we note that since the very early days these courses have continued throughout the life of the Institute and exist in excellent, but significantly evolved, form today . . . after over seventy years! Certainly, I would claim a tradition of excellence—a statement supported by the regular evaluation of these programs by the participants. As indicated above, the course content has changed continuously and often dramatically as entirely new sub-fields of optics have developed.

In the post-Second World War era and the post-Sputnik era, the rapid expansion of optical sciences and engineering required the reformation and reformatting of our summer school. Thus in 1962 a new program titled "Methods of Modern Optics" was successfully launched. This fast "new" course was scheduled for July 8–27, 1962. The news release stated the following: "New workers in optics and persons from other colleges and universities will be enrolled in the program, which will be conducted in three one-week sections. Fundamental optical principles, methods and instrumentation will be covered in the first week, from July 8–13, which is pre-requisite to the more advanced discussions of the following weeks.

"Optical imaging systems and multilayer filter design will be discussed in the second and third weeks, July 15–20, and July 22–27. About 65 persons are expected to be enrolled in each section."

In a postscript to the summer course in the Institute magazine *ION* (3:1), we read, "Quite frankly we were flabbergasted! (with the enrollment). It was necessary to split the group in half and repeat the course a second time." The basic part of the program ran for a number of years under the title "Fundamentals of Optics" with some other special topic courses added, e.g., "Optical Thin Films" with Professor Philip Baumeister as the prime-mover and principal leader. This subject has stood the test of time and is perhaps the most often presented special-topic summer offering.

When I came to the Institute, one of the many tasks to do first (!!) was to make sure that the next summer school was in place. The program was of special interest to me, having been involved in the other "modern optics" courses. Thus, we made some change in the structure and content and changed the name to "Contemporary Optics." The concept was that under this title we would convey the idea that while the fundamentals would still be an important part, the application of those fundamentals to contemporary optical problems would be very much included, The title too would make sure that we always gave the attendees a first-hand view (or anyway a glimpse) of what was going on at the forefront, i.e., what was "contemporary." This general title lasted for many years; but we continuously added additional specialized courses on such topics as "Optical System Design" offered by Rudolf Kingslake for many years; "Fundamentals of Digital and Optical Image Processing," "Image Formation and Detection," "Color Specification and Measurement," "Ultrafast Optics and Optoelectronics," "Nonlinear Optics," "Optical Thin-Film Coating Technology," "Management of Technology," "Lasers and Laser Systems," "Lasers and Optoelectronics," and many more.

On a personal note I must say how much I enjoyed my own involvement in our summer school programs over a long period of time (late 1960s to early 1980s). Certainly I know that the faculty and guest speakers will echo my own sentiments of their personal experiences. The 2004 Summer School is already planned and advertised and will in fact have taken place by the time this article is read. It is the Forty-third Annual Summer Course Series (of the modern era, that is). The offerings are:

- Fundamentals of Optics (with labs);
- Lasers and Optoelectronics (with labs);
- Modern Optical engineering (with labs);
- Biomedical Optics;
- Optical Thin Film Coating Technology.

I have every confidence that 2004 will again be a resounding success for the Institute and its faculty and those attending.

Teacher Programs

The Institute has always welcomed teachers from other institutions to its programs and has often added special activities to meet their needs. It was, of course, recognized that while participants from industry would be sponsored by their companies, teachers would find it difficult to obtain sponsorship. We could sponsor a few positions ourselves, but could not cover the living expenses or travel costs. However, the National Science Foundation and other agencies have been very interested in such sponsorship and have provided grants for the Institute for this purpose. The first of these was, I believe, in 1964 for some twenty college teachers. This process has been repeated a number of times over the years. I recall that in 1971 the University had two such programs—one in the Institute and one in the chemistry department, both sponsored by NSF.

High school science teachers have also benefited from the experience of our programs. In these instances we worked with these teachers to help them develop curriculum elements that they could use in their own high school teaching, but could also be shared with other school districts.

Symposia and Conferences

Another method of outreach to the industrial and research community has been the sponsorship of symposia and conference. Just a few examples will suffice here. In 1952 a "Conference on Optical Methods in Industry" was held. At that time the advisory committee to the Institute had four senior university officials and six senior industrialists on its roster. In addition, George Harrison of MIT served as an outside academic. The areas covered in this conference were optical methods in automotive, oil, glass, chemical, paper and pulp, printing, television and electrical. This list provides a true indication that optical technology was of prime importance in these industries.

Several years later a "Symposium on the Formation and Evaluation of Optical Images" was held. National and international speakers were featured, e.g., Erik Ingelstam and G. ToraIdo di Francia.

Of particular note was the founding of "The Rochester Coherence Conference" by R. E. Hopkins and Emil Wolf. These conferences continue with an expanded portfolio and take place on a regular schedule with very useful published proceedings.

The celebration surrounding the 50th anniversary of the Institute was held in October 1979 with a number of seminar-type activities and exhibitions. This was followed in March 1980 by a symposium to commemorate Eastman Kodak's centennial year which covered major topics under the title, "Michelson, Interferometry and Film." Among the highlights was a presentation by Dorothy M. Livingston, A. A. Michelson's daughter, who spoke about his life and work as detailed in her then-recent book.

Industrial Associate Program

The Institute had from the very start an advisory board made up of senior optical industry representatives. By the 1970s we all felt that there was a real need for a program with industry that was truly interactive rather than just advisory. Through discussions that I had with Charles Miersch of the University development office, he came up with the concept of an industrial associates program. Jointly we pursued this idea with the faculty and successfully launched the program in September 1974. At this point I can do no better than quote from an original document.

Background

A constant growth in the diversity of applications for optical science and technology has greatly expanded the field of optics in recent years. Many industries that made very little use of optics a decade ago are finding that some of their basic operational procedures can be improved by the use of modern optical technology.

This growth has been accompanied by an increased demand for expertise in the optics field, expertise that The Institute of Optics at the University of Rochester has long supplied through the education of optical scientists and engineers as well as through its program of research in both pure and applied optics. In response to this recent demand for optics expertise, The Institute is today training three times the number of Ph.D.'s it was during the mid-sixties. Furthermore, faculty and research activity has been broadened so that new applications are being developed regularly.

Simple expansion in the internal program will not, however, meet the growing need completely. In recognition of this we will initiate the Industrial Associates of the Institute

Industrial Associates meeting, Fall of 2003.

in September 1974. Through this new program we hope to make substantial training and informational benefits available to participating companies while concurrently learning more about the needs and concerns of industry. Such a mutually beneficial exchange can improve industry's ability to utilize modern optical technology while increasing our ability to educate individuals to assume key roles within their companies (nearly 90 percent of Institute graduates go into industry).

The Institute of Optics is, we believe, uniquely suited to house such an association. It has been recognized for more than four decades as the leading center for education and research in optics in America. Further, the spectrum of work accomplished at the Institute is very wide, ranging from very basic research to applied optics and optical engineering. Also, Institute faculty are experienced in cooperative projects with industry, and many have worked full time in industry as well. Finally, the Institute, its Director and faculty have regularly carried out education programs that are (1) aimed at short term, intensive instruction geared to bring individuals only peripherally concerned with optics "up to speed" in a given area, and (2) designed to provide in-depth surveys of narrowly defined areas of optics at a very high technical level. In short, the Institute has the reputation, resources, and experience required to provide significant short-term benefits to industries with interests in optics.

Program

The Industrial Associates Program will comprise:
1. An annual two-day meeting for the members that will include presentations on current work in the Institute and review papers on important topic areas by experts (either Institute faculty or invited outside speakers). A tour of the Institute and related research areas. Group discussions on special topics of interest.
2. A free place for a suitable employee from each company in the various special programs of the Institute (e.g., for 1974 we will offer "Contemporary Optical Engineering" June 3–14, and "Optical System Design" June 17–21).
3. A biannual listing of current thesis topics and recently completed theses. Copies of theses will be available on request,

4.   Complete set of reprints of papers published by faculty and students of the Institute.
5.   Visits by participating company employees to the Institute will be arranged (and encouraged) on request.
6.   A number of Institute faculty will be available as seminar speakers. A list of speakers and possible topics will be sent to participating companies. The expenses involved for the first speaker used in each year by an associate will be covered by the program. (We hope that the associates will not limit that invitation to a single speaker).
7.   A list of members of the graduating class with their thesis topics (if applicable) will be made available as early as possible in each academic year so that associates have the opportunity for an early review of these potential employees.
8.   Library service: The use of the library facilities at the University of Rochester.

Membership

Membership will be by invitation and restricted to a limited number of companies. The minimum membership fee will be $5,000.00 annually although we hope that large companies will participate at a rate above this level. The fees will be given in the form of unrestricted grants, directly to The Institute of Optics. These funds will be used to provide the appropriate services outlined above and to help strengthen the teaching and research programs in the Institute."

The program was very well accepted and has been a continuing success for almost twenty years. To be sure, some program elements have been changed or deleted and new items added to continue to provide for the mutual needs of the Institute and our individual partner. For example, the "annual two-day meeting" is now twice a year and is much more interactive with presentations by Institute faculty and students and by the individual representatives. These are now truly in-depth working level meetings.

All the interaction that has been discussed here has strengthened and helped form an academic enterprise. We will continue to seek further ways to develop new scholarships, new technology, new application and new ways to serve the discipline and the many users of this disciple of optical science and engineering.

Brian J. Thompson has been a member of the faculty of the University of Rochester since 1968. He served as Director of the Institute of Optics from 1968 until 1975. He is currently Provost Emeritus of the University of Rochester, Rochester, NY.

Reference

1   Petry and Sedwick were included because for a few years the Institute had a second mission, "to train men in the testing of sight," in accordance with the requirements of the New York State Optometry Laws.

34. Relationship Between The Institute of Optics and the Optical Sciences Center

James C. Wyant

In 2004 The Institute of Optics at the University of Rochester is celebrating its seventy-fifth anniversary, and the Optical Sciences Center at the University of Arizona is celebrating its fortieth anniversary. While these two optics departments are probably the two best optics education and research units in the world for both undergraduate and graduate students, and there is strong competition between the two departments for both students and faculty, there is a very good friendly relationship between the two departments.

In the early 1960s the Optical Society of America conducted a "Needs in Optics" survey which resulted in a conclusion that the supply of personnel professionally trained in the broad field of optics needed to be increased. At that time The Institute of Optics was the only place in the U.S. where a person could get formal training in optics. The survey recognized that graduate education in optics would be incomplete if students could not participate in advanced research activities, much as was being done at the Institute. The OSA survey inspired Aden Meinel to sought funding to start the Optical Sciences Center. One of the leaders of the OSA survey was Robert E. Hopkins, who at the time was the director of The Institute of Optics. Visits by Hopkins to Tucson and the advice and encouragement he gave Aden Meinel helped the Optical Sciences Center become a reality.

After my junior year in college in 1964 I had a summer job working in optics at Libbey Owens Ford in Toledo. At that time I thought I would go to graduate school in solid state physics, but I found working in optics to be very interesting. Phil Baumeister, who at that time was a faculty member at the Institute, did consulting work for Libbey Owens Ford and as a result I learned about the Institute. Shortly after I went back to Case Institute of Technology for my senior year, I saw my first hologram in senior physics lab. That was it for me. I forgot about solid state physics and I applied to The Institute of Optics for graduate school. When I got to the Institute I found out I was going to work for Parker Givens on holography. I was so happy I felt like I had died and gone to heaven. I was initially in the M.S. program, but I found that I loved optics and the Institute so much that during the first year I switched to the Ph.D. program.

James C. Wyant, Director of the Optical Sciences Center of the University of Arizona.

I first heard about the Optical Sciences Center during my first week of being a graduate student at The Institute of Optics in September 1965. Fellow graduate student Robert E. Fischer had spent the summer working at Kitt Peak Observatory in Tucson, and he came back with a large selection of beautiful photographs of the Arizona desert. At that time I had not traveled west of Chicago, but I had watched a lot of western movies and I was always fascinated by the West, and Bob's pictures of the Arizona desert really excited me about Arizona. He mentioned that the University of Arizona was starting an optics program, and even in my first year of graduate school at Rochester this got me thinking that someday I would like to be part of the optics program at the University of Arizona.

Bob's photographs attracted a lot of attention at The Institute of Optics; another graduate student, Roy Frieden, saw the pictures and also became interested in Arizona and the optics program that was starting up at the University of Arizona. Roy was graduating in 1966, and he applied for a faculty position at the U. of A. Roy interviewed for the faculty position the beginning of February. He liked very much what he saw at the U. of A., but he was not sure he wanted to leave New York State where he had lived his entire life, plus he liked snow. However, on his flight back to Rochester he could not land in Rochester because of a terrible snowstorm, and he was forced to land in Toronto. He then took a train from Toronto to Rochester, but when he got to Rochester he found that all the roads were closed because of the terrible storm, and the only way he could get home was to walk. The next day he accepted a faculty position at the University of Arizona.

In addition to Roy and myself, there have been a number of graduates of The Institute of Optics who have or have had faculty positions at the Optical Sciences Center. The list includes Jim Eyer (former OSC associate director), Bob Shannon (former OSC director), Chris Koliopoulos, Kathy Creath, and Jim Schwiegerling. Chris received his B.S. degree at Rochester and then his Ph.D. at Arizona; Kathy and Jim received their B.S. and M.S. degrees at Rochester and their Ph.D.s at Arizona. Jim remembers that when he was a sophomore at Rochester in 1987, Duncan Moore mentioned in class that there was this upstart optics program at Arizona. This intrigued Jim so he later decided to come to Arizona for graduate school, where he is now an assistant professor with a joint appointment in ophthalmology and optical sciences.

Jim Eyer was a faculty member at both The Institute of Optics and the Optical Sciences Center; in the early days of the Optical Sciences Center he was the associate director. It is interesting that he left his faculty position at Rochester the week before I became a graduate student there in 1965, and he left his faculty position at OSC the week before I joined the faculty there in 1974.

During my graduate school years at Rochester, Bob Shannon worked at the Itek Corp., and every year he would come to the Institute on a recruiting trip. When I graduated in 1968 he hired me at Itek; shortly after I started to work at Itek, he left to join the faculty at OSC. I was heartbroken, but it

B. Roy Frieden, 1966–Present, Emeritus 2002.

James Eyer, (Associate Director) 1967–1974.

Robert Shannon, 1969–Present, (Director, 1984–1992), Emeritus 1992.

Chris Koliopoulos, 1981–1989.

Kathy Creath, 1991–1995, 2003–Present.

worked out very well for me: in 1974 when I was visiting OSC to hire graduates for Itek, Bob asked me if I wanted to become a faculty member at OSC. I thought about it for less than a nanosecond and then said yes.

Two of the graduates from the Optical Sciences Center have had faculty positions at the Institute, John Rogers and Warren Smith. However, they have both left Rochester—John lives in California and Warren lives in Tucson. I think the Rochester winters were too much for them.

Jim Swiegerling, 1998–Present.

The Optical Sciences Center of the University of Arizona.

Each year the Optical Sciences Center recruits at least two or three graduate students from the undergraduate program at The Institute of Optics. We have found them to be extremely well prepared and we are always looking for more. Over the years The Institute of Optics and the Optical Sciences Center have become fierce, but friendly, competitors for graduate students. Each year both departments invite the best U.S. students to visit us for a couple of days at our expense. We always have the visit during the month of February and we always end the visit with a wonderful barbecue under the stars at the Tanque Verde Guest ranch. It is a great experience and I look forward to it every year even though sometimes it gets so cold outside late at night at the barbecue that I have to wear a sweater. The Institute of Optics also has its recruiting visit during February, but I guess they do not end the visit with an outside barbecue.

Former Institute Director Dennis Hall has recently had a large impact on progress at the Optical Sciences Center. In 1998 Dennis chaired the external review committee for the Optical Sciences Center. The final report that Dennis wrote helped convince the University of Arizona administration that the Optical Sciences Center had to have more space; as a result we are now building a 45,000-square-foot addition to our 110,000-square-foot building. Dennis also helped convince the U. of A. provost that we needed to have more control of our undergraduate program; as a result our undergraduate program has grown by more than a factor of three. We very much appreciate Dennis's help.

I feel that I have been very lucky being associated with both The Institute of Optics and the Optical Sciences Center. Not only have I been a graduate student at the Institute, but I have taught in its summer school for nearly twenty years, and I spent the spring semester of 1983 on sabbatical there. Both places are great, and anyone who gets a degree from either place is indeed fortunate.

James C. Wyant is director of the Optical Sciences Center at the University of Arizona. He is an M.S. and Ph.D. graduate of The Institute of Optics.

35. Interview with Brian J. Thompson

Carlos Stroud

I have heard that in your student days you were actually employed as an assistant to Emil Wolf. Could you please tell us that story.

I have chronicled my early interactions with Emil Wolf in a recent paper, "Guide Philosopher and Friend; EmiI Wolf: the Coherent Master of Physical Optics." This paper was the lead paper in a recent conference titled, "Tribute to Emil Wolf: Engineering Legacy of Physical Optics" (4 Aug. 2003 SPIE Conference San Diego). There will be a volume published resulting from this meeting.

Our joint work on two-beam interference with partially coherent light that was conducted starting in early 1956 was submitted to *JOSA* on Dec. 17, 1956 (forty-seven years ago almost to the date of this particular writing!). This particular work became one of the features of *Principles of Optics* by Born and Wolf, with a two-page spread of the illustrations plus several pages of text (pp. 511–514 in the original volumes). I was also asked to prepare a number of the experimental illustrations for use in this book. Thus a lot of interaction between Emil and myself relative to "Born & Wolf," which culminated in my being "hired" to help with the proofreading of the manuscript in galley and page proofs—a great opportunity for me to get involved and immersed in the text in a very detailed way. I had carried out a similar task with my other two mentors, Henry Lipson and Charles Taylor, for their book, *Fourier Transforms and X-ray Diffraction*, which included the preparation of a detailed experimental and illustrative appendix and the galley and page proof routine.

Brian J. Thompson, 1975.

How did you come to become director of the Institute?

It came "out of the blue." I was attending the spring meeting of OSA in 1968 when Lem Hyde caught me in the corridor and told me of his new appointment as provost at NYU University Heights campus. He followed this announcement by telling me that the Institute had started a search for a new director—would I be interested? I responded that if this was a serious request, then yes, I would be very interested. As Walter Cronkite would say, "and the rest is history." Having spent the first eight years of my professional career in the academy (four years at Manchester University and four years at Leeds University), I always knew that I would return to academic life at some point. What better point in time than Sept. l, 1968, and what better academic position was there than professor of optics and director of The Institute of Optics at the University of Rochester? Hence for me, thirty-five years at the University and thirty-five years of involvement with the Institute, and we are still counting!

You have served in several capacities at the University: as director of The Institute of Optics, as dean of the College of Engineering and Applied Science, and as provost. You have had the opportunity to view the Institute from several different vantage points. What would you say are the unique features that distinguish the Institute from other departments in the University? Similarly, how would you distinguish the Institute from the optics departments in other academic institutions?

It has been very rewarding for me to work with and for the Institute over many years and in many capacities. The Institute of Optics has been a special activity for the University from its inception. It was formed to meet a national need and to meet a need by the optics industry for an "academic lighthouse" that would help formulate and develop the intellectual and scholarly underpinning of optical science, engineering and technology. This includes, of course, the education of people at all levels who have been and will continue to be vital for the industrial communities and for the further development of the academic community. It is very different from the usual academic department since its range of activity covers the field of optical science and engineering from the very fundamental concepts, to applied optics, to technology development, to engineering principles, to system design, and now to hybrid systems that interface with many other discipline areas. We are in truth an integrated science and engineering organization that supports our discipline of optical science and engineering to be inclusive of all the sub-areas that have separate and changing names: photonics, electro-optics, fiber optics, opto-electronics, etc. etc. . . .

Over the years The Institute of Optics has spun off a number of centers, labs, and companies. Among those that immediately come to mind are CVS, LLE, the quantum optics group and solid state physics groups in physics, COM, CEIS, COI, Tropel, QED, Gradient Lens Corp., and Rochester Photonics. If the Institute had kept even a small fraction of these activities within the department it would be a greatly expanded enterprise. Could you comment on what you see as the pluses and minuses of the department remaining relatively small while spinning off these successful startups

I am certainly proud of all of the activities that you mention in your questions. They do fall into several categories. First there are the internal University activities that come about because of the importance of optics as an enabling science and technology that can help develop academic units in some specialized area where another major component is needed, e.g., CVS—optics and psychology. LLE and COM are examples of mission-driven programs that must focus on that mission whilst providing an important academic climate for learning; these activities are large enough that they need their own interdisciplinary structure. The quantum optics group and solid state physics group naturally belong in the physics department because the Institute was founded with a very strong coupling to physics, and that coupling has continued to the benefit of both the physics department and the Institute. The spin-off into commercial companies was of significance for the Institute long before it was a popular or financially driven institutional program. This is not the forum to get into the debate about intellectual property.

Finally I can really only see pluses for the historical situation. It would have been impossible to build all those activities into the Institute without turning the Institute from a very strong academic unit into a mini-national Lab that could not exist within a university of our size.

You have put a lot of time and effort into the Institute over the past thirty-five years. Are there particular things that have happened in that time in the Institute that make you proud to have been here?

I have remained proud and supportive of the pre-eminence of the Institute. We are a University of Rochester treasure. We are a major national and international player both intellectually and structurally. We have been the academic model that other programs have been held up against. I am most proud of the leadership that the Institute, its faculty and its graduates have provided to continue to define and redefine our discipline—and to recognize that it truly is a discipline, i.e., an integrated body of knowledge.

In the 1950s, just before the invention of the laser, many people regarded optics as a dead field, unlikely to be the source of any great scientific or engineering breakthroughs. Of course, the field has been one of the most dynamic in all of science and technology in the past fifty years. But with laser science becoming a rather mature field, and with the optical communications boom behind us, some are again questioning the future of optics. What is your vision for the future of optics in the coming decades?

This is the hard question! It is a question that has been posed many times over many decades, and as far as I can tell, nobody had definitive and correct projections! However, I take great encouragement from both history and the current high level of activity. Light is such an important part of our lives and our connection to our external worlds that we will continue to see significant new technology and application of that technology over a set of wide-ranging fields.

The Institute of Optics Faculty 1960–1969

Alley, Carroll O., 1962–63
Altman, Joseph H., 1969–98
Baldini, Giancarlo, 1960–64
Baumeister, Philip W., 1959–79
Blakney, Robert M., 1959–66
Boynton, Robert M., 1955–72
Carpenter, Vance J., 1956–62
Clarke, Frank J., 1964–65
Collins, Francis A., 1964–67
Creuzberg, Martin, 1967–71
Dexter, David, 1953–61
Dutton, David B., 1954–63, 1975–78
Edgerton, Robert F., 1962–63
Evans, John W., 1943–65
Ewald, William P., 1956–65
Eyer, James A., 1959–66
Fang, Sheng-Heng, 1961–62
Forsyth, James M., 1969–85
Garbuny, Max, 1969–70
Givens, M. Parker, 1948–
Gold, Albert, 1962–70
Goldblatt, Norman R., 1967–69
Hamilton, John F., 1969–88
Harrison, Patrick G., 1964–68
Hercher, Michael M., 1965–75
Heurtley, John C., 1968–74

Hopkins, Robert E., 1943–
Hyde, W. Lewis, 1963–68
Illingworth, Robert, 1961–63
Ingelstam, Erik, 1960–61
Kaye, Rachel, 1960–61
Kingslake, Rudolf, 1929–2003
Knox, Robert S., 1960–61
Kristianpoller, Norbert N., 1961–63
Lisle, Claudine, 1964–65
Milne, Gordon G., 1948–66
Murty, Mantravado V. R. K., 1959–64
Nakai, Yoshio, 1959–61
Panizza, E. Hora, 1965–68
Pegis, Richard J., 1961–62
Perrin, Fred, 1958–61
Peskin, James C., 1959–77
Sands, Peter J., 1967–70
Sayanagi, Kazuo, 1966–67
Sinclair, Douglas C., 1965–67, 1970–80
Stewart, Harold S., 1943–46, 1959–62
Stroud, Jr., Carlos R., 1969–
Teegarden, Kenneth J., 1955–
Thompson, Brian J., 1968–
Tuttle, Fordyce, 1940–62
Unvala, Hoshang A., 1966–68
Yonezawa, Seiji, 1968–70

The Institute of Optics
Degrees Awarded 1960–1969

Agliata, Thomas P., M.S., 1969

Alte, Elizabeth D. (nee Liebich), B.S., 1968

Amarel, John A., B.S., 1965

Ansley, David A., B.S., 1962

Appel, James J., B.S., 1967

Arndt, Joseph H., M.S., 1967

Ayers, Wendall G., M.S., 1966

Balasubramanian, N., M.S., 1969

Barlow, Bertram L., M.S., 1966

Bastian, Robert H., B.S., 1964

Baumgardner, John D., Ph.D., 1969

Bebb, Herbert B., Ph.D., 1966

Bennett, Harold F., M.S., 1961

Bliek, David C., M.S., 1967

Blum, Thomas W., B.S., 1965; M.S., 1967

Bray, Clarence P., B.S., 1962

Buchroeder, Richard A., M.S., 1968

Carosella, John H., M.S., 1969

Chesley, Carl H., B.S., 1962

Chirra, Ramalinga R., M.S., 1965

Chisholm, James J., M.S., 1965

Choate, Albert G., B.S., 1969

Clark, Edward L., M.S., 1960

Clark, Guy P., M.S., 1968

Cornejo-Rodriguez, A. Alehandro, M.S., 1968

Costich, Verne R., Ph.D., 1965

Cottrell, Thomas H., Ph.D., 1968

Coulter John K., M.S., 1960

Cree, David A., M.S., 1963

Dame, Jr., Barry T., M.S., 1965

Danielson, Jr., G. Edward, M.S., 1967

DeCew, Jr., Alan E., B.S., 1968

Delano, Erwin, B.S., 1948; M.S., 1956; Ph.D., 1966

Doane, Marshall G., B.S., 1959; M.S., 1961

Dube, George, B.S., 1964; M.S., 1969; Ph.D., 1972

Dublin, Mark H., B.S., 1969

Dumont, Frank J., B.S., 1966; M.S., 1969

Dvorin, Martin, M.S., 1966

Eby, John E., Ph.D., 1960

Edgerton, Robert F., Ph.D., 1963

Fath, Jack M., M.S., 1968

Ferguson, Gerald D., M.S., 1969

Fischer, Robert E., B.S., 1965; M.S., 1967

Forkey, Richard E., B.S., 1965

Forsyth, James M., B.S., 1964; Ph.D., 1968

Frieden, B. Roy, Ph.D., 1966

Gelber, Robert M., B.S., 1967; M.S., 1968

Goad, Joseph H., M.S., 1968

Goodridge, William W., B.S., 1963

Granger, Edward M., B.S., 1957; M.S., 1969; Ph.D., 1975

Grum, Franc, M.S., 1962

Hagerott, Edward C., M.S., 1965

Hahn, Robert E., B.S., 1966; M.S., 1968

Harris, James S., M.S., 1966

Harris, Oswaldo M., M.S., 1967

Harris, Thomas J., M.S., 1960

Harrison, Douglas H., M.S., 1969; Ph.D., 1974

Hercher, Michael M., B.S., 1956; Ph.D., 1964

Hernandez, John P., Ph.D., 1967

Hilbert, Robert S., B.S., 1962; M.S., 1964

Holmes, Dale A., M.S., 1969

Howe, Dennis G., M.S., 1968; Ph.D., 1976

Huggett, George R., Ph.D., 1964

Ikeda, Mitsuo, Ph.D., 1962

John, Puthenpurak K., M.S., 1966

Keil, Thomas H., Ph.D., 1965

Klein, Robert S., B.S., 1968
Klimasewski, Robert G., B.S., 1966; M.S., 1967
Korka, Jr., Jim E., B.S., 1968
Korones, Herbert D., M.S., 1961
Lamberts, Robert L., Ph.D., 1969
Lambrecht, Raymond T., B.S., 1960
Latta, Milton R., M.S., 1969
Lawrence, Robert E., M.S., 1960
Lawson, Walter R., M.S., 1968
Lehmbeck, Donald R., M.S., 1966
Liem, Han-Gie, Ph.D., 1968
Lomer, Lloyd R., M.S., 1967
Maier, Robert L., B.S., 1964; M.S., 1966
Malacara, Daniel, M.S., 1963; Ph.D., 1965
Mauldin, III, Lemuel E., M.S., 1969
McKenney, Dean B., M.S., 1965
McSwain, Berah D., B.S., 1956; M.S., 1962
Miller, Norma D., M.S., 1961
Miller, Theodore L., B.S., 1962; M.S., 1976
Milligan, Frank G., B.S., 1961; M.S., 1964
Minott, Peter O., M.S., 1961
Miyamoto, Kenro, Ph.D., 1961
Montonye, James T., M.S., 1967
Moss, Tuckerman, M.S., 1960
Mostrom, Richard N., M.S., 1967
Munnerlyn, Charles R., Ph.D., 1969
Munroe, James L., B.S., 1964
Naus, David A., M.S., 1967
Neyhart, James H., M.S., 1962
Nord, Donald D., M.S., 1969
Noyes, Gary R., B.S., 1965; M.S., 1967
Oberheuser, Joseph H., M.S., 1968
Paradysz, Louis F., M.S., 1966
Polster, Alan A., M.S., 1968
Potter, Robert J., Ph.D., 1960
Radkowski, Edward J., M.S., 1967
Rajappan, K. Vimaladevi, M.S., 1963
Ramamurti, J., Ph.D., 1967
Rao, Mamidi M., M.S., 1963
Rees, Jr., James D., B.S., 1957; M.S., 1965
Refermat, Stanley J., M.S., 1967
Regensburger, Paul J., Ph.D., 1967
Reilly, Terrence H., Ph.D., 1969

Rimmer, Matthew P., B.S., 1956; M.S., 1963
Rivers, R. R., B.S., 1966
Rosen, Arthur N., Ph.D., 1968
Ruben, Paul L., B.S., 1959; M.S., 1963
Ruff, Bruce J., B.S., 1961; M.S., 1966
Saxe, Douglas M., M.S., 1962
Schwartz, John M., M.S., 1960
Schwartz, Richard A., B.S., 1963; M.S., 1966
Shoemaker, Arthur H., M.S., 1965
Sinclair, Douglas C., Ph.D., 1963
Sleeman, John K., B.S., 1961
Sloan, Thomas R., B.S., 1965; M.S., 1967
Smith, Abbott M., B.S., 1955; M.S., 1957; Ph.D., 1961
Smith, Howard M., B.S., 1960; Ph.D., 1965
Smith, Thomas W., B.S., 1968
Smoyer, Claude B., B.S., 1959; M.S., 1965
Snouffer, Richard K., B.S., 1966; M.S., 1968
Snow, Kenneth A., M.S., 1967
Spencer, Gordon H., B.S., 1957; Ph.D., 1963
Spencer, William T., Ph.D., 1963
Sprague, Robert A., B.S., 1967; Ph.D., 1971
Starkweather, Gary K., M.S., 1966
Steele, Richard K., B.S., 1963
Sterrett, Robert M., M.S., 1962
Straw, Kimball, B.S., 1969; M.S., 1973
Stubbe, III, John A., M.S., 1969
Swaminathan, K., M.S., 1964
Sze, Yu-Kwok, M.S., 1967
Tchejeyan, Sarkis K., M.S., 1962
Thayer, Martha H., B.S., 1965
Todd, Henry S., M.S., 1968
Trindale, David C., M.S., 1968
Urbach, John C., B.S., 1955; Ph.D., 1962
Van Orden, Lynn L., B.S., 1961
Vollmer, David W., M.S., 1969
Wapniarski, William J. S., M.S., 1966
Wertheimer, Alan L., B.S., 1968; Ph.D., 1974

Wetherell, William B., B.S., 1958; M.S., 1961

White, Walter W., M.S., 1962

Whittaker, Gary L., M.S., 1967

Wilhauck, Thomas P., M.S., 1969

Willard, Berton C., B.S., 1962; M.S., 1964

Wojcik, Walter J., M.S., 1968

Wyant, James C., M.S., 1967; Ph.D., 1968

Young, Matt, B.S., 1962; Ph.D., 1967

PART V

A New Home: The 1970s

V. A New Home: The 1970s

The Institute strained within the confines of the fourth floor of Bausch & Lomb Hall as the research program grew, and the appreciation of the broad commercial and scientific applications of the laser became widespread. A development committee was established to plan for the growth of the Institute to take advantage of these new opportunities. It was soon apparent to the committee that new quarters were needed before the Institute could possibly rise to this challenge. The old quarters were both antiquated and cramped. The department had faculty and facilities spread over Bausch & Lomb, the Space Science Center, and Gavett Hall. The committee soon set as its target the designation of the Space Science Center for the new home. By the end of the decade the Institute was comfortably housed in its new home, and primed for a rapid expansion. Brian Thompson had been appointed dean of the College of Engineering and Applied Science, and Nicholas George had arrived from Caltech to lead the effort, aided by a new faculty enhancement grant from the National Science Foundation.

The 1970s saw the rapid growth of an applied optical research center on campus, the Laboratory for Laser Energetics. In a fascinating essay Jim Forsyth describes how one of the largest laser laboratories in the world grew out of a little demonstration experiment that Mike Hercher set up in his lab for Moshe Lubin. One might almost say that this was the spark that fused the idea of LLE in the mind of young plasma physicist Lubin. The Institute not only played a central role in stimulating the startup of the laboratory, but it also supplied many of the people and facilities that were used to build the successively larger laser systems. The optics glass shop and the thin films coating lab were both transferred to LLE to help in the construction. Even Bob Hopkins returned from retirement to help design the optical system for the twenty-four-beam laser system.

Quantum optics grew rapidly in this decade in no small part due to the development of the narrow band tunable cw dye laser that was developed by Ben Snavely's group at Kodak and Mike Hercher's group in optics. Joe Eberly's essay recounts the growth of the quantum optics group, which straddles The Institute of Optics and the Department of Physics and Astronomy, to international stature in this field. Brian Thompson in two essays describes physical optics from philosophical heights to the nitty-gritty of the optical bench.

Finally, we have three humorous essays that give some insight into student life in the 1970s.

36. The Wilmot Building

Hilda Kingslake

The problem of space had been serious most of the life of The Institute of Optics. In recent years it had become acute, a real problem for Brian Thompson to solve if he could.

One research group from The Institute of Optics working with Kenneth Teegarden was accommodated in the partially occupied Space Science Center. This fact no doubt gave rise to the thought of moving the whole Institute into that building. In 1976 the Administration announced that The Institute of Optics would be moved into the Space Science Center. Interestingly enough, the building roughly agreed with the dimensions of the fantastic plan for the proposed Institute of Applied Optics outlined by C. E. K. Mees in 1919.

Nicholas George, successor to Brian Thompson as Director of the Institute arrived just in time to plunge straight into the great move from the fourth floor of Bausch & Lomb Hall to the Space Science Center. The move was a nice problem for both the moving company and the responsible faculty. The weather was Rochester winter's very worst. Duncan Moore, at that time a young Assistant Professor, already known for his work on gradient-index materials, and now very recently appointed Director of the Institute, was to try his hand at planning and directing large-scale moving. Several thousand pieces, varying from heavy equipment to sensitive apparatus in current use, to bundles of reprints and small desk sets, were moved. One bundle of reprints was apparently lost but turned up a year later in the wrong office.

The building was later dedicated to James Peter Wilmot "In recognition of his services as Trustee and his generosity as a benefactor of the University of Rochester." The

Wilmot Building, the new home of The Institute of Optics.

building, situated among the complex of science buildings on the River Campus, received one of three awards made in 1970 in the "Laboratory of the Year" competition sponsored by Industrial Design magazine.

Nicholas George, in reply to a question for *Optics News*, said "Our new facility has added greatly to our spirit of cohesiveness, and I think I can reflect the feeling of everyone at the Institute when I say what enormous pride we have in our new optics building."

37. Mmmmm . . . Donuts . . .

David Aronstein

The Hungarian mathematician Alfréd Rényi said that, "a mathematician is a machine for turning coffee into theorems." Had Rényi visited The Institute of Optics, I suspect that he would have concluded that its denizens are machines for turning donuts into Progress in Optics.

Each Wednesday at 3:44 p.m., you'll find a scraggly and sugar-starved crowd in Wilmot 116 impatiently waiting for the clock's second hand to reach the top of its arc. They're there because 3:45 is Donuts Standard Time, the moment when it's fair game to dig into the spread of donuts, along with bagels and cream cheese, fruit, and drinks, carefully arranged on the front table. The next few minutes are a blur of frenzied activity; I can only liken them to scenes in National Geographic documentaries of cheetahs chasing down and devouring a zebra on the plains of Africa. By 4:15 or 4:30, people diffuse out of Wilmot 116 and head back to work, leaving with twitchy smiles on their faces, a glazed look in their eyes, and a cloud of powdered sugar in their wake.

This visceral and somewhat barbaric ritual can be traced back to 1971: New assistant professor Carlos Stroud fondly remembered the afternoon teas from his graduate-school days in the physics department at Washington University in St. Louis, when students and some faithful faculty members got together each day to chat about physics and whatever else was on their minds. Professor Stroud lobbied the Institute's Graduate Committee to establish such a tradition here. Director Brian Thompson felt that a daily get-together was too often but kindly offered departmental funds to support a weekly "optical smorgasbord" (using the description from the Fall 1971 *Image* alumni newsletter) on the colloquium day, whether or not there was a speaker scheduled. In the years since its inception, the weekly Donuts seem to have drifted away from its roots as an informal get-together towards a sugar-coated feeding frenzy, but it remains a valuable and treasured part of The Institute of Optics experience.

Beyond the continued support and generosity of The Institute of Optics, Donuts is made possible by the help and dedication of the younger graduate students. First-year graduate students are dispatched each week to get the food, set up the spread, and clean up the carnage afterwards. The Institute's Junior Graduate Representative, typically a second-year graduate student, coordinates the weekly schedule with the first-year students. I served as the Junior Grad. Rep. in the 1995–96 academic year; I saw firsthand the seamy underbelly of the entire Donuts ritual, and while it was a pleasure to serve the Institute in this role, it was over a year until the nightmares had subsided and I could eat a donut again.

In the last decade or so, there has been a surprisingly tumultuous history of where we get our beloved donuts. In the early 1990s, the Genesee Bakery on Mt. Hope Avenue supplied us with our weekly fix. After a falling out with them, we turned to the Wegmans grocery store for our sugary treats. During my stint as Junior Grad. Rep., a brewing disagreement with Wegmans over the University's purchase-order system culminated suddenly in Wegmans

David Aronstein finishes his Ph.D. with the help of a few donuts and a little Inglenook.

terminating our standing order. I scampered to contact numerous bakeries in town to see which might be a suitable replacement. Over the next seven weeks, we sampled food from each of the places vying for our business, and I polled the students on which goodies they preferred. (At the time, I touted the process as "Donut democracy" and perhaps fancied myself as a Donut liberator, freeing the Institute from the crime of crummy crullers. In hindsight, I fear that instead I played the role of a Donut dealer, a sort of "sugar daddy," getting the students hooked on a deep-fried high and spiraling them down into addiction.) We ended up going with Calabrese's Culver Bakery, who made us wonderful treats for about a year until they raised their minimum order for delivery above what we could possibly digest. Kathleen Youngworth, then at the Junior Grad. Rep. helm, resumed the hunt for the perfect donut and arranged for Tony & Lou's Fast Food and Variety Bakery to serve us up their finest. My connections on the inside tell me that it might soon be time to shake this up yet again, so I anticipate that there will be an even more complicated bakery saga to share with you for the Institute's hundredth anniversary.

In these troubled financial times, on the heels of a three-year bear market on Wall Street and in the midst of a ballooning deficit in the Federal government, it is natural to worry about the continued fiscal solvency of our revered ritual. The Institute certainly stands firmly behind Donuts and appreciates how it brings us together and nourishes our community (even as it fuels our gluttony), but it has to steer through a maze of University rules to keep the tradition alive: Donuts cannot be funded from College funds, and the unsung heroes in the Institute's administration have found ways to pay the bills through discretionary funds. Donuts could be freed from the financial ebbs and tides of our uncertain times and from the vagaries of the University's bureaucracy by setting up its very own endowment—if our esteemed Donuts rested on a nest egg of perhaps $50,000, the Institute would be able to keep it going forever. If you hear the call to join the Donut Liberation Front, to be part of founding such a Donuts endowment, we urge you to contact The Institute of Optics for more information on how you can help; the fate of Progress in Optics (and of the arteries of its practitioners) may well be at stake.

The author thanks Mark Aronstein, Amy Bieber, Matt Bolcar, Dennis Hall, Joe Howard, Craig Olson, Carlos Stroud, and Kathleen & Rich Youngworth for their help in preparing this essay.

David Aronstein received his Ph.D. from the Institute of Optics in 2002. He is currently an optical engineer at Corning-Tropel Corporation, Rochester, NY.

38. A Philosophical Ode to Physical Optics

Brian J. Thompson

Most of us now believe that there is an integrated body of knowledge that constitutes the discipline of optical science and engineering. That discipline includes, of course, the technology and resultant systems that are associated with, and derived from, that science and engineering. This concept of a discipline comes from the definition that optical science and engineering is concerned with the generation, propagation, manipulation and detection of light from the ultraviolet to the infrared and the application of optics in a wide variety of commercial, industrial and military systems in pure optical form and perhaps more importantly as hybrid systems. Evidence of the acceptance of "optics" as a discipline as well as an enabling technology is apparent in the number of academic programs now available in many schools, colleges and universities around the world. It is interesting to recall that when The Institute of Optics was founded at The University of Rochester, it was one of a very small group of academic programs around the world and the first in the United States. Times have certainly changed!

The now broad field of optics can be examined in three major areas: geometrical optics, physical optics and quantum optics. Or, if you wish, as rays, waves, and photons. This separation into three areas has significant historical importance and each approach can be applied to optical problems and to the design of practical optical systems. The major impact on optical science and engineering is in the interconnection of the three approaches and their interdependence which provides critical insight into the generation, propagation, manipulation, and detection of light but critical insights into the limitation of the approaches and their range of validity.

It was the fundamental concept of rectilinear propagation that really led to the ray tracing techniques which became a very powerful tool for the design and analysis of optical systems including the effects of aberrations. There was, of course, no thought that rays really exist as such. From a physical optics point of view the "rays" are equivalent to the normals to the wave front as that wave front propagates through the optical system. Light waves do exist and electromagnetic wave theory is a particularly important and truly fundamental method in the analysis of the propagation of light and hence to the analysis of optical systems. Historically, geometrical optics was thought of in terms of so-called incoherent systems; physical optics and the phenomena of interference and diffraction were so-called coherent systems. With the development of wave optics the full range of problems could be included—that is, incoherent, partially coherent, and coherent systems, with the spatial and temporal coherence taken into consideration as well as the polarization. Just one example will suffice to make the point. The introduction of the "sine-wave response" of an optical system was a major step in the evaluation and characterization of optical systems, particularly imaging systems. Since the idea was for incoherent systems the "sine-wave" input was really $1 + \sin$ in intensity as a spatial distribution. The ratio of the contrast of the output (image) as a function of the input (object) contrast was the measurement to be made. A full "response function" could be obtained by varying the spatial frequency of the "sine wave" input. This idea led in time to the concept of a spatial frequency response and the Modulation Transfer Function (MTF), and the Optical Transfer Function (OTF). These measures replaced the simple two-point resolution measurement and the somewhat arbitrary three-bar target techniques (i.e. a three bar "square-wave" response). From a wave optics point of view the fundamental parameter for an incoherent system is the intensity distribution in the image (output) of a point object (input). The mathematical Fourier transform of that intensity distribution is the OTF of the system. Hence, the fundamental concept of the point spread function, or the intensity impulse response is to describe that distribution in the image of a point object. In the language of diffraction the above output is the intensity distribution in the diffraction pattern formed in the output plane of the system for a point intensity input. So, in fact, the real fundamental function is the so-called amplitude impulse response which characterizes the amplitude and phase of that output. This then in turn allows a much more general evaluation of the performance and characteristics of the system for any state of coherence of a generalized input.

Quantum optics has added yet a further dimension to our full understanding of optical systems and today's complex detection systems. Interactions of light with matter on the atomic scale have become of paramount importance as have detection issues at very low light levels. No longer is the photon just something to consider in association with the photoelectric effect! The very word "photonics" has become a major part of our vocabulary. (On a personal note, I think that it is very unfortunate for our discipline that people talk about optics and photonics as if they were two distinct but connected fields—it's all optics to me!) I must say I enjoy the debate that is currently underway about photons. In what sense do they exist? Do they exist only as a manifestation of the interaction of light with matter, e.g., in the detection step? I leave the reader to ponder these questions.

Dale Buralli sets up a matched filter.

In the meantime I will take comfort in the thought that physical optics remains a very important area both physically (i.e., for real . . . waves exist!) and philosophically (optical science is part of natural philosophy). In any event, it has been wonderful to work in the field at the very heart of optics and see and be a part of its development. It has been a rare privilege for me and my many colleagues over nearly fifty years (and counting) of which thirty-five have been in association with The Institute of Optics.

An interesting postscript: I had just finished drafting this "ode" on a plane ride headed to Rochester from Portland, Oregon, when I attended a very fine production of Michael Frayn's 2000 Tony Award-winning play *Copenhagen* (also put on by our own Geva Theatre in Rochester). The play centers around conversations between Niels Bohr and Werner Heisenberg with contributions from Margrethe Bohr on political and scientific issues, including their thoughts about wave-particle duality and the uncertainty principle. I took great comfort in my fundamental belief in waves—whether right or wrong!

Brian J. Thompson has been a member of the faculty of the University of Rochester since 1968. He served as Director of the Institute of Optics from 1968 until 1975. He is currently Provost Emeritus of the University of Rochester, Rochester, NY.

39. Quantum Optics

Joseph H. Eberly

Every six years the University of Rochester is host to a conference that draws hundreds of registrants, including Nobel laureates and other distinguished members of the international quantum optics community. The Rochester Conference on Coherence and Quantum Optics that was held at the University in 2001 was the eighth in a series that began in 1960, barely in advance of the announcement of successful operation of the first laser. The first conference was intended as a showcase for work on the theme of optical coherence, which was then emerging as a frontier in optics. The conference was the public signal that the University had already installed research teams to probe the frontier, which gradually became identified with the name quantum optics, a subfield of the general domain known as AMO (atomic, molecular and optical) physics. The first University researchers established a strong identification of the University with the field, and built on their strengths with additional appointments. The success of their strategy has been striking. At the present time the University stands sixth in the national AMO ranking, ahead of traditional and usually much larger science schools including Caltech, Illinois, UC Berkeley, Yale and Chicago.

What is quantum optics? As briefly as possible, it is the study of light and matter at the single-photon and single-electron level. This oversimplification accurately suggests that the field's attraction, and its expected future influence, both arise from its focus on the smallest units of opto-electronics, the photon and electron units that will dictate the development of advanced optical technology. Quantum theory itself arose a century ago in order to explain the way that electrons in atoms absorb and emit light, bringing with it the notion of wave-particle duality. This is the idea that a single photon or a single electron can be interchangeably considered either a particle or a wave, but not both at once. A tension persists to the present day in quantum optics between coherence (the wave aspect, permitting interference) and incoherence (the particle aspect, preventing interference), and this provided part of the intellectual motivation for the 1960 conference.

Robert Hopkins, director of the Institute in 1960, had previously noted that coherence and statistical optics were topics missing among the areas of faculty research, and in 1958 he approached one of Max Born's former research assistants with the offer of a professorial appointment in the Institute.

Leonard Mandel.

This was Emil Wolf, who soon helped to recruit another physicist from England, Leonard Mandel, then studying the statistical behavior of single photons. Mandel joined the University as professor of physics. These were the founders who would become friends and long-time collaborators and participants in the activities of the Institute and the Physics Department, and are recognized world-wide as the originators of the University's quantum optics research groups. The results of their collaboration are summarized in a book that they co-authored, *Coherence and Quantum Optics* (Cambridge University Press, 1995).

By the end of the 1960s, quantum optics was expanding internationally, and additions were made to the local team. Joseph Eberly was appointed to the faculty in Physics, and Carlos Stroud was appointed in The Institute of Optics. Not quite coincidentally, Eberly at Stanford and Stroud at Washington University had worked with the same faculty supervisor, E. T. Jaynes, an early pioneer of quantum optical coherence theory and one of the inventors of the field of cavity quantum electrodynamics. During the 1970s the University's presence in quantum optics expanded greatly. Topics with such descriptions as multiphoton absorption, photon statistics, self-induced transparency, superradiance, Rabi splitting, resonance fluorescence, atomic dark states, non-classical light, cross-spectral purity, time-dependent spectra, and coherence trapping were introduced and discussed and expanded by workers here and around the world. Researchers in pure science were strongly supported by efforts in other areas of optical science and technology that are described in other articles in this volume.

Visitors and other collaborators were frequent participants in quantum optics research activities, with a number of notable results. The well-defined phase of laser light prompted re-examination of the phase-intensity relation in quantum theory as well as a careful treatment by Mandel, Wolf, and field-theorist colleague George Sudarshan of the photoelectric detection of light fluctuations. The first detailed textbook with quantum optics in the title was almost certainly *Fundamentals of Quantum Optics*, published in 1968 by Sudarshan with John Klauder at Bell Labs. It was designed to disseminate consequences of this new line of research. There were also undesigned consequences of the rapid progress being made in Rochester that led to publication. When the existence of two different but similar sets of unfinished lecture notes was discovered during an

Joseph H. Eberly, 1970.

Carlos R. Stroud, 1987.

impromptu dinner during the 1972 IQEC conference in Montreal, Eberly and a former visitor in Mandel's group, Leslie Allen of Sussex University, found that they had practically already written a textbook together. In 1975 their small book appeared with the title *Optical Resonance and Two-Level Atoms*. It was distinguished immediately by the odd fact of having its Japanese translation available in print before the original English edition, and distinguished subsequently by remaining in print to the present day, more than thirty years after the dinner in Montreal. The book has since been translated into two more languages (legally) and is still in use as a classroom resource by Eberly and Stroud. Their introductory graduate course on quantum optics has defined entry into the field for scores of Rochester students and postdoctoral associates in optics and physics over the past three decades. Many of them have since become leaders in academic and industrial institutions in the various rapidly expanding fields of laser science, both in the United States and elsewhere, including England, Poland, Mexico, Russia, Spain, Switzerland, Norway, Netherlands, India, Pakistan, China, Japan, Australia and New Zealand. A related Eberly-Stroud project, almost completed more than once, is an introductory text of about twenty chapters. Another frequent collaborator in the quantum optics group was H. M. Nussenzweig, who authored another early book in the field, *Introduction to Quantum Optics*, in 1973.

In the 1980s Michael Raymer joined the group as a faculty member in optics, and then at the end of the 1980s and at the beginning of the 1990s two more faculty members joined the group: Ian Walmsley in optics and Nicholas Bigelow in physics. More recently John Howell arrived to take a position in physics. Several other current faculty members

Les Allen and Joe Eberly, best selling authors.

of optics have strong overlapping interests in the field, including Robert Boyd, Govind Agrawal, and Lukas Novotny. Collectively the members of this extended group in optics and physics have published well over one thousand research papers, several widely used textbooks, and they have edited literally dozens of books and conference proceedings. They have served and are serving as editors and associate editors of journals and officers of professional societies. Over many years they have received honorary degrees, medals, and awards, and have held distinguished lectureships and memberships in national and foreign academies of science.

Key contributions to quantum optics in its first quarter century have come from the University of Rochester, and several prominent breakthroughs and widely known "firsts" are among them. These contributions have come in the form of both theoretical and experimental innovations, and from many individuals. Prominent themes engaging more than one person or research group over extended periods have included several that deserve particular mention: Optical coherence and statistical optics, the quantum-classical boundary, light generation and laser development, and resonant absorption and atomic coherence.

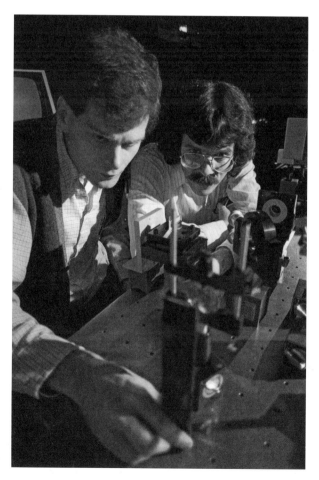

Professor Michael Raymer and student Ian Walmsley in the lab.

Donald Harter (Ph.D. 1982) delivers a check from Allied Signal to support quantum optics research. Professors Stroud, Walmsley, Eberly, and Boyd happily accept the donation.

Optical coherence and statistical optics formed the core themes of the first Rochester Conference in 1960, and their importance and relevance were continuously and vigorously expanded by Emil Wolf and Len Mandel together with their research teams. A wide variety of collaborators included George Sudarshan, whose interest in phase space functions that rigorously connect classical variables with quantum operators led to his co-invention of the so-called Glauber-Sudarshan P distribution, a building block in quantum optical calculations. It prompted the rapid exploitation of the phase-space approach by C. L. Mehta and other students working with Wolf. Particularly notable was the series of papers with Girish Agarwal beginning in 1970 on phase space methods in statistical optics. The first major overview of light coherence and fluctuations following the 1960 conference appeared in an article by Mandel and Wolf, in *Reviews of Modern Physics* in 1965. This was probably the University's first "citation classic," reaching the five-hundred-citation level very quickly in the world literature. Along with two other more recent citation classics, it is listed in bold face in the table.

In a very different project, Eberly and Krzysztof Wodkiewicz established a consistent theory for time-dependent spectra of statistical light fields. This is not the oxymoron it may appear to be, since time-dependent spectra form the background for instrumental developments that came later, including frequency-resolved optical gating (FROG) and Ian Walmsley's invention of spectral phase interferometry for direct electric-field reconstruction (SPIDER).

For almost two decades, announcements of exotic instances of quantum coherence were practically continuously arriving from the Mandel labs. These included the invention of a totally new concept in interferometer design based on two-photon entanglement, the discovery of what is now referred to as the Mandel dip in two-photon interference, and other quantum statistical marvels, such as photon beams that are anti-bunched and/or have sub-Poisson noise. It was in this work that the widely used Mandel Q parameter was introduced.

The quantum-classical boundary is an ill-defined region noted for its strange inhabitants such as the Schrödinger Cat, which is neither alive nor dead but rather is both at once. One of these beasts was actually tracked and captured in Wilmot, a highly publicized result of Rydberg wave packet experiments by Carlos Stroud and his group in the 1980s. Ian Walmsley and Mike Raymer more recently described a similar animal, a molecule with obviously classical vibrational motion but which behaves purely quantum mechanically when subtly observed.

Professor Nicholas P. Bigelow.

Arguments concerning whether light itself belongs on one side or the other of the quantum-classical boundary have a long and honorable history. Are photons necessary to use as the fundamental light unit or not? Direct demonstration that the answer is definitely *yes* became much easier in 1980 when Joe Eberly's group used the context of cavity QED to predict a new phenomenon called quantum revivals, experimental signals that are not compatible with non-quantized light. Revivals have been observed in several ways now, settling the original question, and Stroud's group has found that fractional revivals also exist. They explain a large multiplicity of little quantum cats, Schrödinger Kittens, that can coexist in a single Rydberg atom. Behavior just as unnerving can be exhibited by light pulses. For example, Len Mandel's group showed in a landmark experiment that a photon in an interferometer can be smart enough to tell when an experimenter *could* be watching a second photon, *whether he is watching or not.* John Howell's experiments crowd the quantum-classical boundary from a different direction, by asking how closely can photons be cloned, since Mandel and Peter Milonni and others have shown that nothing can be cloned perfectly, with implications for very practical tasks such as cryptography. The impossibility of perfect cloning, however, doesn't rule out perfect teleportation, but that's another matter.

Light generation and laser development had top priority in many optics labs in the 1960s. Ways were found at that time to make lasers wavelength-tunable by adopting a variety of dyes as laser media, partly through Mike Hercher's work and the concurrent efforts of Ben Snavely's group at Kodak. Later advances in light generation and manipulation came in a number of forms, via stimulated Raman and Brillouin scattering, parametric amplification, free electron lasing, and others. One of the most general and useful remains multi-wave mixing. For example, the visibility of a hologram relies on wave mixing, and Emil Wolf explained how holographic data can provide structure information on semi-transparent objects. Later, the unexpected appearance of Rabi resonances in four-wave mixing was explained by Bob Boyd, Mike Raymer, Paul Narum, and Don Harter. What was certainly the least expected new light form came in the late 1980s from the optics-physics team of Jim Durnin, Joe Miceli, and Joe Eberly, when they announced diffraction-free beams. In the face of world-wide skepticism, their papers provided experimental evidence that so-called

Bessel beams with beam spots as small as 100 microns in diameter have the exotic ability to propagate without observable spreading an order of magnitude farther than the Rayleigh range of a more usual Gaussian beam focused at the same aperture. Despite their counterintuitive character, such Bessel beams are currently being used in a number of optical applications.

Advances in laser operation also led quickly to higher output intensities. Within barely more than a decade of the first laser in 1960, the successive adoption of Q-switching and then mode-locking techniques gave laser powers in the multi-megawatt range, but further increases came very slowly for more than a decade. Then a stunning advance came with the Rochester demonstration of a table-top terawatt laser (called simply the T-cubed laser by everyone). Conceived by Gerard Mourou, and based on chirped pulse amplification, this was the thesis goal of optics student Donna Strickland, and was realized, with other members of Mourou's LLE team, in 1985. To the present day, all subsequent high power solid state lasers, some now operating above the petawatt level, have employed the T-cubed chirped-pulse laser principle.

Such increases in laser power fit perfectly with both theoretical and experimental programs around the world. A hierarchy of predicted high-intensity effects awaited experimental study, and the first efforts were directed to the detection of multiphoton ionization, for which a workable high intensity theory had already been provided by optics professor Al Gold and his student Barry Bebb in 1966. Work with very strong laser fields has been continuous at the University since then, and results have included the first observation of over-the-barrier ionization by the Meyerhofer team, the original simulations by Eberly's group of the suppression of the photo-electric effect under high-intensity irradiation, the dramatic direct conversion of light into matter by the Melissinos-Meyerhofer collaboration on positron-electron pair creation, and new faculty member Chunlei Guo's design of high-intensity experiments to track molecular electrons on attosecond time scales. The two largest international conferences that are focused on strong-field effects in atoms and molecules were founded by Eberly and first held on campus. Both conferences are held regularly and are now being scheduled for off-campus venues such as Budapest, Crete, Monterey, Garmisch-Partenkirchen, Quebec, and even a Volga River cruise boat.

Resonance absorption and atomic coherence became more and more closely connected as tunable lasing allowed formerly impossible experiments to be executed worldwide. These included studies of nonlinear oscillation in laser systems as well as laser threshold studies employing photon-counting techniques pioneered by Len Mandel using the Poisson transform widely known as the Mandel formula, which connects the probability densities of the quantum photocount with the classical intensity of light. Strong resonance effects were most vigorously explored in the sodium D-line manifold with dye lasers based on Rhodamine 6G (a wonderfully intense orange dye, particularly when spraying at high pressure all over a lab from a ruptured hose). The ease of seeing coherent resonance effects focused attention on fictitious (but very popular) two-level atoms. These imaginary atoms were and are real enough to give backbone to quantum optics intuition, and served as the platform for calculations in the 1970s of radiative frequency shifts such as the Lamb shift by Jay Ackerhalt, Peter Knight, and Peter Milonni in Joe Eberly's group to determine the quantum counterparts to neoclassical predictions (see "The Jaynes-Franken Bet," chapter 30), using radiation reaction rather than vacuum fluctuations as their foundation. Two-level theory not only made clear the governing role of Rabi oscillations in coherent stimulated transitions, but also permitted detailed but simplified calculations that revealed a wide variety of effects never seen before. Among the most noted of these were the Rabi splitting of the

Graduate student Felix Schuda illuminated by the light from the first single-mode cw dye laser that he build in collaboration with Michael Hercher.

spectrum of resonance fluorescence into three peaks rather than one, first observed by Felix Schuda, Carlos Stroud, and Mike Hercher, and the prediction and subsequent first observation of anti-bunched photon generation by Len Mandel working with Jeff Kimble and Mario Dagenais.

Highly coherent and strong laser interactions allowed terminology from wave optics to be sensibly applied to atomic dynamics, where conventional rate equations for absorption and emission had to give way to equations for phase-coherent probability amplitudes. New effects such as confluence of coherences, adiabaton pulses, and coherence transfer were announced in theoretical papers of Kazik Rzążewski, Rainer Grobe and Foek Hioe, working with Joe Eberly, and confirmed in experiments later. Tests of quantum theory offered a fundamental application of statistical coherence, and the truly odd features of the quantum side of the classical-quantum boundary began to be appreciated in the 1980s. Len Mandel explained how to design unbreakable cryptographic devices, a forerunner of John Howell's latest work with biphotons from parametric down conversion. Wodkiewicz and Eberly exported the notion of squeezing from photons to atoms, and Nick Bigelow's recent work has led to observations in atoms of macroscopic spin squeezing, the reduction of an uncertainty below the standard quantum limit of the Heisenberg Uncertainty Principle. The final stage of this work probably lies in conditional Heisenberg violation in high quantum entanglement of the type associated with Einstein's famous objections to quantum mechanics published in 1935 with Podolsky and Rosen. One route to reach this goal has recently been elucidated by Eberly with C. K. Law, and collaborative experiments by Bob Boyd and John Howell are moving quickly in the same direction.

A resonance breakthrough occurred as soon as two strong optical fields at different but tunable wavelengths could be exploited in the same experiment. The first double-optical strong resonance studies became possible, and these led to the discovery of the atomic "dark states" that were studied by the Stroud team, explained in Rich Whitley's thesis and confirmed in experiments with Bob Gray. Similar states in cavity QED described by the physics student H. I. Yoo extend the concept of revivals. The discovery by Oreg, Hioe, and Eberly of the unexpected advantage of anti-intuitive pulse ordering in double excitation is now exploited globally in a variety of double resonance applications. Mike Raymer and Ian Walmsley took double resonance right to the classical-quantum border when they showed how classically stimulated Raman scattering gives rise to giant spontaneous quantum fluctuations.

Large-scale collaborations among groups have been founded at the University to exploit the existence of vigorous research teams covering different sectors of quantum optics. The Rochester Theory Center for Optical Science and Engineering was established by the National Science Foundation in 1995. Its mandate has been to provide opportunities for young theorists in a wide range of fields of optical science and technology to interact for one-to-three years with leading optical theorists in the University. Faculty from five different departments and LLE have cooperated within RTC in mentoring more than two dozen post-docs. The recent widespread interest in developing quantum computers has directed new attention to old questions within quantum mechanics and quantum information theory, many of which have optical aspects. In a coast-to-coast collaboration with scientists in four other universities, four faculty members in optics and physics have formed the core of the Center for Quantum Information, supported through the Army Research Office since 1999. The purpose is to coordinate different approaches to research on fundamental aspects of quantum information.

Every discussion of this type could be continued almost indefinitely and still not credit all the important contributions and contributors. The intent has been to focus mostly on the earliest days of quantum optics at the University, and the developments that came from them. The table below is an attempt to finish with a cross-section of University papers from those days that played key roles in the evolution of quantum optics here, and that were also "selected" by the entire world-wide optics community. That is, the articles are those from the quarter century 1965–1990 that have been cited by authors of at least three hundred other published papers. Three of the articles have achieved what is usually called "Citation Classic" status, that is, they have received more than five hundred citations. These are highlighted in bold face.

L. Mandel and E. Wolf,
Reviews of Modern Physics 37, 231 ('65),
Coherence Properties of Optical Fields

E. Wolf,
Optics Communications 1, 153 ('69),
Three-dimensional structure determination of semi-transparent objects from holographic data

G. S. Agarwal and E. Wolf,
Physical Review D 2, 2161–2186 ('70),
Calculus for Functions of Noncommuting Operators and General Phase-Space
Methods in Quantum Mechanics. I. Mapping Theorems and Ordering of Functions of
Noncommuting Operators

F. Schuda, C. R. Stroud, Jr., and M. Hercher,
Journal of Physics B 7, L198 ('74),
Observation of the resonant Stark effect at optical frequencies

H. J. Kimble and L. Mandel,
Physical Review A 13, 2123 ('76),
Theory of resonance fluorescence

R. M. Whitley and C. R. Stroud, Jr.,
Physical Review A 14, 1498 ('76),
Double optical resonance

J. H. Eberly and K. Wodkiewicz,
Journal of the Optical Society of America, 67, 1252 ('77),
The time-dependent physical spectrum of light

H. J. Kimble, M. Dagenais and L. Mandel,
Physical Review Letters 39, 691 ('77),
Photon Antibunching in Resonance Fluorescence

H. R. Gray, R. M. Whitley and C. R. Stroud, Jr.,
Optics Letters 3, 218 ('78),
Coherent trapping of atomic populations

L. Mandel,
Optics Letters 4, 205 ('79),
Sub-Poissonian photon statistics in resonance fluorescence

J. H. Eberly, N. B. Narozhny and J. J. Sanchez-Mondragon,
Physical Review Letters 44, 1323 ('80),
Periodic Spontaneous Collapse and Revival in a Simple Quantum Model

N. B. Narozhny, J. J. Sanchez-Mondragon and J. H. Eberly,
Physical Review A 23, 236 ('81),
Coherence versus incoherence: Collapse and revival in a simple quantum model

H.-I. Yoo and J. H. Eberly,
Physics Reports 118, 239 ('85),
Dynamical theory of an atom with two or three levels interacting with quantized cavity fields

J. Durnin, J. J. Miceli, Jr., and J. H. Eberly,
Physical Review Letters 58, 1499 ('87),
Diffraction-free beams

C. K. Hong, Z. Y. Ou and L. Mandel,
Physical Review Letters 59, 2044 ('87),
Measurement of subpicosecond time intervals between two photons by interference

P. Maine, D. Strickland, P. Bado, M. Pessot and G. Mourou,
IEEE Journal of Quantum Electronics 24, 398 ('88),
Generation of ultrahigh peak power pulses by chirped pulse amplification

Joseph H. Eberly has been a member of the faculty of the University of Rochester since 1967. He is the Andrew Carnegie Professor of Physics.

40. The Tortoise and the Hare

Mary Becker

One spring day in 1975, the Optics graduate students were gathered on the fourth floor of the Bausch & Lomb building. The students were comparing (and boasting about) their experiences on the running track, particularly how fast they could run the hundred-yard dash. Mary (Becker) Citron, who did not even know where the track field was located, asked how fast the "jocks" thought she could run the hundred yards. Mary hypothesized—in a typical analytical method—that the best runner, Eric Krisl at over six feet tall, had a stride twice as large as hers (Mary is five feet short). Mary shared her conclusion that Eric should be able to run his hundred yards as quickly as she could run fifty yards. Unable to refute Mary's assertion, Eric agreed to the tortoise-and-hare race, with Mary's fifty-yard handicap. They scheduled the race for the next Friday afternoon.

Start of the great Tortoise-Hare race featuring Mary Citron and Eric Krisl.

Rumor of the race quickly spread through the corridors. Excitement built enough to generate bets!

Mary talked another runner, Duncan Moore, into being her coach. Duncan began coaching Mary by showing her where the track was. He then showed Mary which part of the track to run her fifty yards, and then he prepared to time her. Mary did her part by wearing lucky yellow sneakers (with pink dye from working in the Stroud's lab!). Duncan timed Mary's fifty yards as being faster than the (then) world record for the hundred-yard dash. They quickly agreed to keep their lips sealed until the race.

A few of the students who had placed bets showed up on Race Day. The race began, then quickly finished, with Mary turning around from the finish line to watch Eric complete his hundred yards!

Heated discussions ensued in the Hall of Bausch & Lomb, fourth floor. Complete analysis of the fifty-yard versus the one hundred-yard course revealed that eighty yards versus one hundred yards would be a fairer rematch. It was decided that this important rematch would take place at the Optics Picnic in October.

More bets were placed at the re-match. Tony Devaney, at that time a post-doc working with Emil Wolf, was heard to say that he calculated, based on the first race, that Mary would win again, but being a man he "had to" bet on Eric.

After Mary won the re-match by a foot (!), it was suggested that Eric and Mary do a third race. Mary logically concluded that she had already won twice and any more races would be redundant.

Mary (Citron) Becker was a Ph.D. student (1971–1977) working with Carlos Stroud. She is currently retired and living in Indianapolis, Indiana.

41. The Institute of Optics and the Laboratory for Laser Energetics: A Personal History

James M. Forsyth

A great strength of the University of Rochester has always been its commitment to teaching by a faculty with aggressive, interdisciplinary research interests. The seventy-five year history of The Institute of Optics is a shining example of this assertion. Superbly chronicled in other chapters of this history, the small team of engineers and scientists who formed the founding team of faculty of the Institute in 1928 proved to be a national asset when special optical devices were required to be designed and built to support the world wide struggle of the Second World War. The world-wide impact of the Institute continues to this day in a wide variety of economic important industries, in health care, and in national defense.

My abbreviated commentary here is intended to focus on the both the seminal and continuing role that the Institute has played in the founding and evolution of the Laboratory for Laser Energetics, a program which has achieved national and international significance and recognition in the field of peaceful applications of thermonuclear fusion technology. A complete chronicle would require a volume in itself. A more modest objective is to acquaint the "present generation" of Institute members and friends as to how LLE was launched, and the role the Institute played in LLE's success and growth during my years at the Institute. I shall concentrate on this objective.

I find it useful to break LLE's history into six periods:

1965–1968 Discovery.
1968–1974 Exploration.
1974–1982 Program/Team/Facility building.
1982–1992 First Rewards on Facility Investment.
1992–2000 Maturation: Facility and Program.
2000–2004 National Facility status for unclassified fusion research.
2004–Initiation of construction of unique, new, world-class laser facility.

My narrative will cover the period 1965–1983.

Discovery

I was a second-year Institute graduate student when, by chance, I witnessed a casual laboratory demonstration which ultimately launched the LLE program. It happened on an afternoon when Assistant Professor of Optics Michael Hercher invited Assistant Professor of Mechanical and Aerospace Sciences (Mechanical Engineering today) Moshe Lubin. Hercher's research interest was in the field of optically pumped, high peak power pulsed solid state laser systems. His laboratory was full of ruby and neodymium doped glass lasers. Lubin's research was concentrated on microwave plasma diagnostics. Lubin was aware of the proposal by Soviet scientists Basov and Prokorov in 1964 that powerful laser pulses might be used to generate plasma conditions where thermonuclear reactions might be observed. A similar proposal was being made at the Lawrence Livermore National Laboratory in California. Hercher's demonstration consisted of passing a Q-switched laser pulse through a lens and producing an air spark. Lubin was profoundly impressed with this demonstration. As Lubin departed, I had the distinct impression of someone who had struck intellectual gold.

James M. Forsyth.

What would Lubin need to translate Hercher's demonstration into Basov and Prokorov's scenario? He needed expertise in pulsed laser technology (Hercher), ready access to state of the art optical fabrication facilities (William Klinkert and Herbert Graf, skilled opticians who worked in the Institute optical shop and who had worked on the world war two projects), advanced optical design (Professor Robert Hopkins), and a pool of talented graduate students. It was all here!

Lubin realized that this project would require a very large laser, much larger than Hercher's demonstration system. Where would he find the required laser material? Enter

Moshe Lubin and early model of Nd:glass slab amplifer.

the Eastman Kodak Company. In the mid 1960s several traditional glass making companies in the US had looked into expanding their filter glass manufacturing, much of which involved production of rare-earth doped crown glass, to include laser glass. Toward the end of the decade, for various reasons, several of these glass makers decided that this market was not one they had the in-house resources to adequately address. This decision was made at both American Optical Corporation and Kodak. Lubin saw the opportunity. He convinced Kodak management to give him access to Kodak's inventory of laser glass, and proceeded to construct large scale (at the time) glass laser amplifiers.

The impressive array of academic and industrial resources were sufficient to convince the Atomic Energy Commission (whose activities today are a part of the Department of Energy) to provide support for serious, university based, unclassified, peaceful uses and applications of thermonuclear fusion to Lubin's program.

The director of the Institute through this period was Professor W. Lewis Hyde. Hyde encouraged the participation of the Institute in this program. He confided to me later that having observed Lubin's boundless energy first hand, that the next phases of the program would have to be populated by a predominantly youthful team.

Exploration

This phase of the program was characterized by construction and testing of a wide variety of components and systems for high peak power laser operation. It was also accompanied by experiments with and theoretical analysis of laser produced plasmas. The results of these activities culminated in the design of a twenty-four-beam glass laser system named Omega) of unprecedented size and performance in an unclassified facility. This phase of the project also involved greatly increased participation by faculty, staff, and students from the Institute. Professor Brian J. Thompson became the Institute's director at the beginning of this phase of the project and he too encouraged the joint efforts which seem to spring up everywhere.

Dr. Jay Eastman, Ph.D. Optics '74, an expert in multilayer thin film coating technology, scoped out a program to test the performance of coatings obtained for the project from outside sources as well as producing sample coatings of new design in house. This program would later be taken over and expanded under Institute graduate Dr. Stephen Jacobs.

In an effort to keep all options open in the early part of this phase, Lubin encouraged me to engage in a study of high peak power gas lasers to see whether sufficiently large systems could be built to produce fusion conditions in a plasma. Conducted along with graduate student Capt. Thomas Jerrick, USAF, our study concluded that high pressure carbon dioxide lasers could indeed be scaled to fusion driver performance. However, ongoing plasma physics studies showed that infrared lasers would not create plasmas of sufficiently high density to make for efficient fusion conditions.

Nevertheless, I was bitten by the bug as the plasma calculations also showed that copious quantities of soft X-rays were generated in laser plasmas under highly nonequilibrium conditions. This suggested to me that a soft X-ray amplifying condition might be found leading to development of a soft X-ray laser. The big payoff here proved to be in the necessity to design and build various soft X-ray diagnostic systems, especially including imaging systems.

At the beginning of this phase modest glass laser hardware and laser matter experiments were carried out in a laboratory in the Hopeman building. Soon, a larger space was remodeled in Gavett hall to house a four-beam glass laser system and experimental chamber. Toward the end of this phase a temporary building was constructed behind Morey hall to house the activities associated with the design and testing of the components to be deployed in Omega.

The question was "where should we house the facility needed for the Omega system?" University President Robert Sproull was anxious to find a space on the river campus in order to maintain an immediacy of contact with faculty, students, and staff from many disciplines. In the end it proved impossible to shoehorn the necessary facility onto the river campus and a separate location on the then unoccupied south campus was selected.

During this phase of the program Lubin received a joint faculty appointment as Associate Professor of Mechanical and Aerospace Sciences and Associate Professor of Optics.

Building the Program, Team, and Facility

At the beginning of this phase Institute Director Thompson was elevated to the position of Dean of the College of Engineering and Applied Science. Dr. Nicholas George from Caltech was recruited to become the next director of the Institute. George was also supportive if the Institute/LLE interaction and established a close working relationship with Lubin.

Groundbreaking for the new laser facility was held on April 2, 1976, a cold, wet, typical early spring day in Rochester. The ceremony was attended by state and federal officials,

Omega system laser bay.

participating industrial sponsors, scientists, and educators. During construction, work continued in the three river campus laboratories located in the Hopeman building, Gavett Hall, and the Morey Hall annex. By 1978 the physical plant on the south campus was ready for occupancy. Equipment and staff from the Morey annex were moved to the south campus, and the Gavett Hall laser was decommissioned. Work began on the construction of six of the twenty-four beam lines and an interim target chamber was installed in a vacant portion of the laser bay floor. Construction of the Omega laser was managed and directed by Jay Eastman. The following year, the Hopeman laser facility was decommissioned and the experimental facility was moved to the south campus. University operated bus service between the river campus, graduate student housing facilities, and the south campus was established so that convenient access for students and faculty to the south campus would be possible. Many students and faculty were provided offices in the south campus facility for the purpose of conducting research.

An important development occurred in laser technology at LLE during this period. Designed by Dr. Stephen Craxton, LLE staff, and brought to fruition under Dr. Stephen Jacobs (Ph.D. Optics '74), large, single crystals of KDP were oriented such as to convert the near infrared output from the glass laser into ultraviolet light at up to 90% conversion efficiency. When later fitted to all twenty-four beams this frequency converter greatly improved the performance obtained from laser fusion targets and is one of the hallmarks of the laser facility. Dr. Jacobs also directs the study and testing of optical damage resistant components used in high pulse power laser systems.

The resources available through LLE's facilities spawned a wide variety of creative and dynamic research activity, not only in the field of laser induced fusion and plasma physics, but in fields ranging from astrophysics to biophysics to ultra-high-speed optoelectronics. An exhaustive list of these projects and their participants is far too large for the

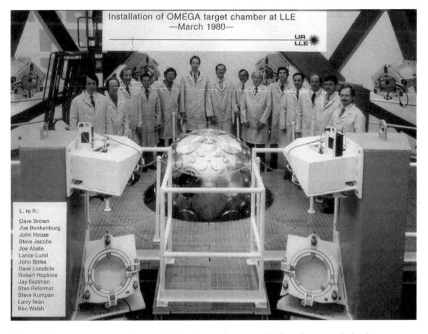

Omega laser system target bay and the team who assembled and operated the laser.

scope of this short narrative. However, two Institute of Optics graduate students during this period went on to occupy important positions today in their affiliated programs. Terry Kessler, M.S. '81, is now responsible for the Laser Engineering program at LLE. Wayne Knox, Ph.D. '82, is now the director of The Institute of Optics.

In 1981 Professor Lubin was hired by one of the project sponsors. Standard Oil of Ohio, to be Vice President of Research and Development, Patents and Licensing. Professor Jay Eastman was appointed acting Director.

Postscript

In 1983 I left LLE and the Institute to pursue a career in the business world. My center of operations continued in the Rochester area and I have been able to follow the continued progress of LLE and the Institute. Both Institutions continue to occupy world class status in their respective disciplines. Of note to me is that the collaboration has given birth to the Center for Optical Manufacturing. Directed by Dr. Harvey Pollicove and located in the south campus facility, it supports LLE's ongoing needs for cost effective manufacture of large optical components while carrying out aggressive new research on the generation and polishing of both conventional and unconventional optical surfaces.

The recent announcement of support to construct a petawatt laser upgrade to the Omega facility is evidence of the health and vigor of the LLE program. I am proud to have been a contributor to the early part of this program and I eagerly look forward to the results obtained in this latest phase of continuing growth.

James M. Forsyth received his B.S. Optics '64, and Ph.D. Optics '68 from The Institute of Optics.

42. The Surprise Party

George Sherman

In the summer of 1975 during the time when I was an Assistant Professsor in the Institute I had a summer appointment at the Technical University of Helsinki in Finland. While there, I worked with a Finnish graduate student named Ari Friberg. In contrast to the more formal relationships between Finnish professors and their students that he was used to, we had a more casual relationship and became good friends. I think he assumed that this was

Danette Ryan, Ari Friberg, and Glenn Tyler at the Optics Picnic, 1975.

just the way it is at American universities. Ari decided he wanted to continue to work with me after I returned to Rochester, so he enrolled as a graduate student in The Institute of Optics. Since I was stopping at two other universities on the way home, we flew to Rochester on different flights and he arrived a couple of weeks ahead of me and stayed in my home while arranging for a place to live. By the time I arrived home from Europe, my wife and kids loved him and he had become a member of the family. After he moved into graduate-student housing, he would often drop by our house to visit us, usually around dinner time.

One night, well into his first term at school, he and several other Institute graduate students were out on the town partying late. Since they weren't ready to stop partying when the bars closed and they had no other source of beer, Ari suggested that they all go to "George's" house where there surely would be plenty of what they had in mind. The other students didn't know who this "George" was; but if he didn't mind Ari coming in for beer at 2:00 a.m. with a bunch of friends, that was fine with them. So they all came, Ari located the hidden key, and they came in and helped themselves to beer from our refrigerator. Before long, I was awakened by boisterous laughter coming from our living room downstairs. Since it didn't seem to be the way that thieves would be behaving, I wasn't overly alarmed, so I put on a bathrobe and went downstairs to check it out.

I will never forget the look of terror on those students' faces when they suddenly realized that they had let themselves into the home of and were drinking the beer of their Physical Optics professor. The only way I could figure out to reassure them that everything was OK was to sit down and have a beer with them. Or maybe it was two beers.

George Sherman was Assistant Professor of from 1970 to 1976.
Ari Friberg was a Ph.D. student in Optics from 1975 to 1981, and is currently Professor of Physics at the Royal Institute of Technology, Stockholm, Sweden.

43. Nicholas George: 1977–1981

Hilda Kingslake

In 1977 Nicholas George, Professor of Electrical Engineering and Applied Physics at Caltech, was appointed the fifth Director of The Institute of Optics. He has had considerable experience in scientific industry and at the National Bureau of Standards.

A professor of electrical engineering! It was to be expected that the conservatives would raise their eyebrows, but the progressives immediately realized that indeed it was an appointment in the right direction: The new technologies demand a happy marriage between classical optics and electronics, no matter whether one regards the electronic age as moving into the field of optics or vice versa.

The Institute of Optics was in the process of moving from its long out-grown quarters on the fourth floor of Bausch & Lomb Hall into the five-story Space Science Center, so that Nicholas George was able to place the very considerable equipment from his California laboratories directly into the new quarters. He also brought with him four graduate students as research assistants, all of whom earned their Ph.D.s, both at Caltech and at The Institute of Optics.

Nicholas George assumes the Directorship.

Nicholas George was barely settled when he was confronted with the plans for the Fiftieth Anniversary Celebration and the National Meeting of the Optical Society of America. However, these interruptions did serve to introduce him to many of the optical scientists in the Rochester area.

In an interview article for *Optics News* published in the summer of 1979, only 18 months after his arrival in Rochester, Nicholas George, the electrical engineer, was able to say: "The Institute of Optics is a beautifully balanced scholarly community, with dynamic young faculty, elder statesmen, and the essential ingredient of a lively inquisitive group of top-ranked scientists-all built around the single focus of optics. This closeness of interest is unique among educational institutions and fosters a most beneficial cooperation and kindred spirit among the faculty. . . . My own specialization has been in electro-magnetic theory and linear systems, and these disciplines fit very comfortably in optics. In fact, for a potential student who may be reading this article, I would like to emphasize that he would do well in our graduate program if he comes from a school with good training in the basic sciences or electrical engineering and mathematics."

Nicholas George appointed the following members of the faculty: R. W. Boyd, J. C. Dainty, M. G. Raymer, D. G. Hall, M. C. Lea, and G. M. Morris. He also renewed the joint appointments of E. Wolf, L. Mandel, and J. H. Eberly from physics, and E. W. Marchand retired from Eastman Kodak Company. He revived the publication of *IMAGE* newsletter, originally started as *I. O. N.* by R. E. Hopkins. He formalized and greatly extended the Industrial Associates program started by Brian Thompson. They now meet twice a year for two days. Papers are presented by faculty members and graduate students, and the Associates have the opportunity to visit the laboratories and talk with the students.

In 1981, Nicholas George resigned from the Directorship to give full time to teaching and research. In 1986 he led the effort that later resulted in a five-year award supported by the U.S. Army Research Office for a new University of Rochester Center for opto-electronic systems research, which he will direct.

No one will ever forget Nicholas George's electrically driven rotating spit for roasting beef and pork at the annual picnics of The Institute of Optics.

44. The Reality of Physical Optics at the Institute

Brian J. Thompson

The model that President Rush Rhees used in conjunction with his industrial counterparts and backers, George Eastman and Edward Bausch, for "his Institute" was the already successful Technical Optics Department at the Royal College of Science of the Imperial College of Science & Technology in London, England. Not only was this the model, but he hired the first two faculty members in England: Rudolf Kingslake, who had graduated from that Technical Optics Department in the second graduating class, for geometrical optics and A. Maurice Taylor for physical optics. These subjects were viewed as the two fundamental branches of the field so those of us who are working, or who have worked in the Institute in physical optics and developed that limb of the "optics tree" can trace our ancestry in part to 1929 and Maurice Taylor. He was a Ph.D. graduate from Cambridge University and co-author of a book, *The Infrared Analysis of Molecular Structures*, with F. I. G. Rawlins. While Kinglake had been appointed by the board of trustees in June of 1929, they didn't act on Taylor's appointment until November of 1929.

The long and productive road from 1929 to 2003 has seen an explosion of understanding, of new fundamental knowledge, and of diverse and interesting, and yes important, applications of physical optics. Maurice Taylor returned to England in 1934 and later became the chairman of the physics department at Southampton University. It so happened that in 1959 I applied for a position in his department as a lecturer ($\approx$Associate Professor) having previously spent several years as an Assistant Lecturer ($\approx$Assistant Professor) at Manchester University. However, I ended up accepting a position at Leeds University. Little did I know at that time that I would follow in Taylor's physical optics footsteps in the Institute, almost exactly forty years after his appointment. Another important connection back to the very start of the Institute was Helen Tobin who was the original secretary to Dr. Wilkins, the acting director, and to the small faculty including Maurice Taylor. Helen became my secretary and administrative assistant when I came to Rochester as director of The Institute of Optics and Professor of Optics in 1968. Helen Tobin retired in 1972 with an amazing record of forty-three years of continuous and dedicated service to the Institute, and the University from which she graduated. Needless to say, she was absolutely invaluable in the director's office.

When Taylor returned to England in 1934, his place was taken by J. Stuart Campbell (Ph.D. Cal-Tech) whose particular interest was in vacuum ultraviolet spectroscopy. Unfortunately, Campbell died suddenly in September of 1939. F. W. Paul joined the Institute in 1939 and was then appointed to the position of Assistant Professor of Physical Optics. Paul's special expertise was in the field of infrared spectroscopy. Paul served the Institute very well until 1947.

A very significant appointment was made in 1947 when M. Parker Givens (Ph.D. Cornell) joined the Institute and accepted the important responsibility for physical optics.

He brought a broad point of view to the full range of physical optics knowledge and research problems. The literature contains many significant papers in both research and teaching on such topics as "Phase in the knife-edge diffraction pattern," "Demonstration experiments in optics using a gas laser," and "Production of zone plates by holographic techniques." One of his papers whose title is "curious" is "Comments on a 'Curious Optical Theorem' " (the curious reader can find it in *Am. J. Phys* 30(9), p. 851, 1968). Finally we must record that Parker's dedication to teaching made him one of our great teachers, whose contributions continued well into his retirement years. We are all very proud of the fact that, thanks to the generosity of the Wyant family, we have a chair named for M. Parker Givens. Jim Wyant had received his M.S. (1967) and Ph.D. (1968) from the Institute and is in the midst of his own distinguished career in the academy and in industry.

In the Kingslake history of the Institute they characterized the period 1955–1968 as "The Rise of Modern Optics." Geometrical, physical and quantum optics were all part of that "rise" . . . but in a very important integrated way. Appointments related to physical optics included Philip Baumeister who developed a major program in thin film design and fabrication that has had a lasting impact and still remains one of significant activity in the world of academic and industrial optics. M. V. R. K. Murty also joined the faculty and pursued studies in interferometry with special reference to rotational-shearing interferometry. In related fields extensive work was carried out in laser research in the 1960s notably by M. Hercher, D. Sinclair and J. Forsyth all of whom received their doctoral degrees and subsequently became important faculty members.

1959 was a particularly important year for optics at the University of Rochester. Emil Wolf accepted a faculty appointment. He was already a very distinguished scholar and teacher at Bristol University, Cambridge University, Edinburgh University, and Manchester University. The year he joined the Institute was the same year that the first edition of the text *Principles of Optics* was published. It is usually referred to as "Born & Wolf" (i.e., the authors' names) rather than its actual title. It is currently in its seventh edition and is still a best seller. Emil Wolf brought to the Institute a rigorous theoretical view of electromagnetic fields and their propagation including, of course, coherent and partially coherent fields. As of this writing, he is still very active publishing original works, review articles and books as well as teaching and guiding the research of graduate students.

Interestingly I first met Emil Wolf in 1955 at Manchester University when I was working on my Ph.D. My interests were in diffraction studies in part as they related to optical analogues to x-ray diffraction and the determination of crystal structures. I was very fortunate to have Henry Lipson and Charles Taylor as my mentors. My initial task was to fully characterize the optical diffractometer (a relatively new instrument) and its performance and to solve a number of specific problems of optical and mechanical alignment, focusing, resolution and coherence control (both spatial and temporal). The last item on my list caused me to search out Emil wolf—I could not believe my good fortune in finding that Dr. Wolf was at that time a Research Fellow in the Theoretical Physics Department at Owens College of the University of Manchester (I was in the University of Manchester Institute of Science and Technology). Thus, Emil became my third major mentor leading to our joint work on "Two-beam interference with partially coherent light," a sample of the published experimental results became a two page illustration in *Principle of Optics*. This association led to the preparation of other illustrations for that same book. Wolf has had significant influence on my own experimental studies, including specific coherence control applications, and also the three-dimensional structure of diffraction by plane apertures; circular, annular and rectangular. This in turn led to early work on optical processing and optical Fourier synthesis.

Not much later I caught up with Emil in the United States when I came to work with George Parent (himself a former Ph.D. student of Emil Wolf's) at Technical Operations in the Boston area in 1963. And, of course, we came back together in Rochester when I joined the Institute in 1968.

Emphasis on a strong physical optics program continued since we had gone from the early days of a single professor representing physical optics to a multiple faculty approach with each faculty member having their own special areas of interest as well as interlocking interest with other faulty in the Institute. The application of physical optics concepts also took us into cooperative activities with colleagues in other disciplines (for example, the development of the Laboratory for Laser Energetics [LLE], medical optics including holographic particle sizing, automated cytology, and image processing with colleagues in electrical engineering and the medical school).

Emil Wolf's influence on physical optics has continued over many years as he wrote on such topics as inverse scattering, evanescent waves, radiometric models, focused fields, quantum optics, partial coherence in the space-frequency domain, red shifts and blue shifts (Wolf shift) and many more too numerous to mention here.

As for myself, I was working on holography with particular interests in particle size analysis as applied to a variety of fields, infra-red holography and holographic interferometry; optical processing (including the Knox-Thompson algorithm); apodisation of coherent imaging and beam propagation systems; hybrid processing; two-step phase microscopy; and the Lau effect amongst other topics. I was blessed with great graduate students and wonderful faculty and post-doctoral fellows who also worked on some of these topics and several related fields. Balasubramanian's infectious enthusiasm got both Parker Givens and myself very interested in coherent optics applied to mapping and photogrammetry (a sample of this work is the subject of an early proceedings of *SPIE* 45, 1974—the proceedings of a conference held in Rochester). John Heurtley and George Sherman joined our faculty and put their own particular spin on our physical optics endeavors.

All of the work in the Institute has been recorded in the scholarly literature of the time that documents a productivity of which we are particularly proud. In addition a significant effort was made in our important area of responsibility to teaching and education. This responsibility manifested itself in the quality and quantity of our course offerings within the Institute and those offered "on-the-road." Our one-on-one teaching and guidance of graduate students significantly expanded, starting in the 1960s. Another part of this mission has been in the preparation and publication of books, monographs, tutorial texts, conference proceedings and editorial leadership in scholarly publications. *Principle of Optics*, aka "Born & Wolf," continues to be a major educational resource book almost forty-five years since it first appeared; *Progress in Optics*, edited by Emil Wolf (forty-four volumes and counting), has been of immense value to our optics community. The original *Physical Optics Notebook* that Goerge Parrent and I prepared for *SPIE* was well received and the very much expanded version, *The New Physical Optics Notebook—Tutorials in Fourier Optics*, prepared with the additional help of John DeVelis and George Reynolds, is still in print. As a final example from a long list I would record the *Optical Engineering* book series published by Marcel Dekker under my editorship since 1982—over eighty volumes and counting.

The leadership of our physical optics activity became Nicholas George's responsibility when he became director of the Institute in 1977. Other new people joined the team, including Chris Dainty and John Rogers, whose interest in lens design led him into the world of holographic optical elements. G. Michael Morris came from Caltech as a doctoral student with Nicholas George; Mike Norris has had his own distinguished career in the Institute and now in industry. But this later era is documented elsewhere in this volume.

It is always difficult to mention names in an article like this for fear of offending people either because they were not mentioned or because they were mentioned but not with sufficient accuracy. I hope that the readers and my colleagues will forgive me if I didn't mention them or I misrepresented them. I gave examples as they came to mind, so on a different day at a different time other examples would have come to mind. The above paragraphs are a few of the many vignettes that record the strength of our efforts as a community of faculty, scholars, graduate students, and undergraduates all learning together for the greater good of our discipline.

Brian Thompson, Karen Jacobson, and Tom Stone watch Peter Gough set up an experiment.

Let me end where I began in stressing the importance of physical optics. Carlos Stroud, the editor of this volume, drew my attention to a paper by Brian O'Brien. Carlos wrote, "Brian O'Brien explains the Stiles-Crawford effect first approximately by geometric optics, but then shows that diffraction in the rods and cones in the eye are necessary to understand the details. I thought that was a nice demonstration that physical optics is important in vision." You are, of course, quite right Carlos. Vision has always been an important part of the Institute, which had a significant role to play in founding the Center for Visual Science. We in the Institute were very pleased when David Williams joined the faculty of the University since he brought a very important physical point of view to the field of vision research. Again, on a personal note, I was particularly pleased to contribute in a small way to some of David's research. David now occupies the W. G. Allyn chair in Medical Optics endowed with a gift from the Allyn family and the Welch Allyn company. W. G. Allyn received his B.S. degree from the Institute in optometry in 1934; so the Institute's seventy-fifth anniversary coincides with Bill Allyn's seventieth reunion year. These events are very special to me since the Allyn family are my personal friends as well as friends of the Institute. I have been proud to serve as a director of this privately owned company for many years and will retire from that board at the next annual meeting. A final closing comment brings me full circle. My first teaching assignment as a very young faculty member in the Department of Applied Physics in the University of Manchester's Institute of Science and Technology was to present a course specifically designed for optometry students!

Brian J. Thompson has been a member of the faculty of the University of Rochester since 1968. He served as Director of the Institute of Optics from 1968 until 1975. He is currently Provost Emeritus of the University of Rochester, Rochester, NY.

45. The Fifty-Year Celebration: 1979

Hilda Kingslake

The fiftieth anniversary, celebrated on Monday, October 8, 1979, occurred in a most favorable period in the life of The Institute of Optics. It was now well established and fully occupying its own very fine building on the River Campus. When in 1976 Brian Thompson was appointed Dean of the College of Engineering and Applied Science he had already arranged for the Fifty-Year History to be prepared in time for the Jubilee Celebration in 1979. Nicholas George, who succeeded him as Director in 1977, continued the advance planning for the anniversary. Further, the Optical Society of America had planned that the Society hold its 1979 Annual Meeting in Rochester in recognition of the fiftieth year of The Institute of Optics, with Nicholas George appointed chairman of the local arrangements committee. Finally, the University granted the Institute the use of the Hartnett Gallery in Wilson Commons for the month of October, thereby ensuring that the whole River Campus shared in the anniversary celebration. The appointed day of celebration, Monday, October 8, had been planned immediately to precede the meeting of the Optical Society.

The Hartnett Gallery. The Hartnett Gallery exhibit was entitled "Fifty Years of Optics in Rochester" and was designed to attract the attention and interest of the learned and unlearned, the young and the old on the River Campus, as well as visiting alumni of The Institute of Optics. Rare books and small exhibits occupied a few glass cases, photographs and portraits and scientific pictures covered the walls, and there were two pieces of standing apparatus, the Munsell "color tree" and a fine hologram which attracted great attention. Conger W. Gabel, a member of the faculty at the time, undertook the arduous job of collecting and setting up the exhibit.

Open House at The Institute of Optics. Formal activities on Anniversary Day began with Open House all afternoon at the Institute's new home on the River Campus. Faculty

Faculty of the Institute of Optics, Fall 1979 celebrating the 50th anniversary.

members were At Home in their offices, with graduate students and research associates in the laboratories to explain the work in hand. Informal tours were given hourly throughout the afternoon. Tours were also arranged to the Laboratory for Laser Energetics.

Alumni Dinner. The Alumni dinner on October 8 was a remarkable witness to the strength of The Institute of Optics and the loyalty of its alumni and supporters. A cocktail hour in the May Room of Wilson Commons preceded the dinner in the Frederick Douglass student dining hall. Well over 500 were present, including alumni, past and present faculty, present students, and friends from civic life and industry. The University President Robert Sproull was in the chair and addressed the meeting in his usual clear and direct style. Dean Brian Thompson also spoke and messages were read from a number of absent friends. Unfortunately, Brian O'Brien, the first Director, was unable to be present but was represented by his son (class of 1944) who was invited to say a few words.

Fifty-Year History of The Institute of Optics, 1929–1979. Elegant copies of the history, written by Hilda G. Kingslake, were passed out as everyone left the dining hall.

The 1979 Meeting of the Optical Society of America. Students and faculty of The Institute of Optics presented no less than 30 papers at the meeting. A luncheon which filled the large hall of the Chamber of Commerce in recognition of the Jubilee Celebration, was planned by the local committee of the Optical Society.

The Institute of Optics
Faculty 1970–1979

Ahrenkiel, Richard K., 1973–77
Altman, Joseph H., 1969–98
Balasubramanian, N., 1973–75
Baumeister, Philip W., 1959–79
Boyd, Robert W., 1977–
Boynton, Robert M., 1955–72
Brody, Edward M., 1970–81
Brown, John L., 1975–78
Creuzberg, Martin, 1967–71
Dainty, John Christopher, 1979–85
Dutton, David B., 1954–63, 1975–78
Eastman, Jay M., 1979–98
Eberly, Joseph H., 1979–
Forsyth, James M., 1969–85
Gabel, Conger W., 1975–88
Garbuny, Max, 1969–70
George, Nicholas, 1978–
Givens, M. Parker, 1948–
Gold, Albert, 1962–70
Gough, Peter T., 1975–77
Hamilton, John F., 1969–88
Hercher, Michael M., 1965–75
Heurtley, John C., 1968–74

Hopkins, Robert E., 1943–
Kay, David B., 1975–78
Kingslake, Rudolf, 1929–2003
Lubin, Moshe J., 1971–81
MacAdam, David L., 1977–96
Mandel, Leonard, 1978–2000
Moore, Duncan T., 1974–
Mourou, Gerard, 1979–94
Peskin, James C., 1959–77
Raymer, Michael G., 1979–94
Sands, Peter J., 1967–70
Santamaria, Javier, 1975–77
Sceats, Mark G., 1977–81
Sherman, George C., 1970–77
Sinclair, Douglas C., 1965–67, 1970–80
Snaveley, Benjamin B., 1970–73
Spitalnik, Steven, 1979–81
Stroud, Jr., Carlos R., 1969–
Teegarden, Kenneth J., 1955–
Thompson, Brian J., 1968–
Uydess, Ian L., 1977–78
Wolf, Emil, 1978–
Yonezawa, Seiji, 1968–70

The Institute of Optics Degrees Awarded 1970–1979

Acchione, Lawrence J., M.S., 1971
Adamo, Daniel R., B.S., 1975
Agostinelli, John A., M.S., 1977; Ph.D., 1981
Allgeier, M. E., B.S., 1972
Altebrando, Joseph M., B.S., 1979
Altfather, K. W, M.S., 1979
Aquilina, Thomas J., M.S., 1977
Arecchi, Arcangelo V., M.S., 1972
Argaman, Ephraim, M.S., 1974
Armstrong, Scott A., Ph.D., 1978
Armstrong, Thomas M., B.S., 1975; M.S., 1978
Arnold, Bruce Y., M.S., 1974
Arnon, Oded, Ph.D., 1979
Aviado, Carlos G., B.S., 1979
Bader, Todd R., Ph.D., 1970
Baer, James W., M.S., 1978
Bates, Robert, M.S., 1971
Baum, Richard C., M.S., 1973
Baxter, Jerome R., B.S., 1973
Becherer, Richard J., Ph.D., 1972
Becker, Mary E. L., M.S., 1972; Ph.D., 1977
Bennett, Brian E., B.S., 1979
Bennett, Victor P., Ph.D., 1974
Bhullar, Pushpinder S., M.S., 1971
Bloomquist, William M., M.S., 1970
Blum, James D., B.S., 1974
Bohache, James J., Ph.D., 1979
Boles, John A., M.S., 1976
Boreman, Glenn D., B.S., 1978
Bourke, Peter W., B.S., 1977
Bragg, Edward B., B.S., 1978
Brandkamp, Warren F., M.S., 1973
Breidenthal, Robert S., B.S., 1971; M.S., 1973
Brown, Matthew, B.S., 1979
Buran, James M., B.S., 1970; M.S., 1973
Burckel, William P., Ph.D., 1974

Burner, Alpheus W., M.S., 1976
Byrd, Ronald E., M.S., 1972
Cameron, Bruce, M.S., 1975
Carniglia, Charles K., Ph.D., 1971
Carollo, Jerome T., M.S., 1976
Castrovinci, Cynthia D. (née Barnes), B.S., 1970
Chadwick, David P., M.S., 1975
Chamberlain, K. T., B.S., 1977
Chan, Francis, B.S., 1979
Chan, Richard, B.S., 1979
Chan, Y. E., M.S., 1977
Chao, Shui L., Ph.D., 1974
Chen, Gih-Horng, M.S., 1974; Ph.D., 1977
Chou, Chien, M.S., 1976
Christo, Douglas J., B.S., 1971
Citron, Mary E. L., M.S., 1972; Ph.D., 1977
Clark, Peter P., B.S., 1971
Coblitz, David B., M.S., 1972
Coult, David G., B.S., 1974
Crichton, John F., M.S., 1971
Critchlow, James A., M.S., 1976
Cuneo, Peter J., M.S., 1976
Davis, John S., M.S., 1973
DeBell, Gary W., M.S., 1970; Ph.D., 1972
Deever, Walter T., M.S., 1974
DeMeijere, Jacob L. F., Ph.D., 1978
DeSmitt, Steven, B.S., 1979
Devaney, Anthony J., Ph.D., 1971
Dey, Thomas W., M.S., 1977
Dil, Jan G., M.S., 1974; Ph.D., 1976
Doherty, V. J., M.S., 1977
Domey, Jacques, M.S., 1972
Donahue, J. Michael, Ph.D., 1970
Donenfeld, Nathan M, M.S., 1979
Doran, Robert E., M.S., 1972
Doty, James L., M.S., 1973
Durbin, John A., M.S., 1972

Dymale, Raymond C., M.S., 1975

Dyn, Mordchai, M.S., 1972

Eastman, Jay M., B.S., 1970; Ph.D., 1974

Edwards, Jr., Oliver J., M.S., 1972

Ehrlich, Daniel J., Ph.D., 1978

Failor, Douglas L., B.S., 1978

Fantone, Stephen D., Ph.D., 1979

Federico, Richard, B.S., 1979

Fehniger, Michael J., M.S., 1971

Fernald, Mark R., M.S., 1976

Flint, Douglas B., B.S., 1973; M.S., 1975

Flores, Ricardo, M.S., 1977

Florkowski, Alan S., B.S., 1976

Fouére, Jean-Claude., M.S., 1973

Freese, Robert P., M.S., 1978; Ph.D., 1980

Frosino, Robert J., B.S., 1971

Fuller, Joseph B. C., M.S., 1970

Gabel, Conger W., Ph.D., 1975

Gallagher, John E., Ph.D., 1970

Gasper, John, M.S., 1972

Gaumer, William B., M.S., 1976

Gaynor, Edwin S., B.S., 1979

Gerchman, Mark C., M.S., 1978

Ghilai, Shay, M.S., 1975

Ginn, Dana A., M.S., 1972

Gino, Joseph D., M.S., 1976

Glassman, Ann T., M.S., 1972

Goldmunz, Michel, B.S., 1978; M.S., 1979

Golnik, Gary, M.S., 1976

Gontard, Denys G., M.S., 1976

Goosey, Jr., William T., B.S., 1973; M.S., 1975

Granger, Edward M., B.S., 1957; M.S., 1969; Ph.D., 1975

Gray, Howard R., Ph.D., 1978

Greener, William J., M.S., 1976

Greenfield, Martin I., B.S., 1974; M.S., 1975; Ph.D., 1979

Greenwald, Roger, M.S., 1975

Gregorka, Lisa, B.S., 1976; M.S., 1978

Greninger, Charles E., Ph.D., 1972

Gruber, Leonard S., M.S., 1971

Gur, Joshua, Ph.D., 1979

Gwyn, Rodney T., M.S., 1972

Hamaguchi, Roy I., M.S., 1971

Hansen, George K., M.S., 1974

Harding, Kevin G., M.S., 1978

Hardy, James, Ph.D., 1979

Harrison, Douglas H., M.S., 1969; Ph.D., 1974

Hatch, Marcus R., B.S., 1972; M.S., 1973

Hauer, Allan, Ph.D., 1977

Hayford, Michael J., B.S., 1978; M.S., 1979

Hearn, Gregory, B.S., 1972

Hecht, Avron, M.S., 1975

Heiney, Allan J., B.S., 1978; M.S., 1981

Herloski, Robert P., B.S., 1978

Ho, Pin-Chin, M.S., 1971

Hochberg, Eric, B.S., 1976

Hoose, John F, M.S., 1979

Horwitz, Bruce A., Ph.D., 1976

Horwitz, J. (née Berman), B.S., 1975

Horwitz, L., M.S., 1975

Howard, James W., B.S., 1978

Howe, Dennis G., M.S., 1968; Ph.D., 1976

Hrycin, Anna L., B.S., 1979; M.S., 1985

Hughett, L. C., B.S., 1978

Husson, Chris J., M.S., 1970

Irving, Bruce, M.S., 1978

Isenberg, John F., M.S., 1978

Jacobs, Richard D., B.S., 1977; M.S., 1979

Jacobs, Stephen D., B.S., 1970; Ph.D., 1976

Jacobsen, Karen D., B.S., 1979; M.S., 1980

Jain, Anil K., Ph.D., 1973

Janeczko, Donald J., M.S., 1972

Jensen, Arthur E., M.S., 1971

Johnson, R. Barry, M.S., 1972

Jones, Peter A., M.S., 1977

Jordan, David C., M.S., 1978

Kafka, James D., B.S., 1977; Ph.D., 1984

Kahn, Cynthia, B.S., 1979

Kamga, FranGois M., M.S., 1976; Ph.D., 1980

Kay, David B., M.S., 1973; Ph.D., 1976

Kelly, John H., M.S., 1976; Ph.D., 1980

Kienholz, Donald F., M.S., 1970

Kimmel, Ronald K., M.S., 1970

Kingsland, David O., M.S., 1971

Knowlton, Robert C., M.S., 1971

Knox, Keith T., Ph.D., 1975

Knox, Wayne H., B.S., 1979; Ph.D., 1984

Koliopoulos, Chris L., B.S., 1974

Konigsmann, Kay C., M.S., 1973

Kostuk, Raymond, M.S., 1977

Kramer, Charles J., M.S., 1972; Ph.D., 1976

Krisl, Eric, Ph.D., 1979

Kumpan, Steven A., B.S., 1971; M.S., 1973

Larkin, Eric W., B.S., 1978

Lebel, C. F., B.S., 1979

Lee, Danny D. Y., M.S., 1973

Lee, John W. Y., M.S., 1974

Lees, David E. B., M.S., 1974; Ph.D., 1979

Lefkowitz, Lester, M.S., 1972

Lehman, Richard F., M.S., 1971

Leiner, Dennis C., B.S., 1975; M.S., 1977

Lettieri, Thomas R., M.S., 1976; Ph.D., 1978

Leung, Thomas C. Y., M.S., 1976

Levin, J. P., M.S., 1974

Lichtenstein, Terri L., B.S., 1979; M.S., 1980

Litynski, Daniel M., M.S., 1971

Maier, Dennis A., M.S., 1971

Malacara, Z., M.S., 1978

Mannello, Richard, B.S., 1979

Markman, Howard P., M.S., 1972

Martin, William C., M.S., 1972

McDonnell, Micheal M., M.S., 1976

McGuire, Stephen C., M.S., 1973

McHugh, Thomas J., B.S., 1974

McKay, Kenneth, B.S., 1979

McLaughlin, Paul O., M.S., 1978; Ph.D., 1983

McVernon, William H., M.S., 1973

Meyzonnette, Jean L., M.S., 1972; Ph.D., 1975

Miller, Bruce E., B.S., 1979; M.S., 1980

Mimmack, William E., Ph.D., 1973

Montgomery, Edward A., M.S., 1970

Moore, Charles E., M.S., 1978

Moore, Duncan T., M.S., 1970; Ph.D., 1974

Moore, Robert C., M.S., 1972

Moorhusen, Robert W., M.S., 1970

Mounts, Darryl I., B.S., 1979; M.S., 1981

Mrdjen, Peter, M.S., 1972

Mullis, Ronald D., B.S., 1974

Murphy, Jr., Robert J., M.S., 1978

Murray, Richard P., M.S., 1978

Najmi, Ashar, B.S., 1977

Nebolsine, Peter E., Ph.D., 1972

Nelson, Roy D., M.S., 1976

Neumann, Gadi, Ph.D., 1970

Neves, Fernando B., M.S., 1977

Nir, Shlomo, M.S., 1978

Nyyssonen, Diana, Ph.D., 1975

O'Neil, Burton D., M.S., 1971

O'Neill, Leo J., M.S., 1972

Oinen, Donald E., M.S., 1970

Oren, Igal, M.S., 1972

Oron, Moshe, Ph.D., 1976

Osada, Hidenori, M.S., 1975

Osborn, Leroy N., B.S., 1974

Oughstun, Kurt E., M.S., 1974; Ph.D., 1979

Parker, Harry L, M.S., 1979

Patel, Vinod N., M.S., 1973

Pfisterer, Richard, B.S., 1979

Pike, Charles D., M.S., 1976

Pike, Harold A., Ph.D., 1972

Popelka, S. R. (née Huberty), M.S., 1977

Powers, Thomas F., B.S., 1977; M.S., 1983

Pritts, James E., B.S., 1971

Purcell, Robert E., B.S., 1974

Ramon, Shmuel J., M.S., 1972

Raymondo, Philip J., M.S., 1973

Rea, Everett J., B.S., 1977

Redderson, Brad R., M.S., 1974

Remijan, Paul W., Ph.D., 1979

Renaud, Blaise, M.S., 1972; Ph.D., 1977

Rifelli, Richard E., B.S., 1974; M.S., 1977

Rinehart, Thomas A., M.S., 1976; Ph.D., 1982

Roseman, Steven A., B.S., 1979

Rosenbluth, Alan E., B.S., 1976; Ph.D., 1983

Rosenstein, J. E., B.S., 1974

Rothschild, Mordekhay, Ph.D., 1979

Royall, William E., B.S., 1974

Roychoudhuri, Chand, Ph.D., 1974

Ruda, Mitchell C., M.S., 1973

Ryan-Howard, Danette P., B.S., 1977; M.S., 1980; Ph.D., 1983

Saccketti, Nicholas B., B.S., 1977

Salvage, Robert T., M.S., 1979
Samuels, Stephen J., B.S., 1974
Sanchez, Joseph, B.S., 1978
Sangmeister, Karen M., B.S., 1976
Satchithananda, Kumar, B.S., 1979
Sauer, Carolyn L., M.S., 1976
Schuda, Felix J., Ph.D., 1974
Seachman, Ned J., M.S., 1973
Seppala, Lynn G., Ph.D., 1974
Shih, I-Fu., M.S., 1977
Shuman, Arnold D., M.S., 1971
Sicard, Dominique M., M.S., 1977
Simbal, John J, M.S., 1979
Simon, R. J., M.S., 1976
Skeps, Micheal J., M.S., 1970
Slaymaker, Philip A., Ph.D., 1979
Smartt, Raymond N., M.S., 1971
Smith, David C., B.S., 1977; M.S., 1978
Snyder, Michael A., M.S., 1975
Sommargren, Gary E., Ph.D., 1972
Spencer, Harvey M., B.S., 1974
Sprague, Robert A., B.S., 1967; Ph.D., 1971
Stamnes, Jakob J., Ph.D., 1975
Stansbury, Frederick C., B.S., 1971
Stark, Gregory L., M.S., 1975
Stark, Richard A., M.S., 1970
Stenton, William C., M.S., 1970
Stoltzman, David E., M.S., 1972
Stone, Thomas W., B.S., 1979; M.S., 1983; Ph.D., 1986
Straw, Kimball, B.S., 1969; M.S., 1973
Stulak, John J., M.S., 1978
Sudol, Ronald J., M.S., 1977; Ph.D., 1982
Swain, David M., M.S., 1974
Swyler, K. Joseph, Ph.D., 1973
Synborski, Charles E., M.S., 1978
Taskett, John, B.S., 1979
Taychert, E. L., B.S., 1979

Tietz, George E., M.S., 1974
Trainer, Michael N., M.S., 1977
Truax, Bruce E., B.S., 1977; M.S., 1978
Tyler, Glen A., M.S., 1974; Ph.D., 1978
Ufford, Curtis J., M.S., 1972
Vaklyes, David W, M.S., 1979
Van Kerkhove, Alan, M.S., 1971
Vandenberg, D., B.S., 1978
Vasanthakumar, Gurram R., M.S., 1972
Venable, Dennis L., B.S., 1978; M.S., 1981; Ph.D., 1989
Volkmer, James L., M.S., 1976
Volonino, Louis, B.S., 1979
Waido, Richard P., M.S., 1973
Waldman, Mark, M.S., 1978
Wall, Stephen D., M.S., 1972
Wallace, Nelson W., M.S., 1977
Walsh, Kenneth F., B.S., 1971
Walsh, Richard J., M.S., 1970
Warren, David W., M.S., 1977
Weber, William L., B.S., 1978
Weibezahl, Thomas, B.S., 1979
Wertheimer, Alan L., B.S., 1968; Ph.D., 1974
Wessel, Jeffrey W., B.S., 1973
Westcott, Mark R., B.S., 1970
White, James R., M.S., 1973
White, Warren T., M.S., 1972
Whitfield, Charles H., B.S., 1975; M.S., 1976
Williams, Kenneth E., M.S., 1973
Willis, Theodore C., M.S., 1978
Woody, Loren M., B.S., 1975
Yang, Jessie H., M.S., 1972
Yau, David W. T., M.S., 1972
Zawacki, David T., M.S., 1974
Zino, Joseph D., B.S., 1974; M.S., 1977
Zyra, Wayne E., M.S., 1971

PART VI

EXPANSION: THE 1980S

VI. Expansion: The 1980s

The stage was set for a rapid expansion of the research and education programs of the Institute in the 1980s. The new building as well as the explosion of applications of laser optics into all sorts of new industries—medicine, telecommunications, manufacturing, inspection, defense, and even super-market checkout—gave rise to increased expectations, and increased accomplishment. The number of students, both undergraduate and graduate, rose quickly. The quality of the credentials of entering graduate students caused the faculty to often comment that it was a good thing that they already had their degrees because they could never get into the program as students now. A number of different research centers were established that greatly increased funding for equipment and student support.

In this section we have essays that describe this growth through the directorships of Kenneth Teegarden and Duncan Moore. We have an essay by Gerard Mourou describing the history of his ultra-fast laser group. It is an interesting story of the synergy between a research program at the Laboratory for Laser Energetics and the educational program in the Institute. This story is told from another viewpoint by Wayne Knox, who describes his experiences in the Institute as a student working in Mourou's group and in returning almost twenty years later as director of the Institute. Nicholas George tells us about education and research in the area of physical optics, and he also reviews the development of large research centers from the 1980s to the present. Finally, we really get a chance to explore student life through a series of short anecdotes, and by Susan Houde-Walter's description of a workshop that she helped organize as a graduate student on "Having It All," a familiar theme for women in the 1980s.

46. The Teegarden Years: 1981–1987

Hilda Kingslake

Kenneth Teegarden, associated with the University since 1954, was appointed Professor of Optics in 1966. He succeeded Nicholas George as Director in 1981. His own field is materials science. He and his research students were certainly the first members of The Institute of Optics to inhabit the Space Science Center, now the Wilmot Building.

Teegarden succeeded to an Institute of Optics bursting at the seams with students and activity. By 1986 there were 13 full-time professors, 3 professors emeritus, 6 part-time appointments, and 4 joint appointments from physics and the Laboratory for Laser Energetics, coping with 340 undergraduates and 140 graduate students. In 1975 the Institute awarded 6 B.S. degrees; this number grew to 67 by 1986. In the same year 37 M.S. degrees and 10 Ph.D.s were awarded. The demand for optical scientists and engineers is still growing.

In recent years the field of optics has undergone rapid expansion in consequence of advances in lasers and integrated circuits. It is expected that in the next decade further achievements will be made in the application of fibers to communication, high-power lasers to energy, and hybrid opto-electronics to industrial process control. Teegarden and Nicholas George believe that The Institute of Optics provides a unique environment for physicists and engineers to conduct research into almost any phase of optics, especially since Rochester has the Medical Center, the Laboratory for Laser Energetics, and the departments of physics and chemistry, all of which are conducting interdisciplinary programs for research.

During the past decade emphasis has been placed on strengthening the educational programs for undergraduates. The Institute has always tried to provide hands-on experience with modern equipment and techniques, especially important for students entering industry. Therefore teaching laboratories, though difficult to provide for large numbers of students, are nevertheless a continuing goal. In 1984 the teaching laboratories were greatly expanded and relocated on the fourth floor of Dewey Hall. Funding for equipment is receiving great attention. An effort is also being made to improve the laboratory facilities for M.S. students.

Kenneth J. Teegarden, Director.

Teegarden is much concerned that The Institute of Optics back up recruiting young faculty with adequate resources for their own work. He stated that, "Because of its current eminence, the Institute is capable of acquiring the funding necessary to apply these resources. The recent establishment of the New York State Center for Advanced Optical Technology, with an annual budget of two million dollars, is an example of the way in which these resources can be acquired."

In 1986, Professor Teegarden returned to full-time teaching and research.

47. Graduate Student Life: Playing Hard

Students of the 1980s

Much of the reason that many of the alumni of the Institute remember their student years with fond nostalgia has nothing to do with their classroom experiences, or even the long hours in the laboratory. Typically optics students work hard and play hard, and there has probably never been a group in the history of the Institute that better excelled at both aspects of life than those who were graduate students in the Institute during the 1970s and 1980s. Many have gone on to distinguished careers, some as faculty, others as founders of companies, presidents of the Optical Society of America as well as other professional societies, one even as an advisor to the president of the United States.

Among the essays in this section we have a series of anecdotes and vignettes concerning the "playing hard" part of their lives. A lot of the play was centered around a house on a little side street off Mt. Hope Avenue near St. Anne's Church. The address of the house is known to all students of the era—21 Brighton Park. Optics graduate students rented this house for about thirty years during the period from about 1971 to 2003, beginning with Jay Eastman and continuing with only a brief hiatus through Jason Porter and Mike Melocchi. The house was the scene of innumerable parties and the beginnings of many traditions—and happy marriages.

Many of the events took place in more remote locations: the shores of Lake Ontario, the glens of the Finger Lakes, the mountains of the Adirondacks, and rock faces of the Niagara Escarpment. Some were taken very seriously by the participants: wine making, beer brewing, and listening to jazz. Present-day standards of political correctness are an anachronism when applied to this era, just as today's standards will raise eyebrows in twenty years time.

Graduate Student Life: Vacuum God

George Harvey

The vacuum god lived in the basement of the Bausch & Lomb building. With pipes ascending to all floors, the vacuum god had a voracious appetite. To appease the god, the graduate students made regular sacrifices in a long-honored tradition. The high priest of optics presented the god with a full roll of toilet paper conveniently obtained from the nearest men's room. The priest's assistant opened the pipe while the priest placed a broom handle through the middle of the roll. Within 30 seconds, the almighty god of vacuum would consume the entire roll, its contents snaking their way through the intricate network of pipes into the bowels of the beast. If times were particularly trying, two or more rolls were sacrificed.

George Harvey received his Ph.D. from the Institute of Optics in 1981. He is currently employed at Tycom (US) Ltd., Eatontown, NJ.

48. Physical Optics, Electromagnetic Theory, and Systems

Nicholas George

For the decades of the 1980s and 1990s The Institute of Optics has continued with its long-term commitment to educate the leaders in the field. Today still, "Optics is a science that greatly enriches other areas of science and technology. Also, optics is a field with far-ranging appeal. Whether students aspire to become theoreticians, experimentalists, engineering scientists or design engineers, the field of optics is broad enough to provide a challenging career and a rewarding profession."[1]

In this section we describe the trends in physical optics and closely related subject areas since 1980. First let us mention that the distinguished faculty of the past has been augmented by an impressive group of new appointees (described below). The excellence of the undergraduate and graduate student body continues as well, with that traditional balance in numbers of graduate and undergraduates that typifies the great research universities. The physical facilities house magnificent laboratories in the Wilmot Building now crowded with people and equipment. Capital equipment expenditures over the past twenty years have exceeded $15 million.

Undergraduate Program in Physical Optics and Related Subjects

Since most students have a relatively limited knowledge of optics when they arrive at the Institute, we offer Optics 101, Optics in the Information Age (Wayne Knox, director). This course has many demonstration lectures and it provides the student with an excellent overview of the entire field, giving one career guidance as well as establishing some enthusiasm and excitement about the future.

Optics 261, Interference and Diffraction (James Fienup), and Optics 262, Electromagnetic Theory (Andrew Berger), are the undergraduate core courses now being taught by a relatively new generation of faculty, together with a modern computing course, Optics 211, Computational Methods in Optics (Thomas G. Brown), taught by the chair of the undergraduate committee who regularly lectures both physical and geometrical optics courses.

Another course for undergraduates that provides major portions of physical and Fourier optics is Optics 242, Aberrations and Interferometry (James Zavislan). This famous old course now includes substantial material on coherence theory as well as computer modeling based on the material in Optics 211. Similarly, Optics 246, Optical Interference Coating (James Oliver), has major components of physical optics. The Optics 256

Laboratory which is housed in the fourth floor of Dewey underwent a major modification in the early 1980s, presided over by G. Michael Morris, M. Parker Givens, and K. J. Teegarden. This laboratory has provided hands-on experience for graduate and undergraduate students for many years. Currently taught by Givens and Teegarden, it is a truly splendid course offering, slated for major funding as it is transitioned into new quarters in the Wilmot Building (2005).

Graduate Program in Physical Optics, Electromagnetic Theory and Systems

Graduate education is strongly emphasized at The Institute of Optics and the strength of this educational program derives from the core courses in the fundamentals and the leading research programs of the faculty. For physical optics and closely related topics, the graduate courses are listed in table 1 together with a listing of faculty who have taught these courses in recent years. The current lecturer is listed first, followed by other recent lecturers. These courses are relatively advanced since our own undergraduates and the new entering graduate students are typically highly qualified. Optics 461 and 462 are the required core courses in physical optics, covering the principles of radiation and propagation based on electromagnetic theory. The treatment includes Fourier optics, information processing, imaging, interference and diffraction, and the elements of statistical optics. Also covered are electromagnetic theory at a rigorous level so important today in fields such as near-field optics and diffractive optics. Additionally, doctoral students are also encouraged to take coursework related to their specialized career interests that are being offered in other departments, typically physics, electrical and computer engineering, mathematics, computer science or chemistry.

J. Christopher Dainty, 1980.

J. Christopher Dainty, Dennis Hall, and G. M. Morris each progressed from junior faculty positions to full professor, making significant contributions in the teaching programs and in leading edge research as well. J. C. Dainty is now enjoying international success first as a chaired professor at Imperial College and more recently as Science Foundation Ireland Fellow, National University of Ireland. Dennis Hall rose to the directorship (1993–2000) and now is the vice-provost for research at Vanderbilt University. G. Michael Morris rose to full professor and also served as OSA president 2003–4. For the past few years he has been an important entrepreneurial figure in Rochester; and currently he is president of two startup corporations, Apollo Corp. (eye implant lenses) and Rochester Photonics Corp. (diffractive optics and display screens).

Table 1. Physical Optics and Electromagnetic Theory (Graduate)

No.	Course Title	Faculty
461	Physical Optics	James Fienup, Nicholas George
462	Physical Optics II	Nicholas George, L. Novotny, S. Houde-Walter
425	Radiation and Detectors	Gary Wicks, Robert W. Boyd
428	Optical Communication Systems	G. P. Agrawal
442	Geometrical and Instrumental Optics	Thomas G. Brown
452	Medical Imaging	Kevin J. Parker
467	Nonlinear Optics	Robert W. Boyd
469	Diffractive Optics	G. Michael Morris
492	Medical Optics	A. J. Berger
528	Advanced Topics in Telecommunication	G. P. Agrawal
561	Advanced Physical Optics	Emil Wolf
563	Statistical Optics	Emil Wolf
564	Electronic Imaging Systems	Nicholas George
592	Nano-optics	Lukas Novotny

Recently James Fienup joined the faculty as the first R. E. Hopkins Chair Professor of Optics. As a student of Joseph Goodman at Stanford and a scientist of international stature for 27 years at ERIM, he is teaching Optics 461, Fourier Optics, and building a major research program in the fields of phase retrieval and imaging science. Nicholas George, Wilson Professor of Electronic Imaging, is now lecturing Optics 462 as well as Optics 564, an advanced course with a definite systems orientation. The graduate students study topics in diffraction theory and signal processing as they apply to systems for imaging, remote sensing, machine vision, and object recognition. Also, he has an impressive research group of nine doctoral scholars studying emerging electronic imaging systems. Four will graduate this academic year in May 2004.

While complete faculty lists are contained elsewhere in this history, we would like to highlight the five recent faculty appointments that are broadly in physical optics. These recent faculty additions will be major contributors in continuing the seventy-five-year tradition of excellence in teaching and research in physical optics.

James R. Fienup: Robert E. Hopkins Professor of Optics; Ph.D., Stanford University, 1975. He performed research for twenty-seven years at the Environmental Research Institute of Michigan and Veridian Systems, where he was a senior scientist. He joined the faculty at the University of Rochester in 2002. Professor Fienup's research interests center around imaging science. His work includes unconventional imaging, phase retrieval, wavefront sensing, and image reconstruction and restoration. These techniques are applied to passive and active optical imaging systems, synthetic aperture radar, and biomedical imaging modalities. His past work has also included diffractive optics and image quality assessment. He has over 110 publications and three patents and was the editor-in-chief of the *Journal of the Optical Society of America A* (1998–2003).

Lukas Novotny: associate professor of optics; Ph.D., Federal Institute of Technology (ETH), 1996. His general research interest is focused on optics on the nanometer scale. He is interested in exploring ways to surpass the diffraction limit of classical optics and in studying the interaction of nanometric systems such as quantum dots or biological proteins with the optical near-field. Of special interest is the combination of near-field optics and nonlinear spectroscopy.

James M. Zavislan: associate professor of optics; Ph.D., The Institute of Optics, University of Rochester, 1988. His teaching interests are in the area of optical system analysis and optical engineering. In 2004 he began teaching the spring semester senior optical laboratory course with Professor Teegarden. His research interests are in developing optical instruments for clinical medical applications. His current projects include the application of confocal and coherence optical imaging toward real-time pathology assessment of in-vivo and ex-vivo tissues for clinical screening and surgical margin assessment. Specific applications include skin cancer screening and breast cancer surgery. He is also an associate professor of dermatology, University of Rochester School of Medicine and Dentistry. He also serves as director of Center for Institute Ventures, a program to provide technology assessment and research services to the venture capital community. He is an inventor or co-inventor of thirty-seven U.S. patents, an author or co-author of twenty papers, and co-editor of a book.

Miguel A. Alonso: assistant professor of optics; Ph.D., The Institute of Optics, University of Rochester, 1996. His general research interest is in finding better ways to model the propagation of waves. In particular, he is interested in the connection between rays and waves, and how to build accurate estimates of wave fields propagating through arbitrary systems, based on ray information alone. Another aspect of his work relates to the theory of partial coherence, and the description of partially coherent wave fields in radiometric terms. Finally, he is interested in generalizations of mathematical tools and concepts relevant to wave propagation, like integral transforms, phase space representations, and uncertainty relations.

Andrew J. Berger: assistant professor of optics; Ph.D., MIT, 1998. His area of interest is medical optics, specifically spectroscopic diagnostic techniques. With recent advances in optical technology, it is now possible to perform sensitive chemical tests on samples (and live subjects) using light rather than reagents or electrodes. The group's present research is centered upon Raman spectroscopy. As offshoots of this basic thrust, other interests include exploring fundamental aspects of light scattering and diffusion in turbid (e.g., biological) media, and developing novel spectroscopic techniques, through both instrumentation and analytical modeling, that extend the range of biomedical phenomena which can be studied using light. The proximity of The Institute of Optics to the medical center offers opportunities for closes interaction with clinical collaborators and patients. Professor Berger also holds a secondary appointment in the Department of Biomedical Engineering.

Trends in Physical Optics Teaching and Research

Since World War II there have been major changes in the material that is taught in physical optics. We would like to make the case that this level of change will continue into the foreseeable future. The reason for this is that research progress in this field is continuing at an unprecedented pace; and when major research findings occur, these necessitate changes in teaching.

To illustrate this one can consider some of the highlights in our field in the fifty-five years since World War II. The work of Dennis Gabor on holography was stimulated by his wartime experiences with radar, microwave physics, and heterodyne mixing. There were also, of course, the major achievements of the laser, the transistor, and the integrated circuit. The work on holography by Gabor and Leith as well as the optical matched filter of A. Vander Lugt were early advances that depended heavily on ideas from communication theory and linear systems theory. The work on synthetic aperture radar, particularly the optical processing by Leith and co-workers, also stimulated important changes in the subject material taught in optics. To illustrate how research changes teaching, one needs only to compare the excellent textbooks by Jenkins and White (1937) with Goodman (1996, 1968) or Papoulis (1968). An analogous discussion can also be made for the pioneering research in the field of statistical optics from van Cittert, F. Zernike, André Maréchal, H. H. Hopkins, L. Mandel, Emil Wolf and many others to the present time. In this case the modern textbooks by Mandel and Wolf (1995) and Goodman's *Statistical Optics* (1985) illustrate the new wave.

For a glimpse or a suggestion of what is coming in the teaching of physical optics, it may be stimulating to look at three separate recent research results by our faculty. These illustrative examples follow in the next three sections.

Integrated Imaging and Computing Systems: Nicholas George

In electronic imaging an integrated consideration of image acquisition and image processing is leading to important new devices—systems that see and think. This notion has been helpful in greatly extending the depth of field (EDF) in imaging systems. W. T. Cathey and E. R. Dowski (1995) reported a new lens type which they called the cubic phase mask for accomplishing EDF. At The Institute of Optics a doctoral student, Wanli Chi, and Nicholas George reported on a different lens type that they call logarithmic aspheres. In brief their imaging lens consists of a symmetric asphere with a radially varying focal length. This lens purposefully blurs the image so that the impulse response has an almost constant shape over a wide range of distances. At any object distance within the design range, there is always a circular annulus that contributes to sharp imaging; and the remainder of the lens causes blur. The digital processing in this application is basically a deconvolution operation. Excellent deconvolution results are obtained using a maximum-entropy algorithm. Let us consider what about this research is novel or not commonly learned in coursework. First is a Fourier optics analysis that is valid in the non-paraxial regime. Second is the iterative digital image processing that utilizes a convergence factor in order to obtain excellent convergence and speed.

While the details are not of great interest here, an interesting finding is that one can obtain (near) diffraction-limited resolution over a distance that is ten times that for a conventional lens. Illustrated in the figure on the following page are images of a two-point object with a separation of 2.57 microns, the diffraction limited resolution distance for a 60 mm lens with an aperture size of 16 mm and the corresponding digitally deblurred image using the maximum entropy algorithm. (a) is the diffraction limited image with an ideal lens

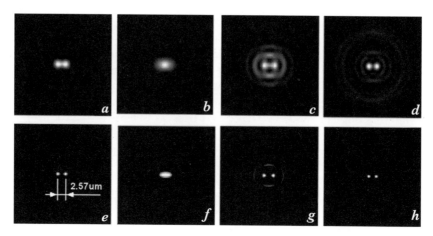

Computer simulations of the resolution of a two-point object separated by the diffraction limit. (a) Blurred image by an idealized lens for the object at 1500 mm; (b), (c), and (d) blurred image by the logarithmic asphere for object at distances 1450 mm, 1500 mm, and 1580 mm, respectively; (e), (f), (g), (h) maximum entropy recovery of images in (a), (b), (c), and (d), respectively.[2]

when the object is at 1500 mm; (b), (c), (d) are the blurred images with the logarithmic asphere when the object is at distances of 1450 mm, 1500 mm, and 1580 mm, respectively. The average signal to noise ratio of the blurred images is close to 100. While it is not shown, but can be readily understood, the images for the conventional ideal lens will be badly blurred at object distances of 1450 mm and 1580 mm. In the maximum entropy recovery, the point spread function used for (a) is the actual diffraction blur of the ideal lens, thus yielding a nice two-point recovery. The point spread function used in (b) (c) and (d) is the average point spread function over an object range of 1400 mm to 1615 mm, the designed depth of field range of the logarithmic asphere. This is ten times the classical depth of field. Thus in the processing, no knowledge of the object distance is assumed. This is important for the extended depth of field enhancement because generally one does not know the actual object distance. In the recovery of (f) (g) and (h), most of the rings in the blurred images disappear. Finally we remark that the two points in (g) and (h) are clearly resolved, which demonstrates the diffraction limited performance over an extended range of the integrated computational imaging system.

Nano-Optics and Physical Optics: Lukas Novotny

Nano-optics is the study of optical phenomena and techniques near or beyond the diffraction limit of light. A key element in nano-optics is strong field confinement. For example, strong field confinement can be achieved by strongly focused laser beams used in confocal microscopy, or by nanoscale material structures (apertures, particles, tips). The theoretical understanding of nanoscale optical fields relies on elements of physical optics. However, many convenient approximations (quasi-static approximation, paraxial approximation, etc.) are not applicable. For example, a realistic theoretical description of the imaging properties of a scanning near-field optical microscope requires the consideration of near-fields and farfields, and for structures ranging from subwavelength to very large size. Hence neither the electrostatic approximation nor Kirchhoff or Fresnel diffraction theory can be used; the full wave equation has to be solved instead. Powerful theoretical techniques used in nano-optics are Green's function methods or the angular spectrum representation. Both of these approaches can be mathematically demanding, but they originate from a clear and intuitive physical picture. Green's function techniques are the result of Huygen's principle where the field at a given space-point is determined by the sum of partial fields emanating from a distribution of point sources. On the other hand, the angular spectrum representation is simply a superposition of plane waves and evanescent waves of different amplitudes, phases, and propagation directions. In Fourier optics, for example, the propagation directions are restricted to a small angular range (paraxial approximation).

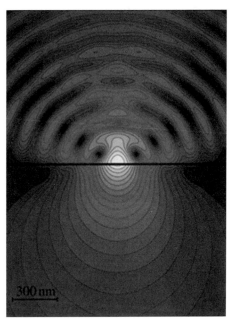

Laser beam focused on the surface of a glass substrate. The calculation relies on an angular spectrum representation. Because the field is incident from the glass side, supercritical plane wave components are totally reflected leading to a standing wave pattern inside the glass medium.

The angular spectrum representation is also ideally suited for the understanding of the diffraction limit and for the essential ideas behind near-field microscopy. While it is reasonable to truncate the evanescent components in the angular spectrum when considering wave propagation in free space, the evanescent fields cannot be neglected close to sources or material boundaries. Inclusion of the evanescent fields lets us overcome the diffraction limit and theoretically achieve arbitrary spatial resolution. Near-field optics aims at understanding these fields close to their source region and making use of them for high-resolution microscopy, manipulation, and localized interactions.

Our knowledge of confined optical fields and their interaction with matter is greatly based on the achievements made in the field of physical optics over the past two centuries. For most applications in nano-optics, classical electromagnetic field theory together with a semi-classical description of light-matter interactions is the ideal theoretical framework.

Phase Retrieval: James R. Fienup

Many problems in optics and related fields are characterized by having partial information available in one domain (such as an image or pupil domain) and some other information available in another domain (often the Fourier domain), and we wish to retrieve or reconstruct all the information in both domains. An example of this came to national attention in 1990 when it was discovered that the Hubble Space Telescope suffered from a severe aberration causing terribly blurred images. NASA needed to find out the exact form

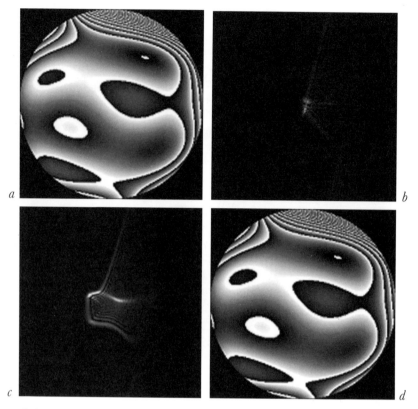

Optical metrology example simulation, by graduate student Greg Brady. (a) Phase of an aberrated wave front (phase wrapped modulo 2π) in a circular pupil, (b) image of a point source in a plane on one side of the nominal focal plane, (c) image in a plane on the other side of the focal plane, (d) aberration obtained from a phase retrieval algorithm using (b) and (c) together.

of the aberration so that astronauts could install correction optics to fix the problem. However, it was not possible to bring the telescope down to Earth for testing. Blurred images of stars taken with Hubble's science cameras were all we had to work with. The problem was to find a phase error estimate in the pupil that, when propagated (in the computer) to the focal plane, gives an image of a star consistent with the blurred star images taken by the camera. The shape of the pupil diameter and the obscurations (such as the central obscuration from the secondary mirror and the struts holding the secondary mirror in place) were the pupil-plane constraint in one domain, while the blurred image of a star was the data measured in the Fourier plane. This problem was solved by phase retrieval algorithms. One such algorithm is the iterative transform algorithm which was developed by Gerchberg and Saxton to solve a related problem in electron microscopy, and by Fienup to reconstruct images of space objects from stellar interferometry data. Another approach is a nonlinear optimization algorithm,[3] akin to those used in lens design, that minimizes an error metric using gradient-search approaches. The successful characterization of Hubble helped to raise phase retrieval from a topic studied by just a few groups to a major area of research. NASA is designing the James Webb Space Telescope, Hubble's future replacement, to use phase retrieval to keep its eighteen hexagonal mirrors aligned to within a small fraction of a wavelength over its six-meter diameter. Meanwhile, phase retrieval, and the closely associated phase diversity technique, are being integrated into other optical systems that employ adaptive optics or actuated mirrors. It also shows great hope as a new tool for optical metrology: measuring the aberrations of optical components.

One can also use phase retrieval to form coherent images, without any imaging optics. Just shine a laser at an object and measure the back-scattered laser speckle intensity pattern in some plane a distance away from the object. It is possible to digitally reconstruct an image by phase retrieval using the measured speckle intensity in conjunction with knowledge that the object has a finite size. Furthermore, if one were to illuminate the object with a sequence of wavelengths from a tunable laser and collect the speckle pattern at each wavelength, then it is possible to reconstruct a 3-D image of the object from this cube of information. This approach employs the principle of obtaining range resolution from frequency bandwidth that is used in swept-frequency radar systems. Increasingly, for image formation it is beneficial to place more of the burden on computer processing as a way of relaxing the requirements on the optics.

Phase retrieval, along with imaging systems that rely on computations to form an image, require additional topics to be included in our physical optics curriculum. Courses that include algorithms and additional mathematics, in combination with existing offerings in Fourier optics and statistical optics, will enable our students to develop novel optical imaging and wave-front-sensing systems.

Nicholas George has been a member of the faculty of the University of Rochester since 1978. He served as Director of the Institute of Optics from 1977 until 1981. He is the Wilson Professor of Electronic Imaging.

References

1   Nicholas George and Karin Strand, "A Profile: The Teaching of Optics by the Faculty of The Institute of Optics," *IEEE* Trans. on Education, E-23 (1980): 108–15.

2   Wanli Chi and Nicholas George, "Computational imaging with the logarithmic asphere: theory," *J. Opt. Soc. Am.* A 20 (2003): 2260–73.

3   J. R. Fienup, J. C. Marron, T. J. Schulz, and J. H. Seldin, "Hubble Space Telescope Characterized by Using Phase Retrieval Algorithms," *Appl. Opt.* 32 (1993): 1747–68.

49. Having It All: Personal Lives and Professional Choices[*]

Susan Houde-Walter

Despite the vigorous involvement of Hilda Kingslake at the inception of The Institute of Optics, there were very few women in the student body for the first few decades. Women made inroads during the 1960s and 1970s. By 1986, the ratio of women to men graduate students was 19 to 100 (the number was 61 to 225 for undergrads).

Jean Bennett was president of the Optical Society of America in 1986, and she paid a visit to the Institute. She met with a number of graduate students.[4] One of these students (your scribe) was seven months pregnant, and it was just beginning to dawn on her that a baby might impact her career in optics. Other students wondered about networking, finding the right mentors, whether to go to industry or academia, and so on. Unfortunately for us students, there were few females on campus at the time who might serve as mentors. Jean suggested we import them for a day. She helped to identify prospective speakers and we organized a day-long seminar. We approached Ken Teegarden, then director of the Institute, for funds, which he generously granted. The University also embraced the seminar as one of the "University Day Seminars" with the improbable name, "Having It All: Personal Lives and Professional Choices." Some excerpts from the transcripts follow.

Irene Engle, professor of physics, United States Naval Academy, Annapolis, Md.
"The 'Old Girl Network' as a Supplementary Professional Support System"

". . . the rate of production of women Ph.D.s [in Physics] has remained almost constant, hovering about 65 per year during the past ten years. So if one is searching for a mentor, particularly a mentor who is a woman, one doesn't necessarily find women available. Now there is always the possibility of finding a good man and most women who have somehow or other survived through the process, have found quite a number of good men who have helped them along the way in various ways. But no matter how many good ones there are, there are just as many areas where it really helps to have women who have the life experience of women as well as the concomitant life experience of scientists."

Teresa M. Motz, optical engineer, Welch-Allyn, Skaneateles Falls, N.Y.
"Being a Professional Woman: Attitudes, Social Structures, and Environmental Considerations"

"I was a foreman in a machine shop, I was the youngster and the only girl there, I had thirty older men that I was supposed to supervise. They had decided to set up a test for me. They brought in appropriate [sic] centerfolds and tacked them on the inside lids of their tool

---

* University Day Seminar, September 17, 1986.

Susan Houde-Walter, 1986.

boxes to see my reaction. Basically they set up a situation where they wanted to find out how I felt about certain social issues, how I reacted in potentially embarrassing situations and furthermore what rights I respected in a supervisor-employee relationship. So I found it—of course this occurred right before a very important management tour was coming through. A lot can be gleaned about a person's character by forcing response to, in this particular case, pornography. Reactions are important, and I found it quite interesting that after a few days, the pictures suddenly disappeared. . . . I don't want whether or not I'm a male or female in any way to influence how they deal with me on a technical level. But basically the teasing that goes on between male and female colleagues is colorful in nature, so to speak, various shades of red being the predominant color for one or both parties involved."

Janet Jackel, Research Scientist, Bell Communications Research, Redbank, N.J.
"Now that you have it all, what do you do with it?"

"About nine or ten years ago when I was very new at Bell Labs I was sent to a workshop—it was called Women in the Work Environment. . . . It was mostly for men in fact and male managers and how to deal with women, and it was run by sort of a psychologist type and we discussed a lot of things. . . . We talked about this and on the very last day—we had gotten to many, many issues, including really important ones like should a man hold a door for a woman and stuff like that—and I just felt that something was missing. . . . Then it hit me—no one had talked about families. Now, in case you haven't noticed it, well—first—most people want families. . . . Really, people did not want to talk about it and then they said, 'Well, if you're going to do that, we don't know what to do. You want to have everything, everything.'

"Things break down constantly. . . . If you can somehow get a job with time flexibility, you're way ahead because the disasters keep coming up. They come up like when somebody calls at three o'clock in the afternoon and they say, 'Well . . . don't get too upset. We took him to the emergency room and there's somebody with him, but the surgeon will not suture the scalp until a parent comes.' "

Ursula Gibson, assistant professor of optics, Optical Sciences Center, University of Arizona, Tucson, Ariz.

"Getting Tough and Getting Through: the Ph.D. and Beyond"

"As part of a Bell Labs grant, I went down to work a couple of summers there. . . . It turns out they had this shielded room, just a mesh room inside the lab where they did all their experiments and part of the tradition had been that they had this 1940s calendar girl on the wall. Part of the ritual was that this 'goddess' would look after things in the screened room while they weren't there to take care of them. So they were very reluctant, despite my arrival in the lab, to take this down. They thought, well gosh, what can we do, I mean, we've got this female scientist coming into the lab and we know that they are special and different and probably can't handle this. And it wasn't a pornographic picture, it was just an old-fashioned calendar girl. And so they decided they'd put curtains on it. I was working in the screen room by myself one day and I saw there was this thing obviously covered up, so I opened it up and there was the (fairly modest) pin-up girl. And so I thought, well isn't that cute, they are worried about being sexist. I covered it back up and went off. That night I went to the grocery store and I bought a copy of *Playgirl*. I figured all's fair in science and war, so I picked out a picture which I thought was similarly revealing, no details necessary, I'm sure. I took it up very early the next morning, I went in and put it next to the pin-up girl and put curtains over it. Then I went off and waited to see what would happen. I came back in for a coffee break about two or three hours later and they were all jabbering away and when I came in it got very quiet. So I knew something was going on. It turned out that by that one act I had completely absolved them of their fears, especially the technicians. They thought it was stupid that just because a woman was coming in, they had to put curtains over their pin-up girl. But the technicians could see the parity involved in the male pin-up and after that there really were no problems."

Elsa Garmire, professor of electrical engineering and physics and director of the Center for Laser Studies, University of Southern California.

"Does Being a Woman Make a Difference?"

"I was a student at Harvard and I did apply to Harvard and MIT to grad school but I wasn't at all sure that I was even going to get in. Well I was offered positions both places along with research money. I look back now and I must have been a pretty good student. . . . I didn't feel like I was a good student. The only reason I went to graduate school was I was married and it was either do that or be a secretary. There really weren't any other options. You made about the same amount of money as a research assistant as you did with a secretarial job so I went to graduate school.

"We've been talking a lot about getting married and having two career families. What I suggest is that you should all go out and marry a wife. . . .

"The technical community is really a very close-knit small community. We're a tribe. I heard a talk once that said that people like to belong to tribes and that tribes used to be the people that lived near you. Now the tribes are the people of the same professional interests and outlook and so the Optical Society is a tribe and the people will be there. So whatever friendships you make, or enemies you make, are going to be with you for your life, so remember that. . . .

"I had an opportunity to work for a woman one summer when I was at Argonne National Labs and I didn't want anything to do with her and I thought you know I just really don't want anything to do with a woman. She passed away a few years ago. It makes me very sad. When she passed away she had been such a wonderful role model for so many young women and I never had the opportunity because I wasn't willing to listen. . . .

"I do believe networking is very, very important. . . . I really want you all to be involved in networking with other women. I would like to get started an organization within the Optical Society of women that will, at least, keep in touch with each other so that when we need jobs, etc., we know who to talk to." [Note: WOSA, or Women of the Optical Society of America, now meets once a year at the OSA annual meeting.]

Sixteen years have elapsed since the Having It All seminar, and conditions for women in the field of optics continue to improve. Many thanks to Jean and the seminar speakers for bringing their experience to us, as well as Ken and the University for providing funds and the event venue. Thanks also to the fellow grad students who cooperated to make the seminar happen. May the progress continue!

Transcripts of the Having It All seminar are available by mailing your surface mail address to shw@optics.rochester.edu.

Susan Houde-Walter received her M.S. and Ph.D. from the Institute of Optics in 1983 and 1987, respectively. She has been a member of the faculty of the University of Rochester since 1987.

50. Multi-Investigator Programs at The Institute of Optics

Nicholas George

Research funding in Optics grew rapidly in the 1980s primarily through the establishment of several collaborative research centers. These centers provided equipment and student support that propelled the Institute to the forefront of research in a number of areas. In this essay we will trace the founding and development of these centers.

Funding patterns for basic research at universities were dramatically changed after World War II. In physics and engineering, the National Science Foundation, the Offices of Scientific Research within the Department of Defense, the Department of Energy, and NASA were funding both single-investigator grants and also major project grants, the latter encompassing major facilities and equipment such as accelerators, telescopes, and special fields such as electronics. Moreover, there was a definite trend toward funding block grants in certain critical key technology areas. In the 1960s and 1970s, AFOSR, ONR, and ARO participated in funding a long-term program called the Joint Service Electronics Program. The JSEP had major funding contracts with all of the big-name research universities in electronics, e.g., MIT, Stanford, Harvard, UC Berkeley, Princeton, and so on. The JSEP has provided block-funded, multi-investigator contracts for more than fifty years. Coincidentally, from 1963 to 1970, the JSEP program director at AFOSR was Colonel William C. Athas, and he funded a single investigator grant to Nicholas George at Caltech as well as an early grant to Moshe Lubin and Gary Conners for the big laser work at Rochester, which ultimately led to the Laboratory for Laser Energetics.

With the knowledge of funding initiatives such as JSEP in electronics, it was natural to formulate an analogous vision for a multi-investigator program in optics that would help to keep the nation in the forefront of this rapidly emerging field. During his period as director of The Institute of Optics, George prepared many briefings and unsolicited proposals containing this vision for a Joint Services Optics Program. In February 1981 this program was initiated by AFOSR (Larry Kravitz, director; John Neff, program manager) and ARO (Herman Roble, director; Robert Lontz and B. D. Guenther, program managers) for $600,000 per year. Table 1 contains a listing of multi-investigator programs at The Institute of Optics since 1980.

New York State Governor Hugh Carey announced an important initiative for multi-investigator funding available on a competitive basis to universities in New York State. With this initiative, substantial matching capital funds were required. Both President Robert Sproull and Dean Brian J. Thompson provided valuable leadership in obtaining large grants from the Eastman Kodak Co., Xerox Corp., Bausch & Lomb, and Corning. K. J. Teegarden, director, authored the proposal and served as program director. The New York State Science and Technology Foundation (NYSSTF), now renamed the New York State Office of Science, Technology, & Academic Research (NYSTAR), has continued to provide funding to optics and to promote interaction between universities and corporations throughout the state.

Table 1. Multi-Investigator Programs in The Institute of Optics

Title of Multi-Investigator Program	Funding Agencies	Faculty Participants	Departments	Funding Level ($)	From	To
Optics and Opto-Electronic Systems Proposal Aug. '80: Nicholas George Program Directors: N. George, Carlos Stroud '82–'89	AFOSR ARO ETL	All Optics	Optics, Physics, LLE	60,000/yr	2/81	6/90
Advanced Technology in Optics Proposal Jan. '82: K. J. Teegarden Program Directors: K. J. Teegarden, D. T. Moore, D. Hall	NYSSTF	All Optics	Optics	1,000,000/yr	7/82	7/94
Center for Optics Manufacturing (COM) Proposal Oct '87: D. T. Moore, PI Program Director: H. Pollicove '88–'04	USAMC DARPA			2,000,000/yr	6/91	6/04
ARO-URI Center for Opto-Electronic Systems Research Proposal Feb. '96: Nicholas George Renewal Jul. '91: Nicholas George Program Director: N. George	ARO	All Optics		16,000,000 4,000,000	7/86 1/92	7/91 1/97
NSF-NYS/IUCRC: Center for *Electronic Imaging Systems (CEIS)* NSF Proposal Jan. '92: Nicholas George (CEIS) NYSSTF Proposal Aug. '92: Nicholas George (CAT-EIS) Program Director: N. George '92–'00	NSF NYSTAR	12	UR & RIT	1,200,000 5,000,000 1,200,000 5,000,000	9/92 7/93 9/96 7/98	9/96 7/98 9/00 7/04
CEIS: Enhanced CAT-EIS & Microelectronic Design Center Program Director: Eby Friedman '00–Present	NYSTAR	57	UR, RIT, Cornell	2,600,000	7/01	7/04
MURI Center for *Quantum Information* Program Directors: Ian Walmsley, Carlos Stroud '01–'04	ARO	9	6 Universities	5,000,000	5/99	5/04

Rationale and Benefits

Certainly the multi-investigator programs are appealing to faculty as a means for funding their research efforts. Ultimately, however, the rewards are much more sweeping than this. As in any complex transaction involving many separate groups, the interests and benefits for the various constituents can be quite different, as described in the following paragraphs.

For Federal governmental agencies, generally, their goals are to sponsor high quality research and promote education. The NYSSTF/NYSTAR is interested primarily in stimulating economic development and secondarily in promoting education. Corporate sponsors have varied interests as well, including specific technologies and education.

In order to address these customer needs and to provide some rationale for engaging in these multi-investigator programs, it was necessary for the faculty to engage in long-term strategic planning. It is clearly evident today that this planning has been beneficial in formulating vision statements for our main fields as well as establishing teamwork among faculty groups and students. For example, in the field of imaging, the Center for Electronic Imaging Systems has successfully developed a new mode for cooperative research that effectively couples university researchers with industrial partners and governmental laboratories. In accomplishing significant research and conducting technology transfer, they have been able to satisfy a diverse marketplace of new, medium, and large corporations without any compromise to faculty freedom and autonomy in research.

Other substantial benefits that have been realized include more diversity in our educational program, transitioning graduate research material into the undergraduate program, improvements in planning faculty additions, and modern management and accounting methods applied to The Institute of Optics.

For CEIS, the grand challenge is to make substantial contributions to imaging in the information age, since one can readily demonstrate that images will dominate the bit stream—even much more than is indicated by the old adage that "one picture is worth a thousand words." The long-term vision for the Center for Electronic Imaging Systems is to establish and maintain a leading national center for all phases of electronic imaging systems. Such a center attracts the best and brightest students, post-doctoral fellows, and faculty. The original goals of CEIS were to contribute to research in electronic imaging, contribute to the educational programs of universities, and contribute to economic development through cooperative programs with industry.

From the interactions with small start-up businesses, it was quickly recognized that expert advice was needed on business questions, perhaps even more so than technology. Hence, CEIS established the idea of the business innovation team (BIT). These teams are composed of MBA students from the William E. Simon Graduate School of Business Administration at the University of Rochester. First under the leadership of Professor Ronald Yeaple and now directed by Peter Waasdorp, MBA students are assigned specific projects of a business nature to assist small companies in a variety of topics depending on their needs. This interaction with the Simon School is an excellent means of building some valuable diversity in our educational programs.

The CEIS was founded by Nicholas George, Wilson Professor of Electronic Imaging and Professor of Optics, who also served as director of CEIS for nine years. Maria Schnitzler, administrator, served at CEIS for approximately nine years and now works in The Institute of Optics. Important contributions of funding were made by Eastman Kodak, Xerox, 3M, and others. Management expertise and technical vision were provided by

Edwin Przybylowicz, Gary Conners, Gary Bottger, Michael Kriss, and James Myers of Eastman Kodak, and Mark Myers, Michael Shahin, Paul Roetling, Keith Knox, and Mary Ann Dvonch of Xerox. Both Gary Conners and Michael Kriss had important management roles at CEIS after their early retirement from Eastman Kodak. A major goal of the visionary NSF/IUCRC program was to build a center that can survive the "sunset" marked by the end of their funding. Today this appears well in hand under the directorship of Eby Friedman, Distinguished Professor of Electrical and Computer Engineering; Associate Director of CEIS Carl Schauffele, and the associate director of CAT-EIS, Dean Ian Gatley of RIT. Faculty participation and corporate projects have increased significantly, as shown in table 1. Overall annual CEIS gross revenue is $5.45 million (2003).

A particularly important center to The Institute of Optics is the Center for Optics Manufacturing (COM) founded by Professor Duncan T. Moore and Harvey Pollicove. The initial concept was developed the day after Labor Day in 1987. The first contract was signed in 1988, and the center was located on the second floor of Wilmot, then moved to Gavett (next to the MBE facility), and finally to the elegant new quarters in the Center for Optoelectronics and Imaging building adjacent to LLE. Moore served as principal investigator on the main contracts for COM from its founding until 1993. Harvey Pollicove was the only director of COM from its founding until early in 2004, serving first as a loaned executive from Kodak and then as a University employee. The center is a partnership of the American Precision Optics Manufacturers Association (APOMA), several universities (Rochester, Central Florida, and Arizona), and the U.S. Army. This award-winning cooperative effort is developing real-world technology solutions that are redefining industry manufacturing capability. The center teams university scientists with industry experts to ensure that project designs and objectives provide manufacturer-usable solutions.

The Center for Quantum Information was founded in 1999 with five years of funding through the Department of Defense MURI Program administered by the Army Research Office. There are nine professors participating in the center from five universities: Cornell, Harvard, Rutgers, Rochester and Stanford. The funding is one million dollars per year. Initially, the project was divided into two parts separately administered by Professor Charles Marcus of Stanford and Professor Ian Walmsley of Rochester. When Marcus moved to Harvard and Walmsley to Oxford, the program was consolidated, with Professor Carlos Stroud as project director for the last three years.

The center carries out basic research in the new field of quantum information through collaborations of leading researchers in classical information theory with researchers in quantum optics and spintronics. Rochester collaborators are Professors Nicholas Bigelow, Joseph Eberly, Carlos Stroud, and Ian Walmsley. The group established a new biennial conference series, the International Conference on Quantum Information. The first conference was hosted in Rochester in 1993 with more than two hundred attendees, and the second at Oxford University with a similar number attending. Nine regular faculty members, two visiting faculty members, and some thirty students and postdocs have participated in this center developing a basic *quantum information toolbox* to serve the needs of the rapidly developing new technologies of quantum computing and quantum communication.

Nicholas George has been a member of the faculty of the University of Rochester since 1978. He served as Director of the Institute of Optics from 1977 until 1981. He is the Wilson Professor of Electronic Imaging.

Graduate Student Life: 21 Brighton Park

Donald Harter

There is a little house located on a small side street off Mount Hope Avenue next to St. Anne's Church which was the site of a lot of historical events in the lives of optics graduate students. The address of this house is 21 Brighton Park. Fourteen optics students rented the house over a period that spanned three decades. The first optics inhabitants were Jay Eastman and his wife Linda. They moved into the house in 1975 when Jay, who received his Ph.D. in 1974, joined the staff of the Laboratory for Laser Energetics. It is unlikely that the owner of the house would have rented directly to a bunch of single graduate students, but the more respectable couple were very desirable tenants. The landlord's experience with these optics-related tenants led him to allow in some who were not necessarily so domestic.

The tenants included Jay Eastman, Steve Fantone, Don Harter, Lloyd Hillman, Bill Molander, Dave Brown, Ian Walmsley, Paul Kane, Jim Zavislan, Ian McMackin, Ed Miller, Mark Beck, Mark Mallalieu, Lee Moore, Jason Porter, and Mike Melocchi. Two were not optics students: Dave Brown, a laser lab staff member, and Lee Moore, a computer science student. Both were made honorary optikers. That these students did not spend all of their time pondering arcane aspects of optics theory is indicated by the number of tenants who met their future wives at 21 Brighton Park. The list is remarkable. Steve Fantone met his wife Betsy (the sister of Linda Eastman); similarly Don Harter and Wendy,

21 Brighton Park, Winter 1999.

Raggedy Ann and Andy Gabel and Generalisimo Renaud at Halloween party 1975.

Lloyd Hillman and Sharon, Bill Molander and Cindy, Ian Walmsley and Kate, Paul Kane and Cathy, and Ian McMackin and Lenore all met there.

The parties held under this roof were notorious enough that one might think that there would be a neighbor problem, but surprisingly the nearest neighbor was a constant friend of the students. Ruth Trompeter, known to all simply as "Ruth," was a long-time resident of 25 Brighton Park. She fed and amused all the students with her charming and outgoing manner and her unique greeting: "Yeah, well, hello Mr. Jay," or "Mr. Steve," or "Mr. Bill," . . . as appropriate. Ruth made soups, cakes, cookies for the guys, and even fed their pets. When she fed Jim Zavislan's dog Cindy some Danish ham, Jim lamented that Cindy had a better lunch than he did.

It is the parties that make 21 Brighton Park memorable even for those who did not live or meet their future spouses there. The Petzval parties are fondly remembered. Of course, Joseph Petzval (1807–1891) is known to every optics student as a name associated with a "curvature" and a doublet lens, but many first year-students had not yet encountered these second-semester topics so they were indoctrinated through a series of get-togethers with international themes—a José Petzval party with a Mexican theme, Giuseppe Petzval party with an Italian theme, etc. The Halloween parties were also famous with a lot of memorable costumes, a few of which are captured in the photographs.

Halloween swell Ian McMackin.

Rich Youngworth and John Heebner clown it up.

Obviously the consumption of intoxicating beverages at these parties and other festive occasions could strain the budgets of those living on graduate student stipends, so thoughts turned to fermenting and brewing. Cider, beer, and wine were all produced by various students, but in the little house on Brighton Park it was mostly beer and wine. Ian McMackin and Mark Beck were the principal brewers, while John Agostinelli and Lloyd Hillman were seriously into wine making. Hillman actually won prizes at the New York State Fair and in national competitions for his varietal Ravat. This was a pretty serious operation. When he moved from New York to Alabama he needed two trucks to carry his belongings—one for the furniture and the other for the wine.

Donald Harter received his Ph.D. from the Institute of Optics in 1982. He is currently employed at IMRA America, Ann Arbor, MI.

51. Duncan Moore Leads the Institute

Carlos Stroud

On July 1, 1987 Duncan T. Moore became Director of The Institute of Optics succeeding Kenneth Teegarden. Moore received his bachelor's degree in 1969 from the University of Maine, and his masters and doctorate from The Institute of Optics in 1970 and 1974 respectively. He joined the faculty immediately on graduation, and like many of his predecessors was very active with a career that combined academic research with participation in industry, government, and professional societies. His research specialty was gradient index optics. He used ion exchange to produce gradients in the index of refraction of glass blanks and then used them in binoculars, endoscopes, and microscopes. In 1980 he founded the Gradient Lens Corporation to exploit the commercial applications of this technology. Unlike many such start-up companies, GLC is still flourishing twenty-four years later.

Moore had a distinctive style as a Director, traveling at least two days a week and keeping a secretary and an administrative assistant very busy. In his last year he also had Professor Dennis Hall appointed as assistant director to help with administrative work. Perhaps the most significant development during his term was the continuation and expansion of the collaborative research centers: the Center for Optical Technology (sponsored by New York State, Eastman Kodak, Xerox, and Corning); the University Research Initiative Center for Optoelectronic Systems Research (sponsored by the Department of Defense); and the founding of the Center for Optics Manufacturing (sponsored by the Department of Defense). Together these centers supported more than half of the research students in the Institute, and brought in more than eight million dollars per year, surpassing the

Duncan T. Moore, Director.

research funding of other much larger departments on River Campus. (These research centers are described in some detail by Nicholas George in chapter 50.)

The research centers and the state-of-the-art equipment that they provided helped to attract large classes of very well-qualified graduate students, with more than 80 percent of the class filled with U.S. citizens. In 1990, the Institute graduated its largest class of Ph.D. students ever, thirteen, along with twenty-five M.S. students. The combination of excellent equipment and talented students greatly enhanced the research program of the Institute. The number of refereed publications grew rapidly from fifty-six in 1988 to 159 in 1991. The number of patents also grew rapidly. In 1988–89 there were twelve patents granted and fifteen additional applications. The remarkable productivity of the faculty was recognized in the compilation of statistics by the National Academy of Sciences comparing Ph.D. granting physics departments in the United States. The Institute was included in the tabulation and ranked in the top five departments in "faculty effectiveness" measured in publications per faculty member, and in the percentage of faculty with external research contract support. The quality of the publications was also evidenced by the frequent appearance of the work in published annual lists of the most significant accomplishments of the year in various fields, and in articles in the popular press including *The Wall Street Journal*, *The New York Times*, and *The Economist*.

The one number characterizing the Institute that decreased during this period was the number of undergraduate majors. There were 97 B.S. graduates in 1987 and the number dropped to 31 by 1991. The total number of undergraduate majors rose from 50 in 1975 to 350 in 1985 and back below 200 in 1990. There were a number of factors that led to the "bubble" of the mid-80s. Lasers had caught the public imagination, with Star Wars and laser fusion research in the newspapers, and holograms and barcode scanners becoming familiar sights. The word was out that this was a hot new field with high-paying jobs. Indeed, in 1987 one westcoast military research company flew fifty of the graduating seniors out to Los Angeles en masse to interview for jobs. One M.S. graduate set a new record by receiving thirty job offers. The twelve faculty members on the Optics faculty did not feel that they could give such large classes the quality of education that an Institute of Optics degree was supposed to represent. There was no time to learn all the students' names much less to supervise individual research projects. The faculty decided to limit the class size by raising the minimum standards. In response to the overcrowding and the enhanced minimum requirements the enrollment in the undergraduate program dropped sharply, eventually dropping below twenty graduates in the late 1990s.

The bursting of the bubble was no happier event than its exponential growth in the first place. A faculty committee chaired by Carlos Stroud and including Dennis Hall and Michael Morris was set up to evaluate the status of the Institute and to suggest changes. The committee recommended that major changes be made in the way that undergraduates were educated. The students were to be integrated into the daily life of the department from the beginning with undergraduate study rooms, carrels, and laboratories mixed in among the faculty and graduate student offices and research laboratories. The program was given the acronym REDI (Rochester Educations Demands Involvement). The University administration and outside donors were approached to fund a building to carry out this experiment in undergraduate education. The reception might well be characterized as "restrained." The economy in general and the University's endowment in particular were strained, and no project which did not guarantee to bring in extra funds was likely to be supported at that time. Although there was general agreement that the plan was educationally sound it was not approved for funding.

The generally gloomy economic atmosphere in the University in the early 1990s was summed up in the last paragraph of the Director's Annual Report for the school year 1991–92.

> The last academic year was an excellent one for The Institute of Optics. However, the winds of change are clearly blowing. We can no longer continue business as usual and must be ready to do more with less resources. The faculty size has decreased by one and budgets have declined, while competitive pressures for salary increases continue. The next few years will pose many problems, but the vitality and historical strength of The Institute should carry us through these difficult times.

Although the University finances were not ideal, the field of optics was just about to undergo another dramatic "bubble"—*photonics*. The field of fiber optic communications was beginning to explode and the Institute was well posed to take advantage of it. The faculty included Dennis Hall, Govind Agrawal, Tom Brown, Susan Houde-Walter and Gary Wicks all making important contributions in this area. Other very strong new appointments had been made including Greg Forbes working in mathematical optics and Ian Walmsley in lasers and quantum optics.

The ground work laid in the REDI plan would prove useful a decade later as plans for the new Optics-Biomedical Engineering building were strongly influenced by the earlier ideas. Similarly, the need to keep faculty salaries competitive with those at other universities and in the industrial sector was soon recognized by the University and a significant increment was made to the faculty salary pool.

In 1993 Duncan Moore took a leave from the University to serve as American Physical Society Congressional Fellow working for two years in the office of Senator John D. Rockefeller IV of West Virginia. Dennis Hall succeeded him as Director of the Institute.

Graduate Student Life: Pig Roasts and Such

George Harvey

The first pig roast in our collective memory was in 1981 at John Agostinelli's parents' home, after his thesis defense. A live pig was purchased from a local farmer by Janis Valdmanis and George Harvey. Before the pig was cooked, George, Janis, and Don Harter put it under Ari Friberg's desk on the fourth floor of the Wilmot Building. This occurred because in a moment of weakness, one late night at the "Rat," Ari confessed he grew up on a pig farm in Finland and loved to rub the bellies of the pigs. We thought he would love to see one under his desk at the Institute. It would be very convenient to rub its belly.

From this escapade we learned three things. It is incredible how deafening the squeals of the pig are in the Wilmot Building elevator. It is also amazing how little time it takes the whole floor of the Wilmot Building to smell like a pig. Finally, Ari did not always show up at his typical early time (2 p.m.) on Saturdays.

It was Lloyd Hillman who "dressed" the pig. We were lucky Lloyd grew up on a ranch near Tucson and had a lot of experience with live farm animals. George made the ultimate sacrifice in staying up all night and basting the cooking pig by spraying it with Jack Daniels. As you may guess, not all the spray fell on the pig, and it wasn't clear who was more cooked by Sunday afternoon.

After this first pig roast, on a regular basis, groups of students would mysteriously converge at random houses for impromptu pig roasts where most supplies were purchased from friendly vendors at the farmers market in the city of Rochester.

The pig is watched over by Michelle Malcuit, Brian Oliver, Becky Oliver, Jeff Maki, and Dan Gauthier.

One year in the mid 1980s Karl Koch and fellow students roasted a full pig in the backyard of their Meigs Street house. "The roasting was pretty uneventful, but by the time we had finished eating the pig, we discovered we had way more firewood than we needed, so we decided to burn it in a bonfire. Well, the flames from the fire got to be taller than our garage roof, which prompted our neighbors to call the fire department. By the time the fire department arrived, the firewood was almost gone, so we were all happy."

Perhaps it was wise to have these pig roasts away from one's habitation, at places such as Chimney Bluffs in Huron, New York, to the east of Rochester, as seen in the photo. The jazz corn roast parties started around 1983, when Karl Koch returned from a few weeks on his uncle's dairy farm with a grain bag full of sweet corn. "We roasted sweet corn on open grills, listened to jazz, and generally had a good time. Occasionally, we had drawings to give away Mandelbrot set pictures that we made on the HP computers of the first floor of the Institute. The parties were billed as mandatory for first-year students and I think it was a good informal way for many of them to meet the other graduate students."

The jazz played at the corn roasts was pretty serious music, according to Koch. According to Dan Gauthier, "These events usually took a turn to the bizarre, often including terrible music." A brochure was generated with the tunes, players, recording year. Karl remembers that one year someone's girlfriend asked, as she looked over the brochure, "Who were the anal-retentive geeks who put this together?" Alex Gaeta and Karl looking sheepishly at her and confessed that it was them. "We had no explanation, we were just obsessive about the details."

George Harvey received his Ph.D. from the Institute of Optics in 1981. He is currently employed at Tycom (US) Ltd., Eatontown, NJ.

52. The Future: Duncan Moore in 1987

Duncan T. Moore

Duncan Moore became the seventh Director of The Institute of Optics on July 1, 1987. He graduated from the University of Maine in 1969, spent some time at the Western Electric Company, then took his Ph.D. at The Institute of Optics in 1974. He has been on the faculty of the Institute ever since. Meanwhile, his knowledge of the world of applied optics, through work with the learned societies and contacts with industry and abroad, has steadily widened his outlook and understanding. Much of his own studies and those of his students has been in the field of gradient index materials. Duncan Moore has made three new faculty appointments: Tom G. Brown, Susan W. Houde-Walter and Gary Wicks.

It seems fitting that he should have this opportunity, as he assumes the directorship, to express his thinking with regard to the future of The Institute of Optics.

—Hilda G. Kingslake

The Institute of Optics is facing a series of challenges. Unlike many departments which have seen declining enrollments and declining funding, The Institute of Optics has increased its graduate and undergraduate sizes and its funding sources. This has provided both an opportunity and a dilemma. The difficulties arise from the student population. In the May 1987 Commencement, 96 seniors received Bachelor of Science degrees as compared to 15 seniors who graduated a decade ago. With a full-time teaching faculty of only 12 at the end of the academic year 1987, the load per unit faculty has increased dramatically. During the same decade the graduate population has nearly doubled, resulting in relatively large research groups. While The Institute of Optics bore the responsibility for providing the total population of Optical Scientists in the United States at the Baccalaureate degree level for the first fifty-five years of its existence, we can no longer do this. Several other programs have started or are approved in the United States. The Institute of Optics will decrease its undergraduate population, to remain the best in the United States. After numerous discussions with faculty members, it has been decided that the optimum number is somewhere between 50 and 60 undergraduate seniors each year. This goal will be an extremely challenging one.

To maintain a first rate research program and reasonable class size, it is imperative to increase the number of faculty members. To that end, the University of Rochester has approved the increase of the number of full-time faculty from 16 to 20. This includes the Kingslake Chair in Optical Engineering. Since the full-time faculty of the Institute has never exceeded 14 in the last two decades, this is a substantial increase.

The emphasis in the research program in the next decade will be to build an optical materials program, to rebuild the optical engineering program, and to create a modern optical engineering program. These programs will be developed with new faculty members. Optical materials is an extremely important focus for the next decade in such areas as optical bistabilities, light emission from silicon, nonlinear properties of materials, and properties of glass and plastics. The Institute of Optics has had a long tradition in optical engineering and that effort will be expanded with new faculty appointments. It is particularly important that our teaching program represent a balance between physics and engineering, both in the graduate and undergraduate courses. New initiatives will be taken in the area of optical fabrication (particularly the single-point turning of glass), lens design optimization theory, aspheric surfaces without rotational symmetry, and metrology. Finally, a new initiative is modern optical engineering, involving optics and devices which operate in a short time domain. The work at the University's Laboratory for Laser Energetics has led to several devices. Parallel processing and digital optical image processing will become even more important, and materials used for these will be necessary. It will be the strong coupling between the optical materials effort and the modern optical engineering effort.

The funding of the Institute has become a complex one. As the cost of conducting first-rate science has increased over the last decade (it is expected to cost approximately $250,000 per scientist per year by 1995) the sources of contracting and grants have become more diversified. Currently we receive funds from four major sources: The state of New York, corporate sponsorship, the University of Rochester, and the Federal Government. The major source of funding from corporations is through the Center for Advanced Optical Technology established in 1983 under Kenneth Teegarden's directorship. This program, which currently has a budget of $2,000,000 (equally divided between the State and corporate participation) was the first large block grant for The Institute of Optics. Corporate support of research must increase in order to maintain the level of scientific work conducted at The Institute of Optics and to fund the next generation of scientists. During this past year we received a University Research Initiative Program from the Department of Defense under Nicholas George's leadership. While block funding is desirable from the simplicity of its administration, and allows for support of a wide variety of optical research topics within one program, it does expose the department to a very large change in funding situation based on political climates in Washington. We therefore must always maintain our individual contract base with individual professors as principal investigators of their own programs.

The future of The Institute of Optics is extremely bright with a strong faculty and excellent students. We will remain a jewel in the crown of the University of Rochester.

Duncan T. Moore received his M.S. and Ph.D. from the Institute of Optics in 1970 and 1974, respectively. He has been a member of the University of Rochester since 1974. He served as Director of the Institute from 1987 until 1993 and is the Rudolf & Hilda Kingslake Professor of Optical Engineering.

Graduate Student Life: Goin' South

John Agostinelli

It was once the talk of Europe. It can be found on the early maps of the North American continent. The explorer LaSalle first recorded its existence in 1669. Many believe it to have the distinction as being the Eighth Wonder of the natural world. Burning Springs, later known more affectionately and quite respectfully as "Fart Springs" around The Institute of Optics, is located in a beautiful little glen in the Bristol Hills near Canandaigua Lake, about an hour south of Rochester. Incredibly, through the centuries, the presence of such greatness in the Rochester vicinity became a fact that slipped into a misty obscurity. Its existence was revealed to some optics students in 1975 by the then-Institute oracle, George Fraley.

It happened that after a particularly nasty stretch of early autumn weather in October 1976, the morning broke with a spectacular sunrise and a warm breeze that caressed the cheek as you entered the outdoors. Cabin fever was already in full play and the springs beckoned. A small band of students struggled to eventually decide that it would be wise to recognize this day as a gift from the creator. The world had gotten along without a clear understanding of quantum mechanics for eons, and so it was decided to GO SOUTH—quantum mechanics class would wait for another day. The decision would later be appreciated as a rare example of wisdom at a young age, and began a tradition that continues today.

Goin' South: On the first nice workday after Columbus Day, head in a southerly direction toward the springs. Soak in the dazzling color of the nearly lasing foliage blanketing the hillsides, trek to the springs and, using several of your senses, discover the location of the best gas sources. Cook up some lunch on a "3-dog fart" (a bubbling natural gas-jet emerging from a rock fissure in the springs' creek-bed having sufficient gas flow such that simultaneous cooking of at least three sausages is achievable on the open flame). Though the epicure might suggest otherwise, a repast prepared in this way and in this setting will be savored and remembered for a lifetime. Following lunch, peruse the glen, and with a renewed spirituality from the wonder of it all, depart the springs and continue with a blood-stirring adventure—hike in one of the many gorges in the area. Invent a new activity for the year. Then gather hickory nuts (in a good year) and finish the experience enjoying a grape pie while viewing an arresting panorama under a breathtaking sunset. The first Goin' South expeditioners were Rich Boucher, Lloyd Hillman, Frank Kalk, and John Agostinelli. Many other optics students and friends have followed and shaped the path in the years since.

The glen at the springs provides an enjoyable hike to a terminus characterized by an imposing vertical waterfall. Along the hike, many jets can be seen, including the muchheralded step-jet whose output bubble stream may be modulated or even stopped by applying weight to a planar ledge of shale at the edge of the creek some six feet from the jet. But the piece de resistance, the creator's chef d'oeuvre in this magical place, is thought by many to be the "eternal fart." The eternal is located at the back of a tiny cave that guards the left flank of the waterfall. Though it is above the creek bed, the cave is fed a constant supply of spring water that covers the cave floor and provides audible evidence of the eternal's existence and precise location. Olfactory evidence, though present here and at many locations within the glen, is generally difficult to localize.

Over the years we have noticed a positive correlation between abundant seasonal rains and the gas flow rates at Burning Springs. Dry years can be particularly challenging, as some of the better jets are not water-covered in the partially exposed creek bed and are therefore invisible, though thankfully not undetectable to the experienced South-goer. The years have also brought application of sound science and engineering understanding to improvements in stove technology (empty beer can with well-placed vents cut in to provide optimum draft and mixture). A quick hot lunch is guaranteed.

The springs are located in the heart of the Finger Lakes region, which offers a plethora of exciting but little-known hiking venues, resplendent with towering cascades and dramatic vistas made even more special at the cusp of seasonal change. Names like Clark's, Brigg's, and Conklin's (the Hi Tor) mark some of the prodigious canyons that continue to exhilarate the South-going thrill-seeker.

And so the ritual has been repeated each year to the present. And each time, we are inspired by both the familiarity and the newness of the feeling, and by the human capacity to wonder. And we marvel at our good fortune to be together amidst the glory of the spectacle, and we toast quantum mechanics for making it all possible.

John Agostinelli received his M.S. and Ph.D. from the Institute of Optics in 1977 and 1981, respectively. He is currently employed at Eastman Kodak Company, Rochester, NY.

53. The Dawn of Ultrafast Science and Technology at the University of Rochester

Gérard A. Mourou

The University of Rochester in the 1980s played an important role in the development of the field of ultrafast science and technology as one of the most active field of optics today. The Institute of Optics and the Laboratory for Laser Energetics (LLE) occupied the central stage. The Institute of Optics provided exceptional students and LLE a unique technical platform. Many of the techniques that the researchers in the field use today, like THz generation, picosecond electron diffraction (PED), electro-optic sampling (EOS), chirped pulse amplification (CPA), and jitter-free synchronization were conceived and demonstrated by the ultrafast science group. The Institute of Optics students—Wayne Knox, Theodore Sizer, Irl Duling, Janis Valdmanis, James Kafka, Donna Strickland, Maurice Pessot, Jeffrey Squier and John Nees—formed the core. Their enthusiasm was infectious and contributed much to attract students from physics, such as Steve Williamson, Theodore Norris, and Kevin Meyer, and from electrical engineering, including Daniel Blumenthal, John Whitaker, and Doug Dykaar, as well as faculty like C. Gabel, R. Knox, C. Stancampiano, T. Hsiang, R. Sobolewski, A. Melissinos, J. Eberly, and D. Meyerhofer.

A group picnic in France.

In the early 1980s ultrafast science was dealing with eV phenomena. Our group extended its range from the meV on one side, with the introduction of THz beams and electro-optic sampling (EOS) techniques, to the MeV-GeV on the other side, with chirped pulse amplification (CPA) and its ability to produce relativistic intensities.

Switching High Voltage with Picosecond Precision: Applications to Active Pulse Shaping, Jitter-free Streak Camera, Time-resolved Spectroscopy

Work in this area mainly started in 1978 after my arrival at LLE. LLE was running a highly programmatic effort on inertial confinement fusion. At that time the director and founder, M. Lubin, and later R. McCrory understood the importance of creating and supporting in parallel to the main research activity a group that would work on weakly related laser fusion projects, that could offer the flexibility and the type of environment that Ph.D. research demands. I would be in charge of this group, known as the ultrafast science group. I was impressed by the work of Dave Auston at AT&T Bell Laboratories that demonstrated that electrical signals could be switched with picosecond precision. I was convinced that this technique could find some important applications in laser fusion, where the program had a need for synchronized high voltage pulses for active pulse shaping or for jitter-free streak cameras. An exceptional undergraduate student, Wayne Knox, shared the understanding of the importance of this line of research. At Wayne's high speed of progress we extended Auston's work to very high voltage [1] and applied it to the synchronization of streak cameras [2]. For the first time the streak camera could be used in accumulation mode. Weak luminescence signals could be accumulated, improving their signal/noise ratio. The jitter-free streak camera found immediate applications in photobiology with the group of Wayne's father, Professor R. Knox. This technique is now routinely used in synchrotron-based femtosecond x-ray diffraction experiments [3]. High voltage switching applications were also in active pulse shaping [4], as demonstrated in collaboration with J. Agostinelli (student of C. Gabel), and in contrast improvement [5] with W. Seka. This technique is still used today [6] in high field science.

Opening the Field of Picosecond Electron Diffraction

A streak camera is a beautiful photon-electron transducer. It makes an electron replica of the photon pulses. The electrons are deflected across the phosphor screen, leaving a phosphorescent track. I was mesmerized by the thought that we could use this perfectly synchronized photoelectron pulse to perform time-resolved electron diffraction in the picosecond time scale by simply locating a sample under study in the camera drift region. We could study solid-liquid transformation simply by using a short optical pulse to produce the phase transition and the electron pulse to probe the structural change that would follow. I asked a new student with great passion for research, Steve Williamson, if he would be interested in this project. This was an enormous challenge, as none of us had any kind of electron diffraction experience in steady state let alone in the transient regime. But Steve was a superb experimentalist, and in one year he built a complete "streak camera" and demonstrated the concept [7]. We applied it by performing the first time-resolved structural transformation in the picosecond domain. It was the solid-liquid phase transformation of aluminum [8]. Further works were conducted by H. Elsayed-Ali, notably on surface melting [9]. The activity was extended later to gas electron diffraction by A. Zewail [10]. More recently—twenty years later—our picosecond electron diffraction experiment on Al was repeated by Dwayne Miller from the University of Toronto with a superior laser and shorter pulses [11]. Note that Dwayne was at the University of Rochester in the chemistry department with a joint appointment in Optics when, in 1982, Steve did his seminal experiment. Today, time-resolved electron diffraction is becoming a very active field, rivaling with time resolved x-ray diffraction.

The First Steps of THz Generation

We knew that the picosecond rise time produced by photoconductive switching could be used to produce THz transients either from the gap itself, by putting a switch in a coaxial waveguide transition, or by exciting a microwave antenna [12]. This simple experiment was performed by a dedicated undergraduate student, Daniel Blumenthal from the electrical engineering department, in collaboration with his adviser, C. Stancampiano, and A. Antonetti from the Ecole Nationale Supérieure de Techniques Avancées in France [13]. The THz field became a very important domain, once it was realized by Auston [14] that the electric field could be time-resolved by the laser pulse itself. The field amplitude and phase could be measured and a new THz spectroscopy technique was born that would replace infrared Fourier-transform spectroscopy [15]. Besides spectroscopy, applications of these transients include THz imaging. Also, the methods of generation have been vastly advanced as demonstrated by X-C Zhang [16].

Electro-optic Sampling (EOS): Opening the Field of THz Electronics

We could switch electrical signals with risetimes in the subpicosecond domain, but it was difficult to measure them. Wide band sampling oscilloscopes could only go to 25 ps., and the only way to measure the picosecond pulses was to use a second photoconductive gap with a fast photoconductive semiconductor. Of course, one solution was to try to use the electro-optic effect. The EO effect can have a purely electronic reaction with a sub-femtosecond response. But there is no free lunch, and this ultrafast response is paid for in terms of sensitivity. Kilovolts are usually necessary to detect a signal. So, it appeared the EO effect could not be a contender for fast measurements, as it was not sensitive enough. Janis Valdmanis, who had the idea to use lock-in detection in conjunction with the electro-optic effect, demonstrated this to be false. With his "golden hands," Janis showed that submillivolt, subpicosecond signals could be measured [17]. The EOS technique became an indispensable tool to visualize THz electrical signals. For the first time, direct propagation of picosecond electrical pulses on transmission lines, both normal and superconducting (with low and high-Tc) [18, 19] could be investigated. EOS was also used in the measurement of the fastest transistor risetimes [20] and the switching of Josephson junctions [21]. It was also used in the direct investigation of subpicosecond carrier dynamics in semiconductors, such as velocity overshoot [22]. Most of the activity was coordinated by D. Dykaar and involved many students, like J. Whitaker, visiting scientist R. Sobolewski and professor T. Hsiang, from electrical engineering, as well as K. Meyer, a student from physics.

CPA for Chirped Pulse Amplification, not for Certified Public Accounting

The generation and amplification of short pulses was, however, our main activity. Short pulses were used for everything. At that time, Ti:sapphire had not been invented, and dyes like rhodamine 6G were the main amplifier media. The leading laboratories were at AT&T Bell Laboratories with the group of C. V. Shank, and with E. Ippen and H. Haus at MIT. In our group, outstanding students were working on dye-based generation and amplification of ultrashort pulses. They were T. Sizer [23], I. Duling [24], J. Kafka [25] and T. Norris [26]. During one of our constant and endless discussions about novel ideas and concepts, we discussed in 1982 with Steve Williamson a possible way to get larger energy per pulse by using good energy storage media. We were at LLE and we knew that Nd:glass was a vastly superior energy storage medium—by a factor 10^3–10^4—than dyes. From a bandwidth point of view, Nd:glass can in principle amplify subpicosecond pulses. However, unlike in dye, Nd:glass is almost too good of an energy storage medium. The major problem is that the pulse energy becomes too large, leading to high intensities and nonlinear effects. The nonlinear effects contribute to destroy the beam quality and ultimately lead to the "destruction" of the optical amplifier. Dyes, on the other hand, do not have this problem. They are mediocre energy storage media, due to their large cross-section. Therefore, the pulse energy stays below the critical intensity level where the nonlinear effects dominate. We were greatly influenced by the work of D. Grischkowsky (IBM Yorktown Heights) and A. Johnson (AT&T Bell Laboratories) that demonstrated that by propagating a relatively long pulse in a fiber, the pulse will be the subject of broadening and stretching by a combination of self-phase modulation (SPM) and group velocity dispersion (GVD). As a result, the pulse is stretched with the spectral content of a much shorter pulse. It exhibits a linear chirp. At this point it can be compressed by using a Treacy grating pair, which exhibits a negative GVD to a value one hundred times the value of the input pulse. It looked to me that it would be simple to try to amplify the pulse in order to extract the amplifier energy and compress it later when the energy would be fully extracted. I asked a new student, Donna Strickland, if she would like to do this experiment. Donna was excited about it but also concerned that it might not be good enough for a Ph.D. thesis. She quickly demonstrated that this concept was working to the millijoule level [26].

The key to CPA: the matched stretcher-compressor. The first approach to CPA was rudimentary and relied on an unmatched stretcher-compressor system. It was not perfect. After a certain amount of stretching, the compressor could not compress the pulse without causing significant wings on the pulse. The fiber-grating pair system was not matched over all orders. What we needed was a matched stretcher-compressor system so we could extract the energy better and compress it better. The matched stretcher compressor became our "Holy Grail." I was continuously thinking about it. One day I was skiing at Bristol Mountain with my wife Marcelle, and on the chairlift I started to think about a paper I read the day before from O. Martinez [27]. This paper was describing a compressor for communication applications at 1.5 μm. At this wavelength the GVD in fiber is negative and the pulses exhibit a negative chirp where the blue frequencies lead the red ones. To recompress the pulse at the fiber output, Martinez proposed a compressor with positive GVD that was a combination of a grating pair and a telescope of magnification unity. I realized that the Martinez compressor in the positive GVD region was in fact the matched stretcher of the Treacy compressor. This was exactly what we were looking for. I interrupted my day of skiing and went back to the laboratory, where I met Maurice Pessot, a new student in my group. I asked Maurice to drop what he was doing and show that the Martinez stretcher and the Treacy grating pair were matched. In a beautiful experiment, Maurice showed that an 80 fs. pulse could be arbitrarily stretched 1000 times by the Martinez device and recompressed by the same factor to its initial value [28]. A major hurdle in CPA was overcome. Fifteen years later, this stretching-compression system is still part of the standard CPA architecture.

The Petawatt. The stretcher-compressor was integrated in our first Joule level Nd:glass system by a visiting scientist, P. Maine, and a post doctoral fellow, P. Bado [29]. With Donna they demonstrated a pulse with one joule in 1 ps., i.e. 1 terawatt on a table top—called the "Maine event" since. It was at night and we were jubilant. R. McCrory, the LLE director, was as usual working late and heard our noisy celebration. He poked his head in the laboratory curious to know what was going on. I told him that we just had demonstrated the generation of one TW with a new amplification technique. It was a thousand times improvement in power over standard techniques, and moreover, this technique could be scaled to a much higher energy than the 1 kJ level using the glass development laser (GDL), a prototype chain at LLE. At that time we paused and asked ourselves what the next scientific prefix after "tera" was. Nobody knew. We went to Bob's office and discovered that it was "peta." So from now on, our next goal would be the petawatt. The first article on the possibility of producing petawatt level pulses was described in a French scientific journal, "En Route Vers Le Petawatt" [30] and the first petawatt pulse was demonstrated by M. Perry at Livermore ten years later.

The name T^3, for table top terawatt, was coined by Jonathan Heritage as he was visiting our laboratory. At that time we decided with Patrick and Donna to call this new amplification technique chirped pulse amplification (CPA). CPA appeared for the first time in reference [29]. Of course Wayne, who was at AT&T Bell Laboratories by that time and always has something to say, called me to argue that people would get the acronym mixed up with "certified public accounting."

We worked a lot to extend the technique to other materials, such as Alexandrite with Jeff Squier and Don Harter [31]. That was before the Ti:sapphire. Alexandrite was at that time the only broadband high-energy storage material available. A lot of the CPA work continued after our move to the University of Michigan with Ted Norris [32], Jeff Squier, Francois Salin [33] and Gary Valliancourt producing the first kHz Ti:sapphire source, which is the workhorse of many ultrafast optical laboratories today. Let's also not forget the indispensable role of Marcel Bouvier, our dedicated electronics engineer who devised the first kHz Pockels cell, the key element of any CPA system.

CPA and Its First Steps in Science

The first paper on the CPA and T³ was presented at the 1986 ICOMP meeting in Boulder [34], where I met Mike Perry from Livermore and Gérard Mainfray from the Commissariat Atomique Energie at Saclay France. Because of the possibility of producing intensities well into the 10^{18} W/cm² regime, the relativistic regime, it was recognized that the CPA technique would revolutionize atomic, plasma and high-energy physics. In a sense the University of Rochester was the perfect cradle. The potential of the T³ and CPA was understood by a number of people. Among the early ones were the tandem of Mike Campbell and Mike Perry from Lawrence Livermore National Laboratory (LLNL). Together we dreamt of the possibility of building a petawatt at Livermore. That dream was fulfilled in 1997 [35], ten years after the first TW, and a few years after the concept of fast ignition was conceived. In 1988 we wrote together the first proposal on petawatt physics) for a LLNL laboratory director's grant. The requested amount was $590 k. Certainly considered too early or too revolutionary, this proposal was not funded. The first experiments on T³ were done in plasma physics by the group of the Institut National de la Recherche Scientifique in Montreal (Quebec) led by H. Pepin [37] in collaboration with a new young professor, D. Meyerhofer. The first atomic physics experiment [38] was performed under the direction of S. L. Chin and J. Eberly (S. L. Chin was on sabbatical with J. Eberly). With A. Melissinos we were thinking about high-energy accelerators by combining fast switching and CPA as well as with K. McDonald from Princeton on nonlinear QED [39]. In 1988 the first CPA Nd:glass was reproduced outside the University by the group of G. Mainfray at the CEA Saclay [40] as well as at the Institute for Laser Engineering (ILE) in Japan by Y. Kato's group with C. Barty and K. Yamakawa [41]. I was relieved to see that our work could be duplicated elsewhere. They were the first of a long series of CPA systems and the birth of a highly active and competitive field involving atomic, plasma, nuclear and high energy physics, astrophysics and cosmology.

Thanks to The Institute of Optics' exceptional students and the Laboratory for Laser Energetics' facilities, the University of Rochester has been the cradle of a number of ultrafast disciplines, notably the thriving high field science area that includes over a thousand researchers and published papers, as well as dozens of conferences per year.

Gérard A. Mourou was a member of the faculty of the University of Rochester from 1979 until 1994. He is currently director of the Center for Ultrafast Optical Science, University of Michigan.

References

1.   G. Mourou and W. Knox, "High-Power Switching with Picosecond Precision," *Appl. Phys. Lett.* 35, 492–95 (October 1979).

2.   W. Knox and G. Mourou, "A Simple Jitter-Free Picosecond Streak Camera," *Opt. Commun.* 37, 203–206 (May 1981).

3.   a) J. Larsson, Z. Chang, E. Judd, P. J. Schuck, R. W. Falcone, P. A. Heimann, H. A. Padmore, H. C. Kapteyn, P. H. Bucksbaum, M. M. Murnane, R. W. Lee, A. Machacek, J. S. Wark, X. Liu, and B. Shan, *Opt. Lett.* 22, 1012 (1997). b) M. Wulff, D. Bourgeois, T. Ursby, L. Goir, and G. Mourou, in *Time-Resolved Diffraction*, ed. J. R. Helliwell and P. M. Rentzepis (Oxford: Clarendon Press, 1997), 195–228.

4.   J. Agostinelli, G. Mourou, and C. W. Gabel, "Active Pulse Shaping in the Picosecond Domain," *Appl. Phys. Lett.* 35, 731–33 (November 1979).

5. G. Mourou, J. Bunkenburg, and W. Seka, "Electrooptic Prepulse Suppression for Fusion Laser Systems," *Opt. Commun.* 34, 252–54 (August 1980).

6. K. Witte, private communication.

7. G. Mourou and S. Williamson, "Picosecond Electron Diffraction," *Appl. Phys. Lett.* 41, 44–45 (July 1982).

8. S. Williamson, G. A. Mourou, and J. C. M. Li, "Time-Resolved Laser-Induced Phase Transformation in Aluminum," *Phys. Rev. Lett.* 52, 2364–67 (June 1984).

9. H. E. Elsayed-Ali and G. A. Mourou, "Picosecond Reflection High-Energy Electron Diffraction," *Appl. Phys. Lett.* 52, 103–104 (January 1988).

10. R. Srinivasan, V. A. Lobastov, Ch. Y. Ruan, A. Zewail, *Helv. Chim. Acta.* 86, 1763 (2003).

11. B. J. Siwick, J. R. Dwyer, R. E. Jordan, and R. J. Dwayne Miller, "An Atomic-Level View of Melting Using Femtosecond Electron Diffraction," *Science.* 1382–85 (November 2003).

12. G. Mourou, C. V. Stancampiano, and D. Blumenthal, "Picosecond Microwave Pulse Generation," *Appl. Phys. Lett.* 38, 470–72 (March 1981).

13. G. Mourou, C. V. Stancampiano, A. Antonetti, and A. Orszag, "Picosecond Laser-Driven Semiconductor Switch," *Appl. Phys. Lett.* 39, 295 (1981).

14. P. R. Smith, D. H. Auston, and M. C. Nuss, *IEEE J. Quantum Electrton.* QE-24, 255 (1988).

15. M. van Exter and D. Grischkowsky, *IEEE Trans Microwave Th. Tech.* 38, 1684 (1990).

16. B. Ferguson and X.-C. Zhang, *Nature Materials*, Vol. 1, 32 (September 2002)

17. J. A. Valdmanis, G. Mourou, and C. W. Gabel, "Subpicosecond Electrical Sampling," *Picosecond Optoelectronics* (Bellingham, WA: SPIE, 1983), Vol. 439, pp. 142–48.

18. a) J. A. Valdmanis and G. Mourou, "Subpicosecond Electro-optic Sampling: Principles and Applications," *IEEE J. Quantum Electron.* QE-22, 69–78 (January 1986). b) J. F. Whitaker, T. B. Norris, G. Mourou, and T. Y. Hsiang, "Pulse Dispersion and Shaping in Microstrip Lines," *IEEE Trans. Microwave Theory Tech.* MTT–35, 41–47 (January 1987).

19. D. R. Dykaar, T. Y. Hsiang, and G. A. Mourou, "An Application of Picosecond Electro-Optic Sampling to Superconducting Electronics," *IEEE Trans. Magn.* 21, 230–33 (March 1985).

20. J. F. Whitaker, G. Mourou, T. C. L. G. Sollner, and W. D. Goodhue, "Picosecond Switching Time Measurement of a Resonant-Tunneling Diode," *Appl. Phys. Lett.* 53, 385–87 (August 1988).

21. D. R. Dykaar, R. Sobolewski, T. Y. Hsiang, and G. A. Mourou, "Response of a Josephson Junction to a Stepped Voltage Pulse," *IEEE Trans. Magn.* MAG-23, 767–70 (March 1987).

22. K. Meyer, M. Pessot, G. Mourou, R. Grondin, and S. Chamoun, "Subpicosecond Photoconductivity Overshoot in Gallium Arsenide Observed by Electro-Optic Sampling," *Appl. Phys. Lett.* 53, 2254–56 (December 1988).

23. G. A. Mourou and T. Sizer II, "Generation of Pulses Shorter than 70 fs with a Synchronously-pumped CW Dye Laser," *Opt. Commun.* 41, 47–48 (March 1982).

24. I. N. Duling III, T. Norris, T. Sizer II, P. Bado, and G. A. Mourou, "Kilohertz Synchronous Amplification of 85-Femtosecond Optical Pulses," *J. Opt. Soc. Am.* B-2, 616–18 (April 1985).

25. T. Sizer II, J. D. Kafka, I. N. Duling III, C. W. Gabel, and G. A. Mourou, "Synchronous Amplification of Subpicosecond Pulses," *IEEE J. Quantum Electron.* QE-19, 506–11 (April 1983).

26. D. Strickland and G. Mourou, "Compression of Amplified Chirped Optical Pulses," *Opt. Commun.* 56, 219–21 (December 1985).

27. O. E. Martinez, *IEEE J. Quantum Electron.* QE-23, 1385 (1987).

28. M. Pessot, P. Maine, G. Mourou, "1000 Times Expansion/Compression of Optical Pulses for Chirped Pulse Amplification," *Opt. Commun.* 62, 419–21 (June 1987).

29. P. Maine, D. Strickland, P. Bado, M. Pessot, and G. Mourou, "Generation of Ultrahigh Peak Power Pulses by Chirped Pulse Amplification," *IEEE J. Quantum Electron.* QE-24, 398–403 (February 1988).

30. P. Maine, D. Strickland, P. Bado, M. Pessot, and G. Mourou, *Rev. Phys. Appl.* 22, 1657 (1987).
31. P. Bado, M. Pessot, J. Squier, G. A. Mourou, and D. J. Harter, "Regenerative Amplification in Alexandrite of Pulses from Specialized Oscillators," *IEEE J. Quantum Electron.* QE-24, 1167–71, (June 1988).
32. G. Vaillancourt, T. B. Norris, J. S. Coe, and G. A. Mourou, "Operation of a 1-kHz Pulse-Pumped Ti:sapphire Regenerative Amplifier," *Opt. Lett.* 15, 317–19 (March 1990).
33. J. Squier, F. Salin, G. Mourou, and D. Harter, "100-fs Pulse Generation and Amplification in Ti:Al$_2$O$_3$," *Opt. Lett.* 16, 324–26 (March 1991).
34. ICOMP, Boulder 1986.
35. M. Perry, P. Pennington, B. C. Stuart, G. Tietbohl, J. A. Britten, C. Brown, S. Herman, B. Golick, M. Kartz, J. Miller, H. T. Powwell, M. Vergino, and V. Yanovsky, *Opt. Lett.* 24, 160 (1999).
36. Petawatt Physics with Livermore.
37. J. C. Kieffer, P. Audebert, M. Chaker, J. P. Matte, H. Pépin, T. W. Johnston, P. Maine, D. Meyerhofer, J. Delettrez, D. Strickland, P. Bado, and G. Mourou, "Short-Pulse Laser Absorption in Very Step Plasma Density Gradients," *Phys. Rev. Lett.* 62, 760–63 (February 1989).
38. S. L. Chin, S. Augst, D. Strickland, D. D. Meyerhofer, and J. H. Eberly, *Phys. Rev. Lett.* 63, 2212 (1989).
39. C. Bula, K. T. McDonald, E. I. Prebys, et al., *Phys. Rev. Lett.* 76, 3116 (1996).
40. X. F. Li, A. L'Huillier, M. Ferray, L. A. Lompré, G. Mainfray, and C. Manus, *Phys. Rev.* A-39, 5751 (1989).
41. K. Yamakawa, C. P. J. Barty, H. Shiraga, and Y. Kato, *IEEE J. Quantum Electron.* QE-27, 288–94 (1991).

54. How I Discovered (and Rediscovered) The Institute of Optics

Wayne H. Knox

I recently found out that my association with The Institute of Optics actually started even before I was born. According to Myrta B. Knox, shortly before I was born, one of the members of The Institute of Optics wives club knitted me a blanket. We have ascertained that it was in fact Ruth Hopkins, wife of Bob Hopkins, who did the knitting. I also recently met Bob Boynton, who reminded me that I lived in his house for a year when I was only three. But then, when I graduated from East High School in Rochester in 1975, I decided to go to the Rochester Institute of Technology, because the school offered a five-year co-op program of work-study, leading to a bachelor's degree with one and one-half years of work experience. I always believed that working in your chosen field concurrently with education was the best way to be sure that you are putting your maximum efforts into what you really want to do—a continuous reality check.

I was a freshman in the physics department at RIT when I overheard Professor Norm Goldblatt talking to several third-year physics students that the Laboratory for Laser Energetics was looking for co-op students. I asked him if I should apply for a summer job, and he encouraged me to do so. I interviewed with Professor Moshe Lubin, founder of LLE, and he immediately offered me student employment. Wolf Seka had recently arrived and needed some help in the lab, so he agreed to supervise me. This was 1976, before the current LLE buildings were finished, shortly after Wilson Commons had been built. I worked in the old Morey Annex buildings that had just been cleaned out of messy monkey cages from a previous project. I helped to build the Delta laser there in Morey Annex, and we spent many long nights building mono-mode and modelocked Nd:Glass, Nd:YAG and Nd:YLF lasers, and characterizing large aperture Pockels cells, making apodized apertures and learning how to operate streak cameras.

One particularly long night, I went to dinner at a German restaurant with Jo Bunkenburg and Steve Kumpan, and I told them that I was really excited about optics. They replied, "Then why don't you transfer to The Institute of Optics?" but I had never heard of the place. I next asked my dad, Robert S. Knox, who was a professor of physics at the University and

Wayne H. Knox graduate student identification photograph.

former department chair of physics, about the optics department. He told me that, in fact, his degree was jointly awarded by the physics department here and The Institute of Optics, since solid-state physics was a part of both departments in the 1950s. I asked him why he had not ever told me about the optics department, and he replied that he thought that if he had told me, I would not be interested. That way, I could claim that I had discovered it myself.

Needless to say, I applied for a transfer, and my transfer was accepted by the director at the time—Professor Nicholas George. I transferred in the spring semester of my sophomore year, and I immediately went into OPT 261 with Professor Brian Thompson. I was immediately hooked, fascinated that you could describe such easily observable phenomena with such great mathematical precision. But, I had missed the OPT 241 geometrical optics course that was being taught by none other than Professor Robert E. Hopkins himself. He had his office at LLE, and I stopped in to ask him what I should do. He told me that he wouldn't want me to get behind, so he would teach it to me over the summer. Imagine that. I took the infamous 471/472 lens design course from Rudolf Kingslake on Wednesday night—I believe the fifty-first time he had taught the course, thirty-five years as an adjunct while working at Eastman Kodak. I took quantum optics from Carlos Stroud, lasers with Conger Gable, physical optics from Nick George.

I greatly enjoyed my undergraduate years, working as a founding member of Gérard Mourou's ultrafast group at LLE, spending considerable time working at LLE with Professor Ken Teegarden (the director at that time) as my academic advisor. Again, the profound synergy between lab work and coursework kept me riveted (it didn't help me very much in my Shakespeare class, though). I stayed for graduate school and continued my research at LLE and finished my Ph.D. in January 1984.

When I finished, I received a staff scientist job offer at Hughes Research Laboratory in Malibu, and a post-doc offer at Bell Labs in New Jersey; I accepted the latter, working with David A. B. Miller and Daniel Chemla in the ultrafast physics of excitons in quantum wells. I also worked in the labs of Charles V. Shank with Richard L. Fork in some very exciting technology advances in femtosecond lasers, amplifiers, spectroscopy techniques and optical pulse compression. I advanced steadily in Bell Labs research until I was appointed in 1997 director of the Advanced Photonics Research Department, in charge of twenty Bell Labs scientists. I continued my ultrafast research focusing mainly in the telecommunications area. In 1998, I was appointed to a visiting trustees panel to review LLE, and I came every October to get an update on the happenings there and in the University in general. At the October 2000 meeting, I heard that Director Dennis Hall had accepted a position at Vanderbilt University, and that the Institute was looking at some possible new directions.

These were the conditions that led me back where I started. Now, I am teaching Optics 101, expanding my research in ultrafast science and technology in biomedical optics, ultrafast manufacturing and telecommunications, and greatly enjoying the academic atmosphere and position of strong growth and support from the administration that we are now in. It is also nice to be back into the Rochester music scene, and have some decent sledding occasionally, as well. One very exciting thing is to have several generations of optics professors teaching and working together here on one common goal—furthering the field of optics through education, research and training in the best way that we know.

Wayne H. Knox received his B.S. and Ph.D. from the Institute of Optics in 1979 and 1984, respectively. He has been a member of the faculty of the University of Rochester since 2001. He has served as the Director of the Institute since 2001.

The Institute of Optics
Faculty 1980–1989

Agrawal, Govind P., 1989–
Altman, Joseph H., 1969–98
Boyd, Robert W., 1977–
Brody, Edward M., 1970–81
Brown, Thomas G., 1987–
Dainty, John Christopher, 1979–85
Davy, L. Nevil, 1987–94
Eastman, Jay M., 1979–98
Eberly, Joseph H., 1979–
Forbes, Gregory W., 1985–94
Forsyth, James M., 1969–85
Gabel, Conger W., 1975–88
George, Nicholas, 1978–
Givens, M. Parker, 1948–
Hall, Dennis G., 1981–2002
Hamilton, John F., 1969–88
Holmgren, Douglas E., 1985–88
Hopkins, Robert E., 1943–
Houde-Walter, Susan N., 1987–
Jacobs, Stephen D., 1988–
Keck, Robert, 1985–88
Kingslake, Rudolf, 1929–2003
Lea, Michael C., 1980–87

Loewen, Erwin, 1988–98
Lubin, Moshe J., 1971–81
MacAdam, David L., 1977–96
Mandel, Leonard, 1978–2000
Marchand, Eric, 1980–94
Moore, Duncan T., 1974–
Morris, G. Michael, 1980–2002
Mourou, Gerard, 1979–94
Raymer, Michael G., 1979–94
Rogers, John R., 1985–94
Sceats, Mark G., 1977–81
Sinclair, Douglas C., 1965–67,
   1970–80
Smith, Douglas, 1989–92, 1999–2002
Smith, Warren, 1988–94
Spitalnik, Steven, 1979–81
Stroud, Jr., Carlos R., 1969–
Teegarden, Kenneth J., 1955–
Thompson, Brian J., 1968–
Walmsley, Ian A., 1988–
Wicks, Gary W., 1987–
Williams, David R., 1988–
Wolf, Emil, 1978–

The Institute of Optics Degrees Awarded 1980–1989

Aaronson, David, B.S., 1982
Agostinelli, John A., M.S., 1977; Ph.D., 1981
Aikens, David, B.S., 1983
Albasio, Marco, B.S., 1986
Albert, Daniel, B.S., 1986
Aldrich, Robert, B.S., 1985
Allardyce, Karen J., M.S., 1985
Allyn, Elizabeth, B.S., 1986
Aloise, James, B.S., 1984
Ames, Gregory H., B.S., 1981; M.S., 1982
Angeley, David, B.S., 1985
Arabos, Vasilios, B.S., 1986
Arackellian, Kevork, B.S., 1984
Arai, Takeo, B.S., 1985
Arrigali, Vincent, B.S., 1982
Atkinson, III, Leland G., Ph.D., 1986
Atlas, David S., B.S., 1980; M.S., 1981
Balkus, Frank, B.S., 1987
Ball, Gary, B.S., 1985; M.S., 1987
Baraban, Edward, B.S., 1989; M.S., 1991
Barber, Paul, B.S., 1989
Barnell, Mark, B.S., 1987
Barrett, Robert, B.S., 1981
Bastiano, Paula, B.S., 1985
Baumgartner, Karolyn, B.S., 1984
Baumgartner, Peter, B.S., 1984
Beck, Mark, B.S., 1985; Ph.D., 1992
Beckhard, Alan, B.S., 1989
Bedard, Sharon, B.S., 1985
Berkoff, Timothy, B.S., 1988
Berthold, Chris, B.S., 1987
Biermann, Mark L., B.S., 1984; Ph.D., 1991
Bietry, Joseph, B.S., 1980
Billow, Nicholas, B.S., 1984
Birdsall, Todd, B.S., 1985
Blablock, Todd, B.S., 1989
Blasenheim, Barry, B.S., 1988
Blaszak, David, B.S., 1988
Bocchiaro, III, Joseph, B.S., 1981
Bond, Christopher, B.S., 1987

Borrelli, John, B.S., 1987
Bortz, John C., Ph.D., 1984
Bothner, Jane, B.S., 1987
Boucher, Richard H., Ph.D., 1981
Bouzid, Ahmed, B.S., 1985; M.S., 1987
Bowler, Karen, B.S., 1982
Bracikowski, Chris, B.S., 1986
Bradfield, Philip L., M.S., 1985; Ph.D., 1990
Bradley, Eric, B.S., 1980; M.S., 1981
Brames, Bryan J., Ph.D., 1986
Brantley, Sheila, B.S., 1982
Brethen, Denise, B.S., 1984
Briguglio, John, B.S., 1987
Brinkman, Jeffrey, B.S., 1989
Brodeur, David, B.S., 1985
Brophy, Chris, Ph.D., 1984
Brown, David L., B.S., 1987; M.S., 1996
Brown, Thomas G., Ph.D., 1987
Brukilacchio, Thomas J., B.S., 1982; M.S., 1983
Buell, Walter, B.S., 1987
Bugenhagan, Jeffrey, B.S., 1988
Bunis, Jenifer, B.S., 1986
Calarco, David, B.S., 1988
Caldwell, J. Brian, Ph.D., 1989
Canal, Nezih, B.S., 1982
Candey, Robert, B.S., 1981
Cappiello, Gregory, B.S., 1984
Carbone, Frank, B.S., 1988
Cardimona, David A., Ph.D., 1984
Cardner, Craig, B.S., 1988
Carellas, Peter, B.S., 1983
Carr, Kevin, B.S., 1982
Carter, III, James, B.S., 1982
Cartwright, Steven L., Ph.D., 1982
Castaneda, Roman, B.S., 1983
Castellani, Robert, B.S., 1988
Castle, William, B.S., 1986
Chambers, David, B.S., 1984
Chen, Pan-Fey, B.S., 1985

Chen, Waikin, B.S., 1987
Chiapperi, Joseph, B.S., 1989
Chipper, Robert, B.S., 1986
Chrien, Thomas, B.S., 1984
Chu, An-Shyan, B.S., 1985
Chu, Hanh Tran, B.S., 1980
Cicchiello, James, B.S., 1988; M.S., 1992
Clark, Michael J., B.S., 1989
Clark, Stephen, B.S., 1987
Clarkson, Andrew, B.S., 1988
Cochran, Eugene, B.S., 1983
Coe, John, B.S., 1986
Cohen, Simon, B.S., 1988
Cohn, Brian D., B.S., 1980; M.S., 1981
Colelli, James, B.S., 1987
Coleman, James, B.S., 1989
Compertore, David, B.S., 1987
Conturie, Yves, Ph.D., 1983
Cook, Catherine, B.S., 1988
Cordi, Anthony, B.S., 1984
Corser, Ellen, B.S., 1987
Costanzo, Chris, B.S., 1983
Cotton, Christopher, B.S., 1986; M.S., 1990
Creath, Katherine, B.S., 1980; M.S., 1981
Creatura, Lawrence, B.S., 1987
Creighton, Daniel, B.S., 1987
Cumbo, Michael J., B.S., 1981; M.S., 1990;
    Ph.D., 1993
Curley, Carole, B.S., 1987
Cusack, Deidre, B.S., 1987
D'Angelo, Lawrence, B.S., 1986
Daley, Michael, B.S., 1989
Darrow, Douglas, B.S., 1985
Daum, Michael, B.S., 1983
Davidson, Barbara, B.S., 1988
de Sterke, Carel M., Ph.D., 1988
Debs, Steven, B.S., 1983
DeJong, C. Dean, B.S., 1986
Delgado, Alvin, B.S., 1986
DeMarco, Michael, B.S., 1987
Demilo, Charles, B.S., 1987
Deutschbein, John, B.S., 1981
Devoe, Catherine, B.S., 1984
Dewa, Paul, B.S., 1985
Diamond, James, B.S., 1986
Diana, John R., B.S., 1988
Dimmler, W. Michael, M.S., 1983
Dir, Gary A., M.S., 1980
Dixon, Sharon, B.S., 1987
Doh, Lucius, B.S., 1989; M.S., 1990
Donaher, John, B.S., 1989
Dougherty, Gregory, B.S., 1983

Downie, John, B.S., 1983
Dufresne de Virel, Francois, M.S., 1981
Duling, III, Irl N., Ph.D., 1986
Dunn, Susan, B.S., 1987
Duquette, Philip, B.S., 1986
Durnin, James E., Ph.D., 1987
Dziura, Thaddeus G., Ph.D., 1987
Economou, Peter, B.S., 1982
Ehmann, Christine, B.S., 1989
Elby, Stuart, B.S., 1982
Elkins, William, B.S., 1980
Eng, Ronnie, B.S., 1985
Engler, Steven, B.S., 1989
English, Jr., R. Edward, Ph.D., 1988
Engstrom, Brian, B.S., 1987
Euquette, Philip, B.S., 1986
Faduski, Charles, B.S., 1989
Farley, Cathleen, B.S., 1987
Farrell, Timothy, B.S., 1980
Fedison, Joseph, B.S., 1987
Feinberg, Lee, B.S., 1987
Ferrin, Deborah S., B.S., 1985
Finck, David, B.S., 1985
Finn, Mary, B.S., 1983
Fonte, William, B.S., 1985
Forer, Jill D., M.S., 1983
Forlenza, Kathleen, B.S., 1989
Forman, Bruce, B.S., 1980
Forman, Warren, B.S., 1987
Forster, Amy, B.S., 1983
Fox, Allen, B.S., 1987
Fox, Richard, B.S., 1980
Franda, Charles, B.S., 1984
Frantz, Christopher, B.S., 1988
Freedbergm David, B.S., 1989
Freese, Robert P., M.S., 1978; Ph.D., 1980
Freymann, John, B.S., 1988
Friberg, Ari T., Ph.D., 1981
Friedman, Douglas, B.S., 1986
Friedman, Marc, B.S., 1984
Friend, John, B.S., 1985
Fry, James, B.S., 1989
Furey, Laurie, B.S., 1982
Gacusan, Lillian, B.S., 1985
Gaeta, Alexander L., B.S., 1983; Ph.D.,
    1990
Gallousis, Gregory, B.S., 1988
Gardner, Leo R., Ph.D., 1989
Garner, Mike, B.S., 1984
Gauthier, Daniel J., Ph.D., 1989
Gentile, Nancy, B.S., 1989
Gianola, Lawrence, B.S., 1984

Gilman, Scott, B.S., 1988
Glass, Thomas R., M.S., 1984
Gobbi, Edward, B.S., 1988; M.S., 1991
Goding, Adrian, B.S., 1986
Goldenberg, Jill, B.S., 1982
Golding, Douglas, B.S., 1989; M.S., 1991
Golini, Donald, B.S., 1986
Golini, Tracey, B.S., 1988
Golob, Laurence, B.S., 1988
Gomba, George, B.S., 1981
Gong, Richard, B.S., 1984
Goodwin, David, B.S., 1985
Gordon, Thomas, B.S., 1986
Gortych, Joseph E., M.S., 1985
Grabarz, Robert, B.S., 1989
Graham, Bruce, B.S., 1987
Greenberg, David, B.S., 1987
Greenland, Alan, B.S., 1985
Greenlee, William, B.S., 1988
Gregory, G. Groot, B.S., 1982
Griffith, Peter, B.S., 1986
Grignol, Kathleen, B.S., 1983
Grimm, Joel, B.S., 1986
Grudus, James, B.S., 1984
Gruhlke, Russell W., Ph.D., 1988
Gruneisen, Mark T., Ph.D., 1989
Guardalben, Mark, B.S., 1983; M.S., 1991
Gum, Steven, B.S., 1981
Gutterman, Pamela, B.S., 1986
Hahn, Walter, B.S., 1987
Hake, Brian, B.S., 1981
Hale, Alex, B.S., 1987
Hanks, Sherry, B.S., 1987
Harmon, Kim, B.S., 1982
Harter, Donald J., Ph.D., 1982
Harvey, George T., Ph.D., 1981
Harvitt, Daniel, B.S., 1987
Hasenauer, David, B.S., 1981
Hassler, Richard, B.S., 1987
Hebb, Ralph, B.S., 1982
Heiney, Allan J., B.S., 1978; M.S., 1981
Heysel, Harrison, B.S., 1982
Hickey, Neil D., M.S., 1980
Hileman, Dane, B.S., 1987
Hillman, Lloyd W., Ph.D., 1984
Hirsch, Jeffrey, B.S., 1986
Hixson, Stephen, B.S., 1982
Hoch, Carlyle, B.S., 1989
Hocheder, Stephen, B.S., 1984
Hochmuth, Diane, B.S., 1984
Hodgdon, Michael, B.S., 1984
Hoke, William, B.S., 1987

Holland, William R., Ph.D., 1985
Holmes, John, B.S., 1985
Hopler, Mark D., M.S., 1987
Horbatuck Suzanne, B.S., 1986; Ph.D., 1996
Houde-Walter, Susan N., M.S., 1983; Ph.D., 1987
Hrycin, Anna L., B.S., 1979; M.S., 1985
Hu, Hui, B.S., 1987
Hubel, Paul, B.S., 1986
Hudyma, Russell, B.S., 1987
Hughart, Bradford, B.S., 1987
Hunter, Vivian, B.S., 1986
Hunter-Hochmuth, Diane, B.S., 1986
Impellizzeri, Craig, B.S., 1985
Intintoli, Alfred, B.S., 1982
Iskenderian, Jr., Arem, B.S., 1982
Jacobs, Arturo A., M.S., 1986
Jacobsen, Karen D., B.S., 1979; M.S., 1980
James, Richard, B.S., 1983
Jaminet, Keith, B.S., 1987
Jin, Michael S., B.S., 1986; M.S., 1988
Johnson, Glen W., Ph.D., 1980
Joj, Katherine, B.S., 1987
Kafka, James D., B.S., 1977; Ph.D., 1984
Kahan, Lloyd, B.S., 1987
Kahn, Ellen (Rich), B.S., 1982
Kalenak, David, B.S., 1988; M.S., 1990
Kalk, Franklin D., Ph.D., 1981
Kamga, FranGois M., M.S., 1976; Ph.D., 1980
Kane, Paul J., M.S., 1984
Kaplan, Michael, B.S., 1985
Karmali, Murad, B.S., 1989
Karp, Chris, B.S., 1988
Kastner, Scott, B.S., 1986
Keegan, Susan, B.S., 1980
Kellogg, Robert, B.S., 1983
Kelly, John H., M.S., 1976; Ph.D., 1980
Kennedy, Roger, B.S., 1986
Kenward, Paul, B.S., 1983
Kessler, Marsha, B.S., 1986
Kessler, Terrance, B.S., 1982
Kiikka, Craig, B.S., 1983
Kilaru, Johnathan, B.S., 1987
Killius, James, B.S., 1983
King, Oliver, B.S., 1985
Kircher, James, B.S., 1984
Kirschner, Roger, B.S., 1980
Knoetgen, Jeanette, B.S., 1985
Knox, Wayne H., B.S., 1979; Ph.D., 1984
Koch, Charles, B.S., 1989

Kohin, Margaret, B.S., 1983
Kohnke, Glenn, B.S., 1989; Ph.D., 1995
Kondysar, James, B.S., 1987
Kondziela, Martin, B.S., 1987
Koshel, R. John, B.S., 1988; Ph.D., 1997
Kotmel, Robert, B.S., 1986
Kouthoofd, Barbara, B.S., 1985
Kramer, Mark A., Ph.D., 1986
Krill, Daniel M., B.S., 1987; M.S., 1990
Kupfer, Sharon, B.S., 1987
Kurdi, Bulent N., Ph.D., 1989
Kurkhill, James, B.S., 1983
Kurtz, Andrew, B.S., 1984
Kwarta, Brian J., B.S., 1983; M.S., 1984
Laird, Ronald, B.S., 1988
Landowne, Gary, B.S., 1982
LeBaron, Jennifer, B.S., 1988
Leidig, Carl, B.S., 1985
Lenney, James, B.S., 1987
Leung, Chin-man, B.S., 1989; M.S., 1990
Levine, Bruce M., Ph.D., 1986
Levine, Michael, B.S., 1989
Lewis, Alan E., B.S., 1981; M.S., 1982
Li, Zheng-Wu, Ph.D., 1989
Lichtenstein, Terri L., B.S., 1979; M.S., 1980
Lindacher, Joseph, B.S., 1989
Little, Alan, B.S., 1986
Lompado, Arthur, B.S., 1988
Lovejoy, David, B.S., 1988
Lunstead, Mark, B.S., 1986
Lutz, Eric, B.S., 1983
Lynn, Stephen, B.S., 1982
Macartor, Trudy, B.S., 1981
Magocks, Stephen, B.S., 1982
Mahnke, Barbara, B.S., 1986
Malcuit, Michelle S., Ph.D., 1987
Malik, Amjad, B.S., 1984
Malyak, Phillip H., Ph.D., 1986
Mandra, Robert, B.S., 1987
Mann, Eileen, B.S., 1987
Mann, Gregory, B.S., 1989
Markason, David, B.S., 1986
Marquart, Margaret, B.S., 1988
Marron, Joseph C., B.S., 1981; Ph.D., 1986
Martin, John D., M.S., 1988
Martin, Sarah, B.S., 1987
Matson, Robert, B.S., 1984
Maxwell, Bruce, B.S., 1984
Mayer, Pamela, B.S., 1985
Mc Mackin, Ian, Ph.D., 1989
McCabe, George, B.S., 1986

McCabe, Jill, B.S., 1988
McCarthy, Matthew, B.S., 1988
McCarthy, Michael, B.S., 1987
McCarthy, Patrick, B.S., 1989
McDonald, Peter, B.S., 1987
McFarlane, David, B.S., 1985
McGuire, Kevin, B.S., 1983
McIntyre, Kevin, B.S., 1988; Ph.D., 1998
McLauchlin, John, B.S., 1986
McLaughlin, Paul O., M.S., 1978; Ph.D., 1983
McNenny, Patrick, B.S., 1983
McTiernan, Michael, B.S., 1985
Meiners, William, B.S., 1989
Mendleson, Alton, B.S., 1986
Meredith, William, B.S., 1989
Mersereau, Keith, B.S., 1984
Methvin, Kimberly, B.S., 1985
Metzger, Robert, B.S., 1985
Miceli, Joseph J., Ph.D., 1983
Michaels, Richard, B.S., 1982
Michaloski, Paul, B.S., 1984
Michalski, James, B.S., 1986
Miciuda, Gail, B.S., 1988
Miller, Brian R., B.S., 1986
Miller, Bruce E., B.S., 1979; M.S., 1980
Miller, Edward J., B.S., 1985; Ph.D., 1991
Miller, Thomas, B.S., 1986
Mills, James P., Ph.D., 1985
Mills, Roger, B.S., 1983
Milowic, Chris, B.S., 1982
Mitchell, Karin, B.S., 1987
Modavis, Robert A., M.S., 1982; Ph.D., 1990
Molander, William A., Ph.D., 1983
Montroll, Andrew, B.S., 1980
Moran, John, B.S., 1989
Moriarity, Kenneth, B.S., 1987
Morien, Steven, B.S., 1988
Morrison, Robert, B.S., 1988
Morse, Samuel, B.S., 1983
Morse, Susan, B.S., 1988
Mott, Andrew, B.S., 1987
Mounts, Darryl I., B.S., 1979; M.S., 1981
Mullen, Siobhan, B.S., 1983
Nadeau, Mary J., B.S., 1982; M.S., 1984
Nadorff, Georg, B.S., 1985
Nash, Daniel, B.S., 1988
Natrella, Vincent, B.S., 1981
Naughton, Denis P., M.S., 1986
Neff, Brian, B.S., 1984
Ness, Colin, B.S., 1984

Ng, Linda, B.S., 1987
Nichols, Craig, B.S., 1987
Niedzwiecki, Colleen, B.S., 1987
Nilsen, Kristin, B.S., 1987
Noll, Thomas, B.S., 1986
O'Brien, Justin, B.S., 1987
O'Donnell, Kevin A., Ph.D., 1983
O'Neill, Mark, B.S., 1988; M.S., 1993
Obear, Jeffrey, B.S., 1984
Okay, Kemalat, B.S., 1988
Oschmann, Jacobus, B.S., 1982
Padnos, Stephen, B.S., 1984
Pagano, Robert, B.S., 1985
Pakyz, Joseph, B.S., 1984
Palvino, Mark, B.S., 1985
Papademetriou, Stephanos, B.S., 1986;
　Ph.D., 1993
Parisis, John, B.S., 1985
Parker, Jeffrey, B.S., 1987
Parker, Jodi, B.S., 1987
Pasciak, Susan M., M.S., 1981
Pavia, Michael, B.S., 1987
Payumo, Vernon, B.S., 1988
Percevault, Elizabeth, B.S., 1988
Percevault, Mark, B.S., 1987
Perlin, Jay, B.S., 1983
Perry, David, B.S., 1982
Pessot, Maurice, Ph.D., 1989
Peterson, Kevin, B.S., 1986
Pfisterer, Richard N., M.S., 1980
Phillips, Paul, B.S., 1981
Placella, Michael, B.S., 1980
Plaessmann, Henry, B.S., 1989
Plotsker, Vadim, B.S., 1988
Plympton, Richard, B.S., 1987
Popli, Sanjeev, B.S., 1988
Portilla, Sixto, B.S., 1987
Powers, Thomas F., B.S., 1977; M.S., 1983
Pratt, Rebecca, B.S., 1985
Prince, Brian, B.S., 1986
Procino, Wesley, B.S., 1989
Progler, Chris, B.S., 1986
Purdy, Edmund, B.S., 1987
Reed, Timothy, B.S., 1982
Rentz, Stephen, B.S., 1987
Reven, Shawn, B.S., 1989
Riggs, John, B.S., 1989
Rinehart, Thomas A., M.S., 1976; Ph.D.,
　1982
Roberts, Eric, B.S., 1986
Roberts, Evelyn, B.S., 1988
Roberts, Harrison, B.S., 1989

Roberts, Thomas, B.S., 1985
Rolleston, Robert J., Ph.D., 1988
Rosenbluth, Alan E., B.S., 1976; Ph.D.,
　1983
Rost, Martin, B.S., 1982
Rudder, Scott, B.S., 1988
Ryan-Howard, Danette P., B.S., 1977; M.S.,
　1980; Ph.D., 1983
Saba, Michael, B.S., 1986
Samios, Gregory, B.S., 1985
Samuels, Joan E., M.S., 1989
Sanca, Amy, B.S., 1983
Savan, Mark, B.S., 1986
Schaub, Jr., Charles, B.S., 1984
Schaub, Michael, B.S., 1986
Schmackpfeffer, Kyle, B.S., 1989
Seligson, Joel Leo, Ph.D., 1981
Shanks, David, B.S., 1984
Sharma, Neelima, B.S., 1989
Shimizu, Jeff, B.S., 1986
Shirley, Lyle G., Ph.D., 1988
Short, Darren, B.S., 1988
Short, Svetlana, B.S., 1981
Shramko, Ellen, B.S., 1982
Silva, Francis, B.S., 1985
Silverstein, Barry, B.S., 1984
Silvestro, John, B.S., 1988
Simons, David, B.S., 1984
Sinensky, Amy, B.S., 1989
Sizer, II, Theodore, Ph.D., 1986
Skeldon, Mark D., Ph.D., 1988
Smith, Linda, B.S., 1989
Smith, Michael, B.S., 1984
Smith-Berryman, Cynthia, B.S., 1982
Smucz, Joseph, B.S., 1987
Snow, Linda, B.S., 1984
Sokach, Stephen, B.S., 1987
Stagaman, Gregory J., Ph.D., 1988
Stagaman, Joan M., Ph.D., 1985
Steele, Paul, B.S., 1981
Steijn, Kirk, B.S., 1981
Stern, Ronald D., M.S., 1982
Stone, Bryan D., B.S., 1985; Ph.D., 1992
Stone, Thomas W., B.S., 1979; M.S., 1983;
　Ph.D., 1986
Storne, Eric, B.S., 1986
Strasser, Arden, B.S., 1984
Strickland, Donna T., Ph.D., 1989
Stuart, Brian, B.S., 1989
Stutz, Glenn, B.S., 1981
Sudol, Ronald J., M.S., 1977; Ph.D., 1982
Suhan, John, B.S., 1987

Sullivan, Kevin G., B.S., 1989; Ph.D., 1994
Sullivan, Robert, B.S., 1987
Sullo, Nancy J., B.S., 1982; M.S., 1983
Suroveik, Lisa, B.S., 1989
Sweeney, Ann, B.S., 1987
Sweredoski, Brent, B.S., 1987
Swim, Cynthia, B.S., 1986
Sylvia, Scott, B.S., 1984
Szukala, James, B.S., 1987
Taggart, Christopher, B.S., 1982
Tatarek, Michael, B.S., 1981
Taylor, Christopher, B.S., 1980
Taylor, Leonard, B.S., 1987
Thibodeau, Kristopher, B.S., 1987
Thomas, Jeffrey, B.S., 1980
Thomas, Michael, B.S., 1989
Thorp, Keith, B.S., 1988
Thurer, Carol, B.S., 1987
Tienvieri, Clair, B.S., 1987
Tinker, Flemming, B.S., 1988
Tirone, Stephen, B.S., 1987
Toomey, Christopher, B.S., 1985
Toomey, Thomas, B.S., 1983
Tracy, Mark, B.S., 1987
Traskiewicz-Webb, Patricia, B.S., 1986
Traylor, Jennifer, B.S., 1989; M.S., 1995
Triou, Scott, B.S., 1987
Tritsch, Constance, B.S., 1986
Trueswell, Melissa, B.S., 1987
Tsufura, Lisa, B.S., 1984
Tudryn, Dawn, B.S., 1989
Turner, Richard M., B.S., 1987; M.S. 1989
Ugolini, Virginia, B.S., 1984
Underhill, John, B.S., 1981
Updike, Todd, B.S., 1983
Utano, Richard, B.S., 1983
Uy, Kevin, B.S., 1987
Valdmanis, Janis A., Ph.D., 1984
Valentine, Paul, B.S., 1987
VanDePoel, Alison, B.S., 1987
VanKerkhove, Steven, B.S., 1989
Vastagh, Richard, B.S., 1984
Vayser, Alexander, B.S., 1989
Venable, Dennis L., B.S., 1978; M.S., 1981;
    Ph.D., 1989
Vent, Debra, B.S., 1988
Vento, Robert, B.S., 1987
Vernold, Cynthia, B.S., 1987
Vogel, David, B.S., 1987
Vogel, Deborah, B.S., 1983

Volatile, Heather, B.S., 1987
Wacks, Martin, B.S., 1980
Wagner, Brenda, B.S., 1988
Wald, Andrew, B.S., 1986
Walmsley, Ian A., Ph.D., 1986
Wang, Anna, B.S., 1989
Wang, David Y-H., B.S., 1985; M.S., 1986;
    Ph.D., 1992
Wang, Ingrid, B.S., 1985
Wang, Shen-ge, Ph.D., 1987
Watkins, Todd, B.S., 1984
Weinberg, Brian, B.S., 1987
Weiner, Bruce, B.S., 1984
Weinstock, Mark, B.S., 1988
Weisman, Andrew, B.S., 1989
Weiss, Richard, B.S., 1988
Weissman, Rachael, B.S., 1986
Welch, Jeffrey, B.S., 1984
Welch, Robert, B.S., 1988
Weller-Brophy, Laura A., B.S., 1980; M.S.,
    1983; Ph.D., 1987
Wells, Conrad, B.S., 1989; M.S., 1991
Whitford, Paul, B.S., 1986
Wierman, Kurt, B.S., 1983
Wilder, Mark, B.S., 1985
Wildy, Marc, B.S., 1987
Wilk, Stephen R., M.S., 1983
Wilkens, Peter, B.S., 1988
Wilkins, Michelle L., B.S., 1983
Wilklow, Ronald, B.S., 1983
Williamson, Thomas, B.S., 1988
Winder, Amy, B.S., 1985
Winiarski, Paul, B.S., 1986
Wohl, Michael, B.S., 1989
Wong, Jennan, B.S., 1986
Wooley, Charles B., Ph.D., 1989
Wyatt, Christopher, B.S., 1983
Yang, Michael, B.S., 1989
Yeazell, John, Ph.D., 1989
Youman, Roy, B.S., 1987
Yu, Jenny, B.S., 1988
Yue, Bobby, B.S., 1988
Zavislan, James M., B.S., 1981; Ph.D.,
    1988
Zeller, Brian, B.S., 1983
Zimmer, Debra, B.S., 1986
Zinter, J. Robert, B.S., 1985; M.S., 1987
Zoeller, Steven, B.S., 1984
Zubritsky, Elizabeth, B.S., 1988
Zweig. David, B.S., 1983

PART VII

PHOTONICS BOOM: THE 1990s

VII. Photonics Boom: The 1990s

The decade of the 1990s was the time of two great related "bubbles," the dot-com bubble and the fiber-optic communication bubble. All commerce would be conducted via the web, and the web would operate via the practically unlimited bandwidth available with fiber optics. A fiber-optics connection to every house in the world was the confident prediction of many. High-tech was the darling of the stock market, and fiber optics the favorite of the high-tech industries. Venture capital funding was available for any good idea, and a lot of bad ideas, in fiber-optics communications and switching—in a word, "photonics." This had an enormous influence on the Institute and the optics world in general. B.S. graduates in optics were offered stock options that might be worth millions in a couple of year's time. Fresh Ph.D.s received offers in excess of $90,000 per year plus lucrative stock options. It was difficult to keep students in school to finish their degrees, and it was difficult to retain faculty when their recent students were making more money than they. It was an exciting time, described in Gary Wicks's description of Dennis Hall's directorship and in Hall's essay on photonics. The long-term effects of the bubbles are not yet clear. It does appear that the cheap communications that they provided are opening up international trade like nothing has done before. While there were disruptions in the optics industry when the bubbles burst, the demand for graduates of the Institute has remained high, even if the signing bonuses were not what they once were.

Essays in this section report two other areas in which there have been major developments in Rochester: nonlinear optics and visual science. A major development in classical optics is also presented in an essay by Don Golini, which discusses high-speed automatic grinding and polishing of lenses with arbitrary figure. A technique for accomplishing this was developed in the Center for Optics Manufacturing and exploited by a spin-off company, QED.

A final series of essays in this section describes student pranks and the faculty club. Both have a venerable history at the University of Rochester.

55. The Dennis Hall Years, 1993–2000

Gary Wicks

In 1993 Dennis Hall became the eighth director of The Institute of Optics. He continued as director until his departure from the University in 2000 to become the associate provost for research at Vanderbilt University.

Prior to becoming director, Dennis had been associate director of the Institute during the latter part of Duncan Moore's directorship. Earlier, in 1980, he joined the Institute's faculty, enhancing the Institute with his excellence in guided wave optics research and in teaching, and also with his humor. When a newspaper reporter in the mid-1980s asked about helping to build the future economy of New York with the newly formed Center for Advanced Optical Technology, Dennis replied, "We're just twelve guys trying the save the universe." The quote appeared as the lead sentence in a Rochester newspaper article reporting the awarding of the CAOT program, and, for a while, was posted in big letters on the front window of the Institute. Of course, Dennis received lots of good-natured kidding about it—lots of fun.

Throughout his directorship, Dennis maintained an active research program. In addition to maintaining his own research funding, he was responsible for obtaining two million dollars in support for Institute graduate student stipends and tuition from Department of Education grants through the GAANN program.

An imaginative, collaborative course was created during the Hall years. Over lunch, Dennis Hall and the English Department chair, Morris Eaves, discussed the radical idea of offering a joint optics/English course. This led to the formation of the course, "Clockwork to Chaos," taught jointly by English Professor Dan Albright and Optics Professor Ian Walmsley. It focused on the ways scientific ideas enter and influence important literature, and how those portrayals contribute to the popular view of the natural world. The course was very enthusiastically received, and was recognized by the University for teaching innovation.

The Institute's summer school and industrial associates programs continued to thrive. A highlight of the thirty-second summer school program in 1993 was the lecture on lens design by one of the Institute's original

Dennis Hall leads the Institute.

faculty members, Rudolf Kingslake. In the early 1990s, a small business category was added to the industrial associates program, enabling the immediate addition of eight small companies to the fold.

The Institute was included in the 1995 study of U.S. physics Ph.D. programs performed by the National Academy of Sciences and the National Research Council. If the Institute had been a physics department, it would have been justifiably proud of its ranking in the study. But considering the incomplete overlap of the fields of optics and physics, the Institute's rankings in the physics study were astounding. Of the 147 physics programs ranked, the Institute placed twenty-fifth overall, including rankings of first in publications per faculty member, second in percentage of faculty with external funding, eleventh in faculty effectiveness, and fifteenth in citations per faculty member.

The student numbers were fairly constant through the 1990s, with around a hundred undergraduates and a hundred graduate students in the Institute. Undergraduate classes typically numbered in the upper twenties or low thirties. M.S. class sized fluctuated the most, from less than ten to nearly thirty. Ph.D. classes were always twelve or thereabouts.

The excellence of the Institute's faculty was recognized by the awarding of many honors during the Hall years. Dennis Hall himself was appointed to the William F. May Professorship in Engineering and Applied Sciences. Nicholas George was named the Wilson Professor of Electronic Imaging. Duncan Moore was awarded the Rudolf and Hilda Kingslake Chair of Optical Engineering. Optics Professor Brian Thompson concluded ten years as provost of the University of Rochester in 1994, and was honored by being naming Provost Emeritus and Distinguished University Professor. David Williams became the Allyn Professor of Biomedical Optics. The endowments for two other professorships were formed. The endowment of the Robert E. Hopkins Professorship of Optics was built by over 350 separate gifts by friends and alumni of the Institute. The groundwork was laid by Dennis Hall for the endowment by James and Louise Wyant of the M. Parker Givens Professorship. Additionally, an endowment for the Institute itself was created.

The latter half of Hall's tenure as director was more challenging, University resources were tighter. A national trend continued of decreasing numbers of students entering the physical sciences and engineering. Throughout these challenges, however, the strength of the Institute continued. The leadership, energy, and friendly support of Dennis Hall kept spirits up and the focus where it belonged, on academics and quality.

Gary Wicks is professor of optics and associate director of The Institute of Optics.

56. History of Research in Nonlinear Optics at The Institute of Optics

Robert W. Boyd

Although the birth of the field of nonlinear optics is often taken to be the first observation of second-harmonic generation by Franken et al. in 1961 [1], in fact the rudiments of this field started much earlier. Parts of this early history can be traced back to work performed at The Institute of Optics, and research in nonlinear optics has thrived at the Institute ever since.

The earliest report of a nonlinear optical effect known to the author is that of G. N. Lewis, who in 1941 reported saturation with increasing excitation strength of the fluorescence intensity of the organic dye fluorescein in a boric acid glass host [2]. In fact, the author with his students Mark Kramer and Wayne Tompkin became very much intrigued by this material system, and in the 1980s developed fluorescein-doped boric acid glass as a highly nonlinear material for use in phase conjugation and other applications [3]. At the risk of digression, it should be noted that G. N. Lewis was one of the most gifted chemists in the United States in the first half of the twentieth century. He held faculty positions at Harvard, at MIT, and at the University of California, Berkeley. Early in his career, Lewis developed the idea that the sharing of paired electrons leads to the formation of a chemical bond. The notion of a Lewis acid (a substance such as the H+ ion that can accept a pair of nonbonding electrons) and a Lewis base (a substance such as the OH− ion that can donate a pair of nonbonding electrons) follows directly from this idea. Moreover, it was Lewis who introduced the word "photon" into the scientific lexicography [4]. Until his time, photons were known as "quanta" of radiation, a term introduced by Planck. So Professor Lewis not only introduced the modern definition of an acid and a base, but also invented the word "photon" and created the field of nonlinear optics.

Work in nonlinear optics at The Institute of Optics can be traced back to the work of Brian O'Brien during the Second World War. O'Brien had directed a number of research efforts aimed at helping the U.S. war effort, described elsewhere in this volume. One such effort, under the immediate supervision of Franz Urbach, involved the development of phosphors that would emit visible light upon excitation by infrared radiation. These phosphors led to the development of various infrared and low-light image converters that were crucial to the U.S. war effort. But an additional application involved the utilization of the nonlinear transfer characteristics of these phosphors. A problem facing the U.S. Navy was that the Japanese were making their bombing attacks on U.S. ships by approaching from the direction of the sun, thus effectively blinding those defending their ships. An imaging device was needed that would dramatically reduce the brightness of the sun while preserving the brightness of immediately adjacent objects. O'Brien and his associates solved this problem through use of saturation of the luminescence of their phosphors. Strong saturation of the luminescence efficiency occurred at those regions illuminated by the sun;

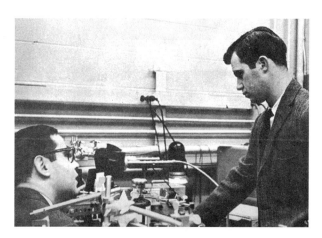

Assistant Professor Mike Hercher discusses possible laser experiments to test Associate Professor Al Gold's theory.

little or no saturation occurred at the adjacent regions, allowing objects in these regions, such as enemy aircraft, to be clearly seen. This device became know as the Icaroscope, named after the Greek tragic hero Icarus.

The invention of the laser led to dramatically new possibilities in the field of nonlinear optics. A spectacular example is the observation at The Institute of Optics in 1964 by Michael Hercher of bulk, laser-induced damage of optical materials such as glass [5]. This observation is at first sight surprising (both in 1964 and today), because a simple estimate of the intensity of the incident laser light suggests that no damage should occur. The current explanation of the phenomenon discovered by Hercher is that, as a consequence of the nonlinear optical process of self-focusing, the laser beam collapsed to a very small spot size upon entering the material. The intensity at the focal spot thus created can be many orders of magnitude larger than that of the incident laser beam. Hercher's discovery has thus through time led to the development of diverse sub-fields of nonlinear optics including self-focusing, optical soliton formation, and the laser processing of materials.

Theoretical work was also stimulated by the development of the laser. Joseph Eberly investigated nonlinear behavior of a free electron in the field of a laser beam and predicted a nonlinear contribution to the Compton wavelength shift [6]. In addition, Barry Bebb and Albert Gold developed one of the earliest theories of multiphoton absorption of laser light [7].

The author of this essay joined the faculty of the Institute in 1977. Michael Raymer joined the faculty soon thereafter, and the pair, along with Donald Harter, began conducting detailed theoretical and experimental studies of how four-wave mixing processes become modified in the presence of laser fields so intense that the atomic energy level structure is modified by the light field [8, 9]. They found that under these circumstances the laser beam transmitted through an atomic vapor cell tends to develop a ring structure surrounding the central component; this process has been called conical emission and has subsequently been investigated extensively.

Raymer and his student Ian Walmsley (who later spent many years on the optics faculty) performed detailed theoretical and experimental studies of how the process of stimulated Raman scattering is initiated by quantum noise [10]. This work motivated

Institute visitors Paul Narum and Kazimierz Rzążewski to perform similar studies of the initiation of the process of stimulated Brillouin scattering [11]; these predictions are useful in predicting the properties of phase conjugate mirrors based on stimulated Brillouin scattering. Dennis Hall also joined the faculty of the Institute at about this same time. His primary research interest was in guided-wave optics, although some of his research was in the field of nonlinear optics. For example, he and Theodore Dziura worked on optical bistability in various photonic systems [12].

My own research has been in the field of optical physics with a concentration on fundamental and applied nonlinear optics. The fundamentals of this field are presented in my textbook *Nonlinear Optics* [13]. During my years in Rochester, I have had the pleasure of supervising and interacting with a large number of exceptional Ph.D. students during my years at the Institute. The remainder of this article outlines some of the results of our research studies.

Local Field Effects and Artificial Materials for Nonlinear Optics

My students, co-workers, and I have performed fundamental studies of the nature of local field effects in dense optical materials, and have shown that local field effects can be exploited to synthesize engineered materials with specially tailored nonlinear optical properties.

This work commenced with a laboratory study by Jeffrey Maki, Michelle Malcuit, John Sipe, and myself of local field effects in a dense atomic vapor. The influence of local field effects was controlled in this experiment by continuously varying the atomic number density. A key result of this project was the first measurement [14] of the Lorentz red shift, a shift of the atomic absorption line as a consequence of local field effects. This red shift had been predicted by Lorentz in the latter part of the nineteenth century, but had never previously been observed experimentally. In addition to confirming this century-old prediction, this work is significant in confirming the validity of the Lorentz local-field formalism even under conditions associated with the resonance response of atomic vapors.

More recently, we have made use of local field effects to tailor the nonlinear optical response of composite optical materials. This work includes the prediction [15] and subsequent laboratory confirmation by George Fischer, Russell Gehr, and others [16] that it is possible to construct a composite material in such a manner that the nonlinear susceptibility of the composite exceeds those of the materials from which it is constructed. A three-fold enhancement of the nonlinear susceptibility has been demonstrated more recently through use of this technique by Robert Nelson and myself [17]. Composite materials hold promise for even larger values of the enhancement in materials formed of alternating metallic and dielectric layers forming a photonic bandgap structure, as shown by Ryan Bennink and others [18]. Quite recently, we have become interested in forming completely artificial materials by coupling micro-ring resonators to optical waveguides. This work is based on the realization that the nonlinear response and dispersive properties of a ring resonator increase very rapidly with the finesse of the resonator. John Heebner has constructed working devices of this sort as part of his thesis work [19, 20].

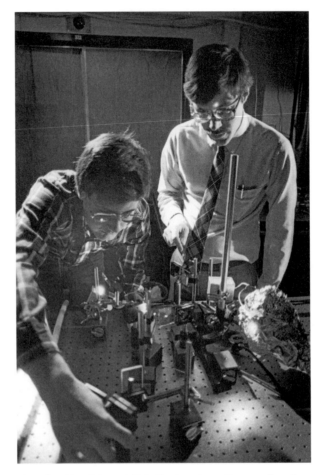

Dan Gauthier (left) and Bob Boyd study nonlinear optics of sodium vapor.

Optical Studies of Chaos, Nonlinear Dynamics, and Optical Pattern Formation

We were also involved in some of the early studies of optical chaos and optical nonlinear dynamics [21]. Our group performed the first laboratory demonstrations of chaotic behavior in a purely passive, resonatorless nonlinear optical system. This work was crucial in elucidating the conditions under which an optical system could become unstable to chaotic behavior; prior to that time optical chaos had been observed only in lasers and in passive nonlinear optical systems in the presence of external feedback. Our work entailed the observation by Daniel Gauthier, Narum, and myself of chaotic behavior in a photorefractive phase conjugate mirror [22]. Our work also involved the prediction by Alexander Gaeta and others [23] and subsequent observation by Gauthier, Malcuit, and myself of chaotic behavior in the polarizations of counterpropagating laser beams in an atomic sodium vapor [24]. More recently, we have become involved in research on spontaneous pattern formation in nonlinear optical systems, leading to the observation and theoretical description of honeycomb patterns and other regular patterns formed spontaneously in a laser beam propagating through an atomic sodium vapor [25].

Fundamental Studies in Quantum and Nonlinear Optics

Malcuit, Maki, David Simkin and I conducted a successful experiment [26] aimed at elucidating the relationship between superfluorescence and amplified spontaneous emission (ASE). The idea of this experiment was to fabricate a gain medium (monovalent molecular oxygen doped into single-crystal potassium chloride) for which the dipole dephasing rate could be controlled by varying the temperature of the sample. We found that at low temperatures the emission occurred through the process of superfluorescence, that is, the emission took place in the form of a well-defined pulse occurring after a short time delay. At higher temperatures, the emission occurred as a result of ASE, and the emission was in the form of a longer, noisy pulse with no time delay. The experiment also showed how the nature of the emission changed as the dephasing rate was varied continuously between the two limiting values. These results led to some excitement in the theoretical community as attempts were made to model the experimental results [27, 28].

We have also performed fundamental studies in the field of nonlinear optics, including an investigation by Gauthier, Jerzy Krasinski, and myself of the role of atomic Rydberg states in leading to resonantly enhanced ultraviolet generation [29]. Malcuit and Gauthier worked with me on studies of how various nonlinear optical processes can compete with one another, at times in enormously subtle ways, such as the nearly complete suppression of one nonlinear optical process by another [30]. Martti Kauranen, William Davis, Elna Nagasako, and Gaeta worked on various aspects of how quantum noise can modify the behavior of various nonlinear optical processes [31]. Mark Gruneisen, Kenneth MacDonald, Gaeta and I worked on the construction of optical amplifiers based on four-photon nonlinear optical coupling [32, 33]. Robert Bridges worked on the influence of space-time coupling on the mode-locking of laser systems [34].

More recently we have has been actively engaged in studies of electromagnetically induced transparency (EIT) in various atomic systems. For example, Bennink, Vincent Wong, Carlos Stroud and I have studied EIT in two-level atomic systems [35]. In addition, Marlan Scully and I have investigated the use of quantum coherence effects to increase the sensitivity of infrared detection [36], and Q-Han Park and I have shown how to control fundamental quantum optical processes through use of phase-coherent media [37]. Moreover, Girish Agarwal, Elna Nagasako, Sean Bentley and I have demonstrated theoretically the possibility of performing "quantum lithography" using light produced by a high-gain parametric amplifier [38].

Optical Phase Conjugation, Stimulated Light Scattering, and Fiber Nonlinear Optics

In the area of optical phase conjugation, we have performed theoretical studies of the role of quantum noise in phase conjugation [39], of the polarization properties of the phase conjugation process [40, 41], of the process of Brillouin-enhanced four-wave mixing [42], of phase conjugate interferometry [43], and of techniques for single-pass aberration correction [44]. Edward Miller performed experimental studies of ultrafast stimulated light scattering [45]. Thomas Moore performed detailed studies of the energetics of the process of stimulated Brillouin scattering [46] and observed chaos in the Brillouin interaction [47]. Mark Bowers and co-workers [48] designed and constructed phase conjugate laser systems based on stimulated Brillouin scattering.

We have also been very interested in the nonlinear optical properties of optical fibers. Gaeta studied the nonlinear dynamics of the process of stimulated Brillouin scattering in optical fibers [49]. Andrew Stentz studied soliton formation in optical fibers [50]. Eric Buckland studied the various mechanisms of nonlinearity in optical fibers and concluded that in many circumstances electrostriction can make up to a 20 percent contribution [51, 52].

The present essay has summarized the history of the field of nonlinear optics from the perspective of The Institute of Optics. A historical account from a broader perspective has been presented by Bloembergen [53]. The field of nonlinear optics remains an extremely exciting field of scientific investigation. The Institute of Optics has played a key role in the history of the development of this field.

Robert W. Boyd has been a member of the faculty of the University of Rochester since 1977. He is the M. Parker Givens Professor of Optics.

References

1. P. A. Franken, A. E. Hill, C. W. Peters, and G. Weinreich, *Phys. Rev. Lett.* 7, 118 (1961).
2. G. N. Lewis, D. Lipkin, and T. T. Magel, *J. Am. Chem. Soc.* 63, 3005 (1941).
3. M. A. Kramer, W. R. Tompkin, and R. W. Boyd, "Nonlinear Optical Interactions in Fluorescein-Doped Boric Acid Glass," *Phys. Rev. A* 34, 2026 (1986).
4. G. N. Lewis, *Nature* 118, part 2, 874–75 (1926).
5. M. Hercher, *J. Opt. Soc. Am.* 54, 563 (1964).
6. J. H. Eberly, *Phys. Rev. Lett.* 15, 91 (1965).
7. H. B. Bebb and A. Gold, *Phys. Rev.* 143, 1 (1966).
8. D. J. Harter, P. Narum, M. G. Raymer, and R. W. Boyd, "Four-Wave Parametric Amplification of Rabi Sidebands in Sodium," *Phys. Rev. Lett.* 46, 1192 (1981).
9. R. W. Boyd, M. G. Raymer, P. Narum, and D. J. Harter, "Four-Wave Parametric Interactions in a Strongly Driven Two-Level System," *Phys. Rev. A* 24, 411 (1981).
10. I. A. Walmsley and M. G. Raymer, "Observation of Macroscopic Quantum Fluctuations in Stimulated Raman Scattering," *Phys. Rev. Lett.* 50, 962–65 (1983).
11. R. W. Boyd, K. Rzążewski, and P. Narum, "Noise Initiation of Stimulated Brillouin Scattering," *Phys. Rev. A* 42, 5514 (1990).
12. D. G. Hall and T. G. Dziura, "Transverse Effects in the Bistable Operation of Lasers Containing Saturable Absorbers," *Opt. Commun.* 49, 146 (1984).
13. R. W. Boyd, *Nonlinear Optics* (Boston: Academic Press, 1992).
14. J. J. Maki, M. S. Malcuit, J. E. Sipe, and R. W. Boyd, "Linear and Nonlinear Optical Measurements of the Lorentz Local Field," *Phys. Rev. Lett.* 68, 972 (1991).
15. J. E. Sipe and R. W. Boyd, "Nonlinear Susceptibility of Composite Optical Materials in the Maxwell Garnett Model," *Phys. Rev. A* 46, 1614 (1992).
16. G. L. Fischer, R. W. Boyd, R. J. Gehr, S. A. Jenekhe, J. A. Osaheni, J. E. Sipe, and L. A. Weller-Brophy, "Enhanced Nonlinear Optical Response of Composite Materials," *Phys. Rev. Lett.* 74, 1871 (1995).

17. R. L. Nelson and R. W. Boyd, "Enhanced Electrooptic Response of Layered Composite Materials," *Appl. Phys. Lett.* 74, 2417 (1999).
18. R. S. Bennink, Y.-K. Yoon, R. W. Boyd, and J. E. Sipe, "Accessing the Optical Nonlinearity of Metals with Metal-Dielectric Photonic Bandgap Structures," *Opt. Lett.* 24, 1416 (1999).
19. J. E. Heebner and R. W. Boyd, "Enhanced All-Optical Switching by Use of a Nonlinear Fiber Ring Resonator," *Opt. Lett.* 24, 847 (1999).
20. J. E. Heebner, R. W. Boyd, and Q.-H. Park, "Slow Light, Induced Dispersion, Enhanced Nonlinearity, and Optical Solitons in a Nanostructured Waveguide, *Phys. Rev. E* 65, 036619 (2002).
21. R. W. Boyd, M. G. Raymer, and L. M. Narducci, eds., *Optical Instabilities* (Cambridge: Cambridge University Press, 1986).
22. D. J. Gauthier, P. Narum, and R. W. Boyd, "Observation of Deterministic Chaos in a Self-Pumped Phase Conjugate Mirror," *Phys. Rev. Lett.* 58, 16 (1987).
23. A. L. Gaeta, R. W. Boyd, J. R. Ackerhalt, and P. W. Milonni, "Instabilities and Chaos in the Polarizations of Counterpropagating Light Fields," *Phys. Rev. Lett.* 58, 2432 (1987).
24. D. J. Gauthier, M. S. Malcuit, and R. W. Boyd, "Polarization Instabilities of Counterpropagating Laser Beams in Sodium Vapor," *Phys. Rev. Lett.* 61, 1827 (1988).
25. R. S. Bennink, V. Wong, A. M. Marino, D. L. Aronstein, R. W. Boyd, C. R. Stroud, Jr., S. Lukishova, and D. J. Gauthier, "Honeycomb Pattern Formation by Laser-Beam Filamentation in Atomic Sodium Vapor," *Phys. Rev. Lett.* 88, 113901 (2002).
26. M. S. Malcuit, J. J. Maki, D. J. Simkin, and R. W. Boyd, "The Transition from Superfluorescence to Amplified Spontaneous Emission," *Phys. Rev. Lett.* 59, 1189 (1987).
27. J. J. Maki, M. S. Malcuit, M. G. Raymer, R. W. Boyd, and P. D. Drummond, "Influence of Collisional Dephasing Processes on Superfluorescence," *Phys. Rev. A* 40, 5135 (1989).
28. K. Rzą_żewski, M. G. Raymer, and R. W. Boyd, "Delay Time Statistics of Cooperative Emission in the Presence of Homogeneous Line Broadening," *Phys. Rev. A* 39, 5785 (1989).
29. D. J. Gauthier, J. Krasinski, and R. W. Boyd, "Observation of Resonantly Enhanced Sum-Frequency Generation Involving Sodium Rydberg States," *Optics Letters* 8, 211 (1983).
30. M. S. Malcuit, D. J. Gauthier, and R. W. Boyd, "Suppression of Amplified Spontaneous Emission by the Four-Wave Mixing Process," *Phys. Rev. Lett.* 55, 1086 (1985).
31. W. V. Davis, M. Kauranen, E. Nagasako, R. J. Gehr, A. L. Gaeta, R. W. Boyd, and G. S. Agarwal, "Excess Noise Acquired by a Laser Beam in Propagating through an Atomic Potassium Vapor," *Phys. Rev. A* 51, 4152 (1995).
32. M. T. Gruneisen, K. R. MacDonald, and R. W. Boyd, "Induced Gain and Modified Absorption of a Weak Probe Beam in a Strongly Driven Sodium Vapor," *J. Opt. Soc. Am. B* 5, 123 (1988).
33. M. T. Gruneisen, K. R. MacDonald, A. L. Gaeta, and R. W. Boyd, "Laser Beam Combining in Potassium Vapor," *J. Quantum Electron* 27, 198 (1991).
34. R. E. Bridges, R. W. Boyd, and G. P. Agrawal, "Effect of Beam Ellipticity on Self-Modelocking in Lasers," *Opt. Lett.* 18, 2026 (1993).
35. R. S. Bennink, R. W. Boyd, C. R. Stroud, Jr., and V. Wong, "Enhanced Self-Action Effects by Electromagnetically Induced Transparency in The Two-Level Atom," *Phys. Rev. A* 63, 033804 (2001).
36. R. W. Boyd and M. O. Scully, "Efficient Infrared Imaging Upconversion via Quantum Coherence," *Appl. Phys. Lett.* 77, 3559 (2000).
37. Q. H. Park and R. W. Boyd, "Modification of Self-Induced Transparency by a Coherent Control Field," *Phys. Rev. Lett.* 86, 2774 (2001).
38. G. S. Agarwal, R. W. Boyd, E. M. Nagasako, and S. J. Bentley, "Comment on 'Quantum Interferometric Optical Lithography: Exploiting Entanglement to Beat the Diffraction Limit,' " *Phys. Rev. Lett.* 86, 1389 (2001).

39. A. L. Gaeta and R. W. Boyd, "Quantum Noise in Phase Conjugation," *Phys. Rev. Lett.* 60, 2618 (1988).

40. M. S. Malcuit, D. J. Gauthier, and R. W. Boyd, "Vector Phase Conjugation by Two-Photon Resonant Degenerate Four-Wave Mixing," *Opt. Lett.* 13, 663 (1988).

41. M. Kauranen, D. J. Gauthier, M. S. Malcuit, and R. W. Boyd, "Polarization Properties of Phase Conjugation by Two-Photon Resonant Degenerate Four-Wave Mixing," *Phys. Rev. A* 40, 1908 (1989).

42. M. D. Skeldon, P. Narum, and R. W. Boyd, "Non-Frequency Shifted, High-Quality Phase Conjugation with Aberrated Pump Waves by Brillouin-Enhanced Four-Wave Mixing," *Opt. Lett.* 12, 343 (1987).

43. D. J. Gauthier, R. W. Boyd, R. K. Jungquist, J. B. Lisson, and L. L. Voci, "Phase-Conjugate Fizeau Interferometer," *Opt. Lett.* 14, 325 (1989).

44. K. R. MacDonald, W. R. Tompkin, and R. W. Boyd, "Passive One-Way Aberration Correction Using Four-wave Mixing," *Opt. Lett.* 13, 663 (1988).

45. E. J. Miller, M. S. Malcuit, and R. W. Boyd, "Simultaneous Wavefront and Polarization Conjugation of Picosecond Optical Pulses by Stimulated Rayleigh-Wing Scattering," *Optics Letters* 15, 1188 (1990).

46. O. Kulagin, G. A. Pasmanik, A. L. Gaeta, T. R. Moore, G. J. Benecke, and R. W. Boyd, "Observation of Brillouin Chaos with Counterpropagating Laser Beams," *J. Opt. Soc. B* 8, 2155 (1991).

47. T. R. Moore, G. L. Fischer, and R. W. Boyd, "Measurement of the Power Distribution During Stimulated Brillouin Scattering with Focused Gaussian Beams," *Journal of Modern Optics* 45, 735–45 (1998).

48. M. W. Bowers, R. W. Boyd, and A. K. Hankla, "Brillouin-Enhanced Four-Wave-Mixing Vector Phase Conjugate Mirror with Beam Combining Capability," *Opt. Lett.* 22, 360–62 (1999).

49. A. L. Gaeta and R. W. Boyd, "Stochastic Dynamics of Stimulated Brillouin Scattering in an Optical Fiber," *Phys. Rev. A* 44, 3205 (1991).

50. A. J. Stentz, R. W. Boyd, and A. F. Evans, "Dramatically Improved Transmission of Ultrashort Solitons through 40 km of Dispersion-Decreasing Fiber," *Opt. Lett.* 20, 1770 (1995).

51. E. L. Buckland and R. W. Boyd, "Measurement of the Frequency Response of the Electrostrictive Nonlinearity in Optical Fibers," *Optics Letters* 22, 676 (1997).

52. E. L. Buckland and R. W. Boyd, "Electrostrictive Contribution to the Intensity-Dependent Refractive Index of Optical Fibers," *Opt. Lett.* 21, 1117–19 (1996).

53. N. Bloembergen, *IEEE Selected Topics in Quantum Electronics* 6, 876 (2000).

57. The Faculty Club

Carlos Stroud

The Faculty Club was a very important part of the optics faculty social interactions at least from the 1960s through the 1990s. At lunch time in the 1970s almost every day a Faculty Club excursion group gathered outside of Len Mandel's office on the third floor of B&L, including Len Mandel, Emil Wolf, Joe Eberly, George Sherman, and Carlos Stroud. They were frequently joined by other faculty, postdocs and visitors, including H. M. Nussenzweig, C. L. Mehta, Hank Carter, Robin Asby, Peter Knight, Les Allen, and others. The discussions ranged widely, but were seldom far from optics. The paper placemats were indispensable, by the end of lunch generally covered on both sides by equations and diagrams. Sometimes it was necessary to request extras. The waiters and waitresses joked about the "equations table." The discussions carried over to coffee in the lounge and—sometimes when the weather was nice—walks along the river, always a favorite of Len Mandel and Emil Wolf. The discussions helped many of us get over blocks encountered in a morning's research, and actually led directly to the only publication co-authored by Len Mandel, Joe Eberly, and Carlos Stroud. The fourth author was a student, Bill Lama, whose thesis project stimulated the discussion.

The club was also important in the afternoon and evening. Many quantum optics seminars were merely interrupted by the end of the seminar hour, and resumed almost immediately with continued lively discussion over beer and pretzels in the Faculty Club. For a while in the early 1970s there was a happy hour on Friday afternoons when beer and munchies were provided to the membership. Frequent attendees at these events included the junior faculty of the Institute, George Sherman, Ed Brody, and Carlos Stroud. More impressive was the gourmet evening fare.

In the 1960s and 1970s the Faculty Club was widely conceded to be the best restaurant in Rochester, with multi-course gourmet dinners scheduled occasionally and a wine list that was the envy of almost every faculty club in the country. The list was well enough known so that when Kumar Patel was invited to give a seminar, he agreed to come at his own (Bell Labs') expense, on the conditions that the post-seminar dinner be held in the

Vintage wine from the Faculty Club cellar enjoyed and the label signed by Solid State Seminar speaker Kumar Patel and faculty members.

Faculty Club and he be allowed to pick the wine. His host, Professor Eberly, happily agreed. There was no shortage of local faculty anxious to see that their guest receive proper hospitality, and the wine selected was *Chateau Lafite Rothschild 1962*. The Faculty Club sommelier, like the assembled faculty, had always wished for an occasion to sample the premier wine on the list. Somehow it turned out that when he had distributed the precious liquid to all glasses, just a small sample remained in the bottle. He offered that if he could have that sample he could make available with dessert a Madeira from the first decade of the century that was not on the list, an offer that was quickly accepted. Seated a few tables away in another party was University President Robert Sproull. He observed the seminar party taking an empty wine bottle with them as he was leaving the club and remarked that they seemed to be enjoying themselves. The bottle, signed by all participants, sits on Professor Eberly's bookshelf to the present day. A few days later a new accounting rule was announced in the College of Arts and Science, capping the cost of a bottle of wine that could be charged to a departmental account. As a reminder of the rate of inflation, the '62 Lafite was billed at $34.95! A similar bottle was recently sold at auction for more than $500. Fortunately there was no such rule restricting the range of tastes permitted to engineering faculty, so its imposition naturally encouraged collegial joint seminars.

The quantum optics faculty continued their regular luncheon gatherings through the 1980s, but the custom spread much wider. Particularly during the first part of Dennis Hall's directorship, a large fraction of the optics faculty gathered each noon for lunch at the Faculty Club. There was little need for formal faculty meetings as everything of importance was hashed out over lunch and coffee, long before it could appear on a meeting agenda. On Fridays the conversation was unlikely to turn to such serious matters until the previous evening's episode of *Seinfeld* had been thoroughly reviewed.

Unhappily, by the 1990s the University became serious about the costs associated with a facility that was no longer serving the same clientele. Evening meals at the Faculty Club were not attended with enough regularity for several good reasons, and the days of service were gradually reduced, each cutback stimulating a greater decrease in patronage. By then there were many excellent restaurants in Rochester, and newer faculty tended to live more remotely from campus and were not anxious to come back to campus for dinner. What was worse, many faculty members felt too pressured to spend time eating lunch with their colleagues at the Faculty Club. They either skipped lunch or brown-bagged at their desks. An institution was under siege. Some of the optics faculty were alarmed and tried to save the club. Joe Eberly and Carlos Stroud both served terms on the Faculty Club Board and on committees trying to save it. It was not to be: The Faculty Club closed and was replaced by a campus eatery shared with students.

While the old club is sorely missed by some of us, the luncheon gatherings are slowly coming back. Lukas Novotny's entire group of graduate students and postdocs gathers every noon for a joint luncheon. There is no regular gathering of faculty for lunch, but often there is an informal gathering of one or sometimes even two tables of optics faculty at the new Meliora eatery. There are even paper placemats, but if we are to carry out research over lunch these days we will have to await a lunch room with wireless connections, and perhaps soup-resistant keyboards, for our laptop computers.

58. Photonics at The Institute of Optics

Dennis G. Hall

During the first century B.C., the Roman poet and satirist Horace observed that once a word has been allowed to escape, it cannot be recalled. And so it is that I find myself asked to write an essay about, of all things, photonics at The Institute of Optics. Such a request would have been unthinkable in the late 1980s, when some within the optics community were arguing that light was capable of ever so much more than an old-fashioned word like *optics* could communicate. The futuristic *photonics*, they admonished, projected a modern, exciting image that was big enough to convey both what the field had been and what it was destined to become. The broader field of photonics, they argued, would place the photon on an equal footing with the electron, to usher in a new era in technology.

Of course, if one already happened to have a great deal invested in the word *optics*, as did (and do) the members of the Optical Society of America (OSA) and the students, staff, faculty and alumni of The Institute of Optics, and if one already regarded *optics* as a field as big as all outdoors, then it was hard not to react to this upstart term *photonics* with some alarm. Where would this end? Would Emil Wolf be driven to change the title of Born & Wolf to *Principles of Photonics*? Would the University become the home of The Institute of Photonics? Inquiring minds in Rochester wanted to know! OSA members ended months of debate by voting in the fall of 1989 to retain the O in OSA, after which the entire issue receded into the background. OSA's members had considered patiently Shakespeare's advice in *Romeo and Juliet* that a rose by any other name would smell as sweet, but in the end had sided with Winston Churchill's (1952) more recent advice that "Short words are best and the old words when short are best of all."

Today, photonics has become a hopeful moniker for the subset of optical science and engineering that's associated with optical communication and information technologies, and especially, but not quite exclusively, with those involving optical waveguides. With that general landscape in mind, one might say that photonics at The Institute of Optics was foreshadowed by Brian O'Brien's suggestion in 1951 that surrounding each glass fiber in a fiber bundle with a lower refractive-index cladding would improve that bundle's performance as an image-transmission system.[1] Each fiber in such a bundle transmitted light by means of total internal reflection, with the lower-index cladding serving both to isolate each fiber from the others and to reduce surface scattering. Nearly a decade went by before Bob Potter completed, in 1960, the Institute's first Ph.D. dissertation in fiber optics,[2] a dissertation supervised by Bob Hopkins. Bear in mind that these contributions appeared very early indeed—T. H. Maiman's paper reporting the first laser[3] appeared in the latter half of 1960, almost simultaneously with Potter's dissertation.

Nineteen seventy was a defining year for photonics. Interest in optical-fiber waveguides as non-imaging transmission media became intense in late 1970 when researchers at the nearby Corning Glass Works demonstrated and reported glass fibers with transmission losses as low as $20\,\mathrm{dB/km}$ at wavelength $\lambda = 0.6328\,\mu\mathrm{m}$.[4] That same year brought the first

Bob Potter (Ph.D., 1960) in the lab.

reported continuous-wave operation at room temperature of a III–V, AlGaAs/GaAs semiconductor laser. One year later, fiber transmission losses were down to 2 dB/km and the technology was off to the races. Soon every major corporation was gearing up to explore and exploit these and a host of related developments involving optical waveguide technologies.[5]

Nick George invited me to join the optics faculty in 1980 to teach and to build a research program in guided-wave optics. I remember commenting to Nick during a visit to the Institute in March 1980 that I had some reservations about Rochester's legendary winters. Without missing a beat, Nick, who himself had moved to Rochester from Caltech only a few years earlier, said, "Don't worry about that; you'll be too busy even to notice the weather." I can't say that I wasn't warned. The Institute's research infrastructure worried me a little at the beginning. Having spent the previous two years working on fiber-optics, integrated-optics and semiconductor-laser problems at McDonnell-Douglas Corp. in St. Louis, I knew only too well that The Institute of Optics of 1980 lacked the materials and processing laboratories that virtually everyone believed was needed to do publishable research on optical waveguide phenomena. I learned quickly, however, that the Institute had something far more precious than modern, solid-state laboratories. It had outstanding graduate students.

By 1980, the required, senior-level undergraduate laboratory (Optics 256) already had two fiber-optics experiments, one that used a fast oscilloscope to compare the optical-pulse delays introduced by step-index and gradient-index multimode fibers, and another that used an electro-optic modulator to transmit a television signal through a few meters of optical fiber. It was via the former experiment that students learned in a personal way how much care it takes to inject the invisible, near-IR output of a tiny semiconductor laser into something even as large as a 50-μm-core-diameter multimode fiber. Some found it so challenging that they were certain that there was something wrong with the experiment, but most felt pretty good when they finally mastered it. A few faculty had small fiber-optics side-projects underway in 1980. For example, Duncan Moore had an interest in rays propagating in gradient-index fibers and in the use of gradient-index lenses to facilitate coupling light into fibers, and another, Ken Teegarden, was helping a local Rochester company

Hall research group luncheon meeting.

explore an idea for a fiber-optic pressure sensor. My appointment to the faculty reflected the Institute's decision to make optical waveguide phenomena part of its teaching and research core.

I developed a new graduate course titled guided-wave optics and taught it for the first time as a special-topics course in the spring of 1981. The next year it was assigned a regular course number, Optics 468. The course covered the basics of planar optical waveguides, coupled-mode theory, elementary waveguide devices such as Bragg reflectors and directional couplers, propagation and pulse-broadening in optical fibers, and an introduction to the band-theory of solids and semiconductor lasers. There was no single book at that time that covered all of this material, so I taught the course entirely from my own lecture notes. The course catered primarily to first- and second-year graduate students, but it was open to adventurous undergraduate seniors, too. I taught that course each spring for six years before turning it over to others.

Major help with laboratory development arrived on the scene when, thanks to a proposal effort led by Ken Teegarden, the Institute was designated in 1982 as the home of the New York State Center for Advanced Optical Technology (known as the CAT program). Several such centers were created throughout the state in a number of different technical fields as part of New York's master plan for economic development. With its long and distinguished history in optics, the University was the natural site for the state's CAT program in optics. The CAT program brought to the Institute two million dollars per year in combined state and industrial funding targeted for five technologically important areas, one of which was guided-wave optics. That infusion of funds made it possible to build a clean room and a photolithography laboratory, to purchase a variety of vacuum deposition systems and other specialized equipment needed to fabricate thin-film structures, and to hire a laboratory engineer (Oliver King, then a new optics M.S. graduate) to help keep the equipment working and to work with graduate students to develop the solid-state fabrication and processing techniques required for their research.

The mid-1980s was a boom time for the Institute. External support for research reached unprecedented levels. The success of winning CAT designation from the state of New York was matched by winning a multi-million-dollar, multi-year program from the Department of Defense, the University Research Initiative (URI) program in optoelectronics and optoelectronic systems, thanks to a proposal effort led by Nick George. Photonics proved to be such a broad and fertile field for research and became so visible internationally that many more outstanding Ph.D. students were drawn to it than could be accommodated by a single faculty member. The Institute responded in 1987 by hiring two of its own Ph.D. graduates as new assistant professors, Thomas G. Brown, who had completed his Ph.D. in my research group, and Susan N. Houde-Walter, who had completed her Ph.D. in Duncan Moore's group, *and* a new associate professor, Gary W. Wicks, all three of whom had strong interests in optical waveguides, optical materials, semiconductor lasers and related subjects.

Tom Brown had carried out research on coherent fiber-optic communications at GTE laboratories before taking up graduate studies in the Institute, where his dissertation research had centered on radiative impurity complexes in single-crystal silicon. Susan Houde-Walter's intellectual journey had taken her from an undergraduate degree in studio arts from Sarah Lawrence College all the way through a Ph.D. from The Institute of Optics, where her research had focused on forming refractive-index gradients in glass by means of an ion-exchange process. Both Tom and Susan had cut their teeth on guided-wave optics as graduate students by taking Optics 468. Susan went on to teach that course after she joined the faculty. Gary Wicks had earned his undergraduate and Ph.D. degrees in applied and engineering physics from Cornell University, where he had remained for another six years as a research associate to help Les Eastman lead his large semiconductor research group. By 1987, Gary had already made a name for himself as a specialist in the growth of III–V semiconductor layers and layered structures by the method known as molecular-beam epitaxy (MBE), a sophisticated crystal-growth technique carried out in an ultrahigh-vacuum chamber, referred to (sometimes with affection) as a "mega-buck evaporator." Immediately

Mike Koch, Gary Wicks and Fred Johnson operate the MBE facility.

upon his arrival, Gary developed and taught a new course, Optics 421, optical properties of semiconductors.

The Institute's decision to hire Gary Wicks, to purchase an MBE system and to establish a well-equipped III–V MBE laboratory and research effort recognized that advances in modern optical technologies depend heavily upon specialized materials growth and processing. One high-energy physicist at the University criticized this hiring decision, arguing that the Institute had strayed from its charter, demonstrating that high-energy physics might not be the best lens through which to view the field of optics. Advances in optical science and engineering have always been intimately connected with advances in materials science. That optics was undergoing another historic change, one that made the semiconductor an important *optical* material, was an established fact in the off-campus world. The Institute of Optics faced a clear choice: Either change and help lead, or be left behind. A decision between two such alternatives can be made very quickly.

Two years later, in 1989, the Institute seized the opportunity to add to its faculty Bell Labs scientist Govind Agrawal, already a highly visible theoretician in the field of optical communications, recognized for his work on semiconductor lasers and nonlinear effects in optical fibers. Govind created a new course titled optical communications (Optics 428) as soon as he arrived, and over the course of the next three years developed his course notes into a book, *Fiber-Optics Communication Systems*, now in its third edition and used throughout the world.[6] Since joining the Institute's faculty, Govind has published four additional books on related subjects. In 1994, the Institute hired another of its Ph.D. alumni, Turan Erdogan, to carry out research in fiber optics. After completing his Ph.D. in my research group in 1992 by demonstrating and investigating the properties of a novel semiconductor laser, Turan accepted a postdoctoral position at Bell Labs, where he explored the use of ultraviolet laser emission to write Bragg gratings directly into the core region of an optical fiber. That work proved so successful that it made it possible for fiber Bragg gratings to be

Turan Erdogan returned to the Institute after a postdoctoral position at Bell Labs.

incorporated into practical fiber-optic communication systems. Turan declined a permanent position at Bell Labs in order to accept an appointment as an assistant professor in the Institute. Professors Brown, Houde-Walter, Wicks, Agrawal, and Erdogan all established vigorous, productive research programs in photonics very quickly after their respective arrivals.

During most of the 1980s and 1990s, The Institute of Optics had fourteen full-time, tenured or tenure-track faculty. That six of the fourteen faculty worked principally in what today might be called photonics demonstrates how important that specialty had become by the end of the twentieth century. Those six faculty made their interests felt both in the curriculum and in research. It would take more space than is available in this essay to describe the many research accomplishments that have emerged from those six groups, but let me offer a snapshot.

Gary Wicks's research program in III–V semiconductors produced advances of its own and provided fuel for the ideas and efforts of others. For example, he and his students, along with MBE laboratory engineer Mike Koch, developed a solid-phase phosphorus source that made it possible to use MBE to grow phosphorus-containing semiconductor layers without using dangerous gases.[7] That source is now used universally to grow phosphide compounds via MBE. Gary's group used that technique at the Institute to fabricate and demonstrate, for instance, low-threshold InAsP/GaInAsP semiconductor lasers that emit light at wavelength $\lambda = 1.3\,\mu\text{m}$.[8] Without the local control over the growth process that Gary's effort made possible, and without his advice about semiconductor subtleties, it would have been much more difficult, and perhaps impossible, for (then) graduate student Turan Erdogan, working in my research group, to complete so successfully his dissertation project, the creation of a novel concentric-circle grating, surface-emitting AlGaAs/GaAs semiconductor laser.[9] Turan was awarded OSA's 1995 Adolph Lomb Medal for that achievement. Many other faculty and graduate students both within and outside of the Institute benefited from the capabilities and advances within the MBE group.

III–V semiconductors are not the answer to every question, however. Tom Brown and graduate student N. Darius Sankey turned heads by becoming the first to observe all-optical switching in a nonlinear, periodic, Bragg-resonant medium, and they did so using a *silicon*-based optical waveguide system.[10] All-optical switching is, in some sense, a holy grail of nonlinear optics. The idea of controlling light with light summons images of optical logic elements, all-optical switching networks, and even all-optical computing. Theoretical predictions about switching in nonlinear Bragg structures began appearing in the mid to late 1980s, but no physical system that exhibited such switching could be found. Tom and Darius were able to show that a silicon-on-insulator optical waveguide configured with a surface grating *does* exhibit (non-thermal) all-optical switching.

Susan Houde-Walter's work has investigated the relationship between atomic-level properties and the resulting macroscopic optical properties of both glass and III–V semiconductors, but she and her students have also developed a strong presence in the theoretical analysis and design of optical waveguide systems. As an example of the former, she and her students have used various accelerator facilities in the United States and Europe to apply the EXAFS (extended x-ray absorption fine structure) technique to developing a microscopic understanding of the properties of optical glasses.[11] Her work in the latter area has included investigations of how the optical mode changes as light passes from one component to the next in multi-component, integrated-optical devices. That work included the development of new tools to track down such modes as layer configurations and refractive-index profiles vary and become complicated.[12] Beginning in 2005, Susan will take up her duties as president of the Optical Society of America.

Govind Agrawal and his students have contributed mightily to the quantitative understanding of many phenomena that occur in optical fibers and semiconductor lasers. One prominent example is identifying the root cause of the so-called filamentation that occurs in broad-area semiconductor lasers, something that had been observed for at least two decades.[13] Other examples include analyses of soliton propagation and other nonlinear effects in optical fibers, the properties of vertical-cavity, surface-emitting semiconductor lasers, optical effects in semiconductor laser amplifiers, and the behavior of fiber Bragg gratings. At the time of this writing, Govind's publication list includes some three hundred entries.

It deserves mention that other members of the faculty made occasional forays into photonics. For instance, Robert Boyd's research program in nonlinear optics has included the study of soliton-propagation effects in optical fibers.[14] Indeed, optical-waveguide phenomena became so widespread during the 1980s and the 1990s that it touched the research of most or all of the optics faculty at one time or another. By the year 2000, *photonics* (a.k.a. guided-wave optics, optoelectronics, etc.) had become one of the pillars of research and teaching in The Institute of Optics.

Dennis G. Hall was a member of the faculty of The Institute of Optics 1980–2000; he served as its director from 1993 to 2000. He is currently associate provost for research and graduate education, and professor of physics and electrical engineering, at Vanderbilt University in Nashville, Tenn.

References

1 See, for example, Jeff Hecht, *Understanding Fiber Optics*, 3rd ed. (Garden City, N.J.: Prentice Hall, 1999), 6.

2 Robert J. Potter, "A Theoretical and Experimental Study of Optical Fibers," Ph.D. dissertation, The Institute of Optics, University of Rochester, 1960. This appears to be the first Ph.D. dissertation on fiber optics written in the U.S.

3 T. H. Maiman, *Nature* 187, August 6, 1960, p. 493.

4 F. P. Kapron, D. B. Keck, and R. D. Maurer, *Appl. Phys. Lett.* 17, 423 (1970).

5 The light within the cavity of a semiconductor laser is confined laterally within an optical waveguide.

6 G. P. Agrawal, *Fiber-Optic Communications Systems*, 3rd ed. (New York: Wiley, 2002).

7 G. W. Wicks, M. W. Koch, J. A. Varriano, F. G. Johnson, C. R. Wie, H. M. Kim, and P. Colombo, *Appl. Phys. Lett.* 59, 342 (1991).

8 C. C. Wamsley, M. W. Koch, and G. W. Wicks, *J. Crystal Growth* 175/176, 42 (1997).

9 T. Erdogan, O. King, G. W. Wicks, D. G. Hall, E. Anderson, and M. J. Rooks, *Appl. Phys. Lett.* 60, 1921 (1992).

10 N. D. Sankey, D. F. Prelewitz, and T. G. Brown, *Appl. Phys. Lett.* 60, 1427 (1992).

11 S. N. Houde-Walter, J. M. Inman, A. J. Dent, and G. N. Greaves, *J. Phys. Chem.* 97, 9330 (1993).

12 R. E. Smith, S. N. Houde-Walter, and G. W. Forbes, *Opt. Lett.* 16, 1316 (1991).

13 J. R. Marciante and G. P. Agrawal, *IEEE J. Quantum Electronics* QE-32, 590 (1996); see also *Appl. Phys. Lett.* 69, 593 (1996).

14 See, for example, A. J. Stentz, R. W. Boyd, and A. F. Evans, *Opt. Lett.* 20, 1770 (1995).

59. Optics Pranks

Carlos Stroud

Student pranks are a tradition as old as academia itself. While the record of pranks in the first few decades of the history of the Institute is rather sparse, if one is allowed to extrapolate the record of the recent decades backward, there can be little doubt that things were always lively. Some pranks were simple like the scanning Fabry-Perot which had been sitting on the shelf in my lab for a couple of years unused because its mirrors appeared to be damaged. When it was finally disassembled to examine the damage the problem was quickly apparent: a piece of lens tissue with the scrawled message "Kilroy was here." But many were much more elaborate, involving extensive planning and careful execution. The pranksters were often the top students in the department. Usually the faculty and administration took the pranks in good humor, perhaps because of some memories of their own youthful indiscretions. In fact two of the most notorious pranks were carried out by students who were destined to become future directors of the Institute. In the following pages we will recount a few of the classic pranks.

Pranks: Safety Violations

Carlos Stroud

In the early 1970s Bala Manian (then called Naranyan Balasubramanian) was a new faculty member in the Institute of Optics setting up his laboratory in the west wing of the fourth floor of Bausch & Lomb Hall. His seriousness, coupled with good humor and an infectious optimistic nature, made him a favorite of the faculty and students alike, but also a natural target for some mischievous young graduate students.

When Bala left for a few-week visit to his home in India, three students whom we will call "Duncan, Jay and Kim" for concreteness (you may be assured that any similarity to actual student names is strictly coincidental) were quick to see their opportunity. They attached a padlock to Bala's laboratory door with a sign stating that safety inspectors of the New York State Department of Laser Safety (a totally fictitious organization) had found a number of violations in the laboratory and that it was forbidden under penalty of law for anyone to enter the room. A telephone number was included to "call Commissioner Bird for further information."

The ruse was made even more believable by putting a series of messages in Bala's mailbox from Commissioner Bird. The first was relatively mild: "Please call." The fourth worked up to "URGENT CALL!" They also "found" some stationery from the dean's office and wrote a letter to George Fraley indicating that there was a problem in the Institute and for him to look into it. All of these were in Bala's mailbox when he returned to Rochester on a Friday morning. When Jay arrived at the Institute, Bala was in a panic.

So they arranged for Commissioner Bird (whose telephone number on the notice on Bala's lab was the Seneca Park Zoo) to call the phone in Evie Snyder's office so that they could overhear the conversation. Commissioner Bird (aka Kim) called, and although they could hear only hear Bala's end of the conversation, it contained phrases like: "I know this is a terrible situation," "Can we arrange for another inspection?" and "I am sure that this is a mistake." Worried that the prank was getting out of hand, Duncan said to Bala, "Come here and let me show you something." Whereupon a group of about eight people came out of hiding where they had been eavesdropping on Bala's conversation and paraded to the door where the padlock had been placed. Duncan took out the key and started to unlock the padlock. Bala pulled him away from the door. Duncan said, "Bala,

Bala Manian.

this is a joke," but Bala responded, "It is no joke. This will be another violation of the laser safety code."

Finally, after another day of lab-lessness, Bala caught on. Definitely his good humor was put to the test that week, but the pranksters have thus far escaped serious retribution and indeed are now respected members of the optics community.

60. A Brief History of QED Technologies

Donald Golini

> "One new and exciting technology that could have a profound influence on optical fabrication, and ultimately, the basic design forms we work with is *'Magnetorheological Finishing' (MRF)*."
>
> —*Photonics Spectra*, January 1993

The concept of using magnetorheological finishing (MRF) as an automated process to polish high precision optics was first introduced to the Center for Optics Manufacturing (COM) at the University of Rochester in 1993. In 1996 the MRF technology became the foundation of a new start-up company, QED Technologies, whose vision was to develop commercial MRF equipment. After a decade of research and development, MRF has earned industry-wide acceptance and is used by optics manufacturers around the globe. MRF has significantly changed the way precision optics are manufactured, and QED Technologies remains on the leading edge of optics manufacturing technology.

Overview

QED succeeded in the challenging task of transforming a novel university R&D technology into a robust optics manufacturing product with broad commercial acceptance. QED's automated polishing machines use a magnetic fluid to finish high precision optical elements in minutes or even seconds, replacing the artisan-based, manual technology that previously took hours or weeks. Before MRF, precision optics fabrication was mired in processes that had seen few improvements since the 1950s and relied on highly skilled master opticians and labor-intensive techniques. QED overcame initial resistance from a change-averse industry and is now recognized for introducing an enabling technology that will meet next-generation optics manufacturing challenges in the semiconductor, telecommunications, and many other high technology applications. In 2003 QED introduced an innovative metrology system, the Subaperture Stitching Interferometer (SSI). QED's SSI leverages developments in software and hardware to improve the capacity, accuracy, and flexibility of traditional interferometers.

QED's roots trace back to 1989 and the formation of the Center for Optics Manufacturing.

The Center for Optics Manufacturing at the University of Rochester

In 1989 a unique partnership was created at the University of Rochester. Harvey Pollicove, an executive on loan from Eastman Kodak, joined forces with former Institute of Optics director, Professor Duncan Moore, and enlisted the help of the American Precision Optics Manufacturers Association (APOMA) and the U.S. Army Materiel Command. Together they created a collaboration of academic, industrial, and military resources to develop advanced optical technology and equipment for U.S. optics manufacturers.

In 1990 COM was officially launched, thanks to a $4.8 million contract from the U.S. Army Materiel Command. COM was chartered with meeting the needs of a faltering U.S. optics manufacturing industry that was losing ground to overseas manufacturers and in decline for more than a decade. Pollicove was named COM's first director and undertook the challenge of modernizing the optics industry for both commercial and defense sectors. According to Pollicove, "New equipment will be only one product of the center. . . . the center embodies a whole new approach to manufacturing that will revolutionize the way we make optics." Traditional optics manufacturing consisted of rigid and repetitive processes of grinding, polishing, testing, and correcting—largely requiring the knowledge and skill of master opticians. The long-range goal of COM was to introduce novel processing technologies to help manufacturers become less dependent on expensive, artisan-based labor. With a focus on determinism and automation, optics manufacturing becomes less sensitive to labor costs, creating a more level global playing field.

COM quickly adopted the motto, "Implementation is the only hallmark of success." Technology transfer, training, and education were key to COM's mission. "The center is in a unique position to be able to assemble expert resources from leading academic, government and industrial institutions to provide an invaluable technology transfer base," said Moore. The first project COM tackled was the development of an automated, CNC-based grinding machine to manufacture optics. Dubbed "Opticam," the new manufacturing approach allowed glass and ceramic optical components to be made as easily as metal parts. The center's goal was to have a prototype within two years. To this end, COM

The Center for Optics Manufacturing at the University of Rochester is located within the Center for Optoelectronics and Imaging building.

organized a process science committee—an advisory panel of volunteers from the optics industry who helped guide the center's research and development work, ensuring the program would meet the needs of industry. Don Golini, then with Litton/Itek Optical Systems, agreed to chair the committee.

In 1992 the University broke ground on a 96,000-square-foot facility—the new home of the growing center. That year COM demonstrated that the prototype Opticam System was capable of manufacturing optics with surface finishes of 100 to 300 angstroms (rms), 1–2 microns of subsurface damage and peak-to-valley surface figure of 1 wave or less. This unprecedented breakthrough could not be achieved using conventional equipment. In that same year, Golini joined COM full time to manage the manufacturing sciences program, concentrating his efforts on grinding and polishing process innovations. The manufacturing sciences team grew to seventeen faculty and more than twenty graduate students who produced dozens of technical publications. In a relatively short time, the group improved the state of the art in grinding optics, reducing cost, and improving process yields for manufacturers. However, the final polishing step was still expensive, time consuming, and required the "black art" expertise of the master optician.

In 1993 a private investor approached COM about the potential use of a magnetic slurry for polishing optics. This radical approach sparked skepticism from the optics industry, but Pollicove, Professor Stephen D. Jacobs, and Golini were impressed. A collaboration between Byelocorp Scientific Inc. (BSI), a technology development firm, and COM was launched to develop a proof-of-concept demonstrating that MRF could become a viable optical finishing technology.

Magnetorheological Finishing (MRF)

MRF was first developed by a team of scientists lead by William Kordonski at the Luikov Institute of Heat and Mass Transfer in Minsk, Belarus in 1988. Kordsonki and his team developed the use of magnetically sensitive—or magnetorheological (MR)—fluid to polish optics. The MRF process is based on this "smart fluid" which changes viscosity in milliseconds when a magnetic field is introduced. The fluid is a slurry consisting of water and other materials, mainly carbonyl iron and an abrasive material such as cerium oxide. The MR fluid temporarily hardens when exposed to a magnetic field and conforms to the surface of the glass to be polished, making it ideal to polish many types of components. It offered a truly revolutionary opportunity to overcome many of the limitations of conventional polishing.

Under the new collaboration with COM, Kordonski came to Rochester to work with Jacobs and Golini to perfect MRF and develop a stable finishing process. The team spent the next three years studying and refining MRF. Institute of Optics Professor Gregory Forbes and doctoral candidate Paul Dumas developed the complex algorithms required to deterministically control and automate the polishing process. In 1994 a prototype MRF machine was created and validation tests began. The COM-BSI team demonstrated that MRF could achieve unprecedented results deterministically. Optics with less than 10 angstroms rms surface roughness and $\lambda/10$ p-v figure error were produced in less than an hour. The once-skeptical optics industry began to believe in the technology. However, a commercialization plan for MRF did not yet exist.

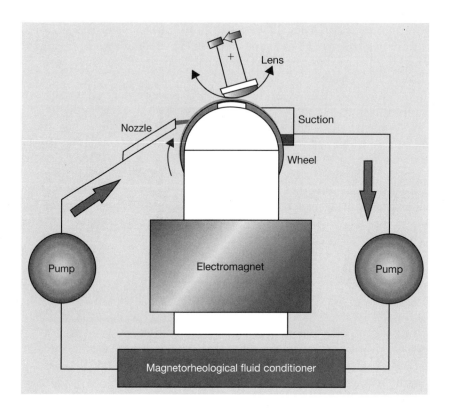

"MRF represents one of the single most exciting advances in optical fabrication in many, many years."—Photonics Spectra, *1993.*

QED Technologies

In mid-1996 Golini recognized the opportunity, wrote a business plan, and approached BSI, the investor who initially brought MRF to COM. This partnership became the foundation of QED Technologies. By 1998, QED introduced the Q22 MRF System, a multi-axis, computer-controlled machine that was capable of polishing optics up to 200 mm in diameter. The Q22 could simultaneously eliminate subsurface damage while improving surface figure by varying the amount of time the optic is immersed in the fluid. The flexibility of the Q22 and the conformal nature of its magnetic fluid polishing tool made it extremely effective to produce a wide array of optical components. Today, QED offers a family of MRF machines capable of polishing flats, spheres, aspheres, optical windows, prisms, and cylindrical optics in diameters as large as one meter. QED's intellectual property portfolio has grown to over a dozen fundamental international patents, and the company has sold more than eighty machines world-wide.

QED's newest product, the Subaperture Stitching Interferometer (SSI), is a six-axis computer-controlled interferometric workstation that provides automated, high-precision metrology for large clear aperture (CA up to 200 mm in diameter) and high numerical aperture (NA) plano, convex, and concave parts. QED's motivation to develop a metrology tool was simple. Metrology is critical to the optics fabrication process and often, the lack of accurate and affordable metrology ultimately limits the lens quality. One famous optician said, "If you can't measure it, you can't make it." QED's SSI uses novel developments in software and hardware to improve the capacity and accuracy of traditional interferometers, overcoming many of the limitations previously faced with interferometric stitching techniques. Partnering the SSI with the Q22 MRF Systems allows QED to offer

Q22-Y MRF system is QED's flagship machine, enabling the manufacture of precision optics while reducing overall production time, increasing yield and reducing costs.

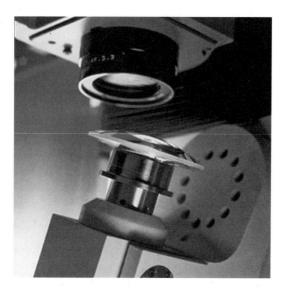

The subaperture stitching interferometer (SSI) is QED's latest innovation.

customers a complete state-of-the-art finishing solution that increases speed and yield, while decreasing costs.

In recognition of significant technological achievements, QED has been awarded the Photonics Spectra Circle of Excellence Award, the Laser Focus World Commercial Technology Achievement Award, the Department of Defense Manufacturing Technology Achievement Award, and the R&D 100 Award, for the innovative and revolutionary Q22 MRF system. In 2002 QED Technologies was named Rochester's fourth fastest-growing company. Most recently, QED was named recipient of the 2003 Rochester Business Ethics Award, awarded in recognition of a Rochester company that exemplifies the highest ethical standards in its everyday business practices.

QED Technologies maintains a valuable partnership with COM, The Institute of Optics, and the University of Rochester, and is indebted to the expertise, professionalism, and dedication of the many people who have contributed to our unique success story.

Donald Golini received his B.S. from the Institute of Optics in 1986. He is currently President of QED Technologies, Inc., Rochester, NY.

Pranks: April Fools' Day

Jake Bromage

Joan Christian knew that something was wrong. She'd walked along the first floor corridor of the Wilmot Building many times, but this morning, April 1, 1992, it felt different. And then it hit her.

As she stared at the row of portraits that lined the corridor her eyes slowly widened. Usually the eight photographs showed each of the directors of the Institute, extending back over its sixty-five-year history, looking proud and distinguished. This morning, however, strange faces stared back at her. Some were grotesquely distorted. Another looked like a young boy, barely twelve years old. Others wore strange clothing and disguises to hide their identity. Then Joan realized what was going on.

"Those students," she muttered as she returned smiling to the secretaries' office. The news spread quickly, and soon everyone knew of the April Fools' Day prank.

After a few days, the original directors' photographs mysteriously returned, and disciplinary action was averted. It was only recently that the strange and ugly photographs surfaced once more. They were found during a routine cleaning of the directors' portraits, carefully hidden behind the real photos. Shown here is one of the few considered suitable for publishing.

BRIAN J. THOMPSON
1968-1975

A young Jake Bromage photograph that was substituted for Brian Thompson's photograph in the Rogue Gallery of Directors. Clearly all Englishmen do not look alike.

Jake Bromage received his Ph.D. from the Institute of Optics in 1999. He is currently a scientist at the Laboratory for Laser Energetics, University of Rochester, Rochester, NY.

61. Center for Visual Science

David Williams

Historically, optics and vision have always been closely related. Some of the greatest scientific minds, such as Isaac Newton, Thomas Young, Hermann von Helmholtz, and James Clerk Maxwell, have made significant contributions to both disciplines. Not surprisingly, The Institute of Optics has had a long history of vision-related research. The Institute had an early focus on optometry. (See essay 4 in this volume for the history of this aspect of the program.) Later Brian O'Brien became interested in the notion that photoreceptors were optical waveguides. O'Brien built a Styrofoam model of a photoreceptor scaled up in size to microwave wavelengths. To test the model, he placed it on the balcony at the back of the fourth floor of B&L and illuminated it with a microwave transmitter in Gavett Hall. O'Brien also studied color vision with a dual interferometer that could produce red-green gratings, and devised a device to test prospective military pilots by observing their eye movements.

In 1963, Bob Boynton established the Center for Visual Science, and its ties to the Institute are described in his contribution to this volume. Following Boynton's departure from Rochester in 1974, links between vision science and optics faded. Indeed, I was only dimly aware of the existence of The Institute of Optics when I arrived at Rochester in 1981 and would never have imagined that it would be so central to the development of my academic career as it ultimately turned out to be. I was attracted to Rochester because of its unusual focus on vision research, instantiated in the interdepartmental research program, the Center for Visual Science. Walt Makous, who had just assumed the directorship of the center a year earlier, and Jim Ison, chairman of the Department of Psychology, had plans to expand the center, and I was the lucky beneficiary of their visionary recruiting efforts throughout my early years at Rochester. Peter Lennie and Mary Hayhoe were hired into the center shortly after my arrival. We formed a nucleus of faculty that ultimately led to a significant expansion of CVS to twenty-six faculty today in the medical school and the college.

Though I did not overlap at Rochester with Bob Boynton, I was a graduate student at UC San Diego, in a vision group started there by Bob in 1974 immediately after he left Rochester. Bob hired Don MacLeod onto the UCSD faculty, and Don took me on as his graduate student in 1975. I got to know Bob very well during this period, as he played a very active role in the education of all the graduate students in the vision lab. Indeed, Bob even served as a subject in the experiments that led to my Ph.D. We spent long hours together in a darkened laboratory testing Bob's vision, and I heard many stories about the University of Rochester, especially how cold it was. I would not have guessed at the time that I was just two years from moving to Rochester myself, let alone that I would eventually inherit the directorship of the center he founded there in 1963.

As a new assistant professor at Rochester laboring under the usual anxieties about career development and tenure, I was searching for a productive direction for my fledgling

David Williams.

research program. I thought the role of photoreceptor sampling on human visual resolution might be an interesting possibility. At the time, thinking of human vision as an array of spatial filters was very much in vogue, but there had been relatively little work on the spatial sampling as well as the spatial filtering characteristics of the visual system. The consequences of spatial sampling in man-made imaging systems were already well understood, and I was keen to learn everything I could about this so that I could apply these same principles to the eye. I sought out Brian Thompson, and despite his busy schedule as dean of engineering, he generously offered me an hour of private tutoring every week. He taught me much about Fourier optics, sampling theory, and aliasing. Before long I was using his five-watt argon laser to generate power spectra of photoreceptor mosaic patterns, simulated on photographic film. The laser was water-cooled and one day I left the water running after finishing our experiments, which caused a major plumbing problem for the Institute. I suspect Brian wondered at that point whether it had been a wise decision to give a psychologist free reign in his laboratory, but he reprimanded me quite politely. The experiments continued and I landed a publication in *Science* based on this work.

I then began to build an interferometer to study human visual resolution without the influence of blur by the eye's optics. My interferometer was an elaboration of instruments previously developed by John Krauskopf, my postdoctoral mentor at Bell Laboratories, and Walt Makous in CVS. Measurements with this device suggest that the eye is much more sensitive to interference fringe contrast than had been shown by the classic results of Campbell and Green. I had a suspicion that ultimately turned out to be wrong, that their results were attributable to a contrast artifact in their interference fringes. Brian pointed me to Nick George, who helped me estimate the contrast of Campbell and Green's interference fringes based on the bandwidth of their laser. I learned a lot about interferometry from both Nick and Brian. The rich technical expertise of The Institute of Optics was rapidly becoming an essential cornerstone of my research program, allowing me to conduct experiments using advanced optical technology that was inaccessible to vision scientists elsewhere. I used this new interferometer to demonstrate conclusively for the first time how the foveal cone mosaic and brain establishes a limit to human visual resolution, showing that aliasing results when the eye is exposed to interference fringes with spatial frequencies exceeding the resolution limit.

With the initial photoreceptor sampling work under my belt, I applied for tenure. Duncan Moore, who was then director of the Institute, was chosen to sit on the review committee. Duncan, who has always been fascinated by the diversity of eye designs in the animal kingdom (as he is fascinated by a myriad of topics ranging from science, to engineering, to politics), approached me about my work and offered me a secondary appointment in The Institute of Optics. This was a wonderful opportunity for me because it gave me access to the Institute's graduate students, who came into my laboratory with unparalleled training in optics. I began to teach a graduate course for the Institute, principles of eye design, Optics 448, that I continue to offer today. Students who studied in both the Institute and CVS could now acquire a rather unique combination of skills in optics and vision.

David MacAdam joined the faculty in the Institute following his retirement from Kodak in 1977 Dave had an international reputation in the field of color vision, especially in the area of color representation and discrimination. Until his death in 1998. Dave participated in our weekly CVS research meetings from time to time, especially when the topic was color.

Brian Thompson had developed long-standing relationship with the Allyn family of Welch Allyn, the medical instrument company based in nearby Skaneateles. He persuaded the patriarch of the Allyn family, Bill Allyn to donate $1.5 million to establish the Allyn Chair of Medical Optics in the Institute. The Institute asked me to serve on the search committee to fill the chair and we spent two years at this task. Each year we identified an outstanding candidate who we felt was likely to accept the chair, only to be turned down late in the recruiting effort. One of these candidates was Rob Webb, the inventor of the scanning laser ophthalmoscope, and I was especially disappointed that he did not accept the position since he would have been another bridge at Rochester between optics and vision. Much to my surprise, in 1997 Dennis Hall, director of the Institute, offered me the Allyn Chair. I was very flattered. Not only was this a great honor for me personally, it signaled the value that the Institute placed on its relationship to vision science. All the same, I was disappointed to see the chair spent on an internal candidate. While accepting the chair would have saved the College a good deal of money, it did not bring in new faculty in the area of biomedical optics. I agreed to accept the chair if Tom LeBlanc, dean of the College, would provide a junior faculty position in the Institute in medical optics. Fortunately, Tom agreed, and we ultimately hired Andrew Berger into that position.

The laser interferometer that had been the key instrument in my laboratory since the early 1980s provided a way to avoid optical blur for sine wave gratings delivered to the retina, but it did not avoid optical blur for light scattered off the retina. This of course is the light that must be collected to image the retina. We knew that it was theoretically possible to image single cells in the retina if only the aberrations of the eye could be corrected, but no one had succeeded at this so far. I had developed a friendship with Mike Morris back when we were both assistant professors. Mike had worked with Nick George at Caltech and joined the Institute at about the same time I joined CVS. Mike and I teamed up to try to image the retina at high resolution, employing a technique Mike had suggested related to stellar speckle interferometry. We co-supervised a graduate student, Don Miller, who, in 1995, published the first pictures ever of single cone photoreceptors in the living human eye. This exciting result prompted Junzhong Liang and Don Miller, as postdoctoral fellows in my laboratory, to build the first adaptive optics system for the eye that could correct higher order monochromatic aberrations. We now had a new tool for exploring the living retina at a spatial scale that had never been accessible before. Austin Roorda and I eventually used this instrument to image all three cone classes in the human eye, and we continue to use descendants of this instrument today to learn new things about the diseased as well as the normal eye. The principles of wavefront sensing and correction moved very quickly into the field of refractive surgery, and are now beginning to change many aspects of vision correction including the design of phoropters, autorefractors, contact lenses, intraocular lenses, and spectacles. These exciting developments are leading to fundamental advances in the fields of ophthalmology, optometry, and vision science. There is no doubt that the relationship between The Institute of Optics and the Center for Visual Science provided the unique environment without which these developments would never have occurred.

In addition to expanding its relationship to CVS, the Institute is steadily gaining momentum in the field of biomedical optics, successfully recruiting faculty with interests in this area such as Andrew Berger, Jim Zavislan, and Jim Feinup. Its new director, Wayne Knox, is committed to biomedical optics and is forming new relationships with the departments of ophthalmology and biomedical engineering. These exciting developments originated with those members of the Institute who were able to look beyond their immediate scientific discipline and see the potential synergy of optics and vision and more broadly of optics and biomedicine. I can't wait to see where this will take us.

David Williams has been a member of the faculty of the University of Rochester since 1981. He is currently Director of the Center for Visual Sciences and the William G. Allyn Professor of Medical Optics.

Pranks: Wilmot Mouse

Carlos Stroud

Perhaps it was the recent newspaper article in which Dennis Hall's humorous comment to a reporter that the faculty of the Institute were just "12 men out to save the universe" was duly quoted. Maybe it was just an irresistible urge to celebrate a Rochester spring that was finally arriving. In any case, just in time for graduation in May of 1986, there appeared on the observatory dome atop the Wilmot Building a beautifully crafted set of mouse ears with matching eyes and nose. Wilmot Mouse was born.

This was not some crude fabrication installed after an overly long night of indulgence at the Distillery. The ears stood up proudly, complete with slits to allow them to remain erect even in a thirty-mile-per-hour breeze. They had been carefully tested by tying them to the roof of a car. Unfortunately their ability to withstand the spring winds while atop the dome was never properly tested, as Institute Director Ken Teegarden did not feel that they represented the statement the department wanted to make at graduation. He had them removed immediately.

Who would have predicted that the group of pranksters from optics and physics would later achieve notable success? They included a current optics faculty member, a successful entrepreneur, an Oxford don, and the first author on a paper cited for a Nobel Prize.

Wilmot Mouse.

The Institute of Optics
Faculty 1990–1999

Agrawal, Govind P., 1989–
Altman, Joseph H., 1969–98
Boyd, Robert W., 1977–
Brown, Thomas G., 1987–
Davy, L. Nevil, 1987–94
Eastman, Jay M., 1979–98
Eberly, Joseph H., 1979–
Erdogan, Turan, 1992–2001
Fauchet, Philippe M., 1994–
Forbes, Gregory W., 1985–94
George, Nicholas, 1978–
Givens, M. Parker, 1948–
Hall, Dennis G., 1981–2002
Hopkins, Robert E., 1943–
Houde-Walter, Susan N., 1987–
Jacobs, Stephen D., 1988–
Kingslake, Rudolf, 1929–2003
Loewen, Erwin, 1988–98
MacAdam, David L., 1977–96
Mandel, Leonard, 1978–2000

Marchand, Eric, 1980–94
Moore, Duncan T., 1974–
Morris, G. Michael, 1980–2002
Mourou, Gerard, 1979–94
Novotny, Lukas, 1999–
Oliver, James B., 1998–
Raymer, Michael G., 1979–94
Rogers, John R., 1985–94
Seka, Wolf, 1994–
Smith, Douglas, 1989–92, 1999–2002
Smith, Warren, 1988–94
Stone, Bryan D., 1994–2000
Stroud, Jr., Carlos R., 1969–
Teegarden, Kenneth J., 1954–
Thompson, Brian J., 1968–
Walmsley, Ian A., 1988–
Wang, Shen-ge, 1994–2000
Wicks, Gary W., 1987–
Williams, David R., 1988–
Wolf, Emil, 1978–

The Institute of Optics
Degrees Awarded 1990–1999

Achziger, Josh, B.S., 1992
Albright, Dan, M.S., 1993
Allard, Jr., Peter, B.S., 1990
Allen, Bradley, B.S., 1996
Allen, Jr., George, B.S., 1991
Allen, Matthew, B.S., 1997
Alster, Stacey, B.S., 1992
Alonso, Miguel A., Ph.D., 1997
Altmann, Griffith, B.S., 1990; M.S., 1991
Andre, Richard, B.S., 1996; M.S., 1997
Anzellotti, Jay, B.S., 1993
Arden, Amy, B.S., 1992
Armstrong, J. Joseph, B.S., 1991; M.S., 1992
Asack, Scott, B.S., 1994
Attanasion, Daniel, M.S., 1991
Aude, Carl, B.S., 1991
Badar. Timothy, M.S., 1990
Baldwin, Kevin, B.S., 1990; M.S., 1991
Bancroft, Deborah, B.S., 1994
Banerjee, Somnath, M.S., 1994
Baraban, Edward, B.S., 1989; M.S., 1991
Barber, Kenneth, B.S., 1998
Barkocy, Kendra, M.S., 1996
Bartlett, Christopher, B.S., 1990
Bassingthwaite, Jason, B.S., 1993
Battistoni, Donald, B.S., 1991
Baughman Richard, M.S., 1990
Beal, Madeleine M., Ph.D., 1990
Beck, David, B.S., 1993
Beck, Mark, B.S., 1985; Ph.D., 1992
Benecke, Glenn, M.S., 1991
Bentley, Julie, B.S., 1990; Ph.D., 1996
Berger, Dennis, M.S., 1990
Bickel, Nathan, B.S., 1998; M.S., 1999
Bieber, Amy E., Ph.D., 1996
Biermann, Mark L., B.S., 1984; Ph.D., 1991
Bilker, Lawrence, B.S., 1991
Blitz, Dara, M.S., 1993
Blough, Christian G., Ph.D., 1992
Blumer, Robert, B.S., 1991

Boldosser, Patrick, B.S., 1993
Boothroyd, Michael, M.S., 1997
Bordyn, Brett, B.S., 1992; M.S., 1993
Bouk, Theodore, M.S., 1992
Bowen, John, Ph.D., 1991
Bowers, Mark W., Ph.D., 1998
Bradfield, Philip L., M.S., 1985; Ph.D., 1990
Bradley, Jonathan, B.S., 1998
Brady, Doreen, M.S., 1992
Bridges, Robert, Ph.D., 1995
Bromage, Jake, Ph.D., 1999
Brooks, Patricia, B.S., 1991
Bryant, Kyle, B.S., 1998
Buckland, Eric L., Ph.D., 1997
Bui, Thu-Huong, B.S., 1992
Bunzey, David, M.S., 1992
Buralli, Dale, Ph.D., 1991
Burke, Paul, B.S., 1993
Burkwit, Mary, B.S., 1991
Bussjager, Rebecca, B.S., 1990
Caccuitto, III, Michael, B.S., 1991
Cairns, Brian, Ph.D., 1992
Canning, David, B.S., 1996
Cannon, John, M.S., 1994
Carter, Thomas, B.S., 1994
Caruso, Angelo, M.S., 1991
Casaverde, Pablo, B.S., 1998; M.S., 1999
Catlin, Scott, B.S., 1992
Cavalcanti, Marcel, M.S., 1999
Caya, Timothy, M.S., 1998
Centanni, Paul, B.S., 1991
Chakmakjian, Stephen H., Ph.D., 1990
Chan, Eric, B.S., 1990; M.S., 1992
Chan, Yim, B.S., 1993
Chang, Thomas, M.S., 1991
Chao, Yvonne, B.S., 1990
Chatterbuck, Timothy, M.S., 1990
Chen, Min, M.S., 1997
Chen, Stephanie, B.S., 1995; M.S., 1999
Cheng, Yuh-Jen, M.S., 1990

Chernosky, Mark, B.S., 1992
Chiu, John, B.S., 1990
Cho, Doo Jin, Ph.D., 1990
Cicchiello, James, B.S., 1988; M.S., 1992
Cohen, Jonathan, B.S., 1990
Coleman, Edward, M.S., 1992
Conolly, Christopher, M.S., 1993
Corless, John D., Ph.D., 1997
Cormier, Mary, B.S., 1990
Cornell, James, B.S., 1993; M.S., 1994
Corum, Curtis, M.S., 1994
Coston, Scott, Ph.D., 1992
Cotton, Christopher, B.S., 1986; M.S., 1990
Culver, Thomas, B.S., 1990
Cumbo, Michael J., B.S., 1981; M.S., 1990; Ph.D., 1993
Cummings, Christopher, B.S., 1995
Curtin, Katherine, B.S., 1990
Dady, Joella, B.S., 1990
Daneshkhah, Shahin, B.S., 1995
Dass, Sasha, B.S., 1991
David, Stuart, B.S., 1990
Davis, Arthur, B.S., 1996; M.S., 2000
Davis, William V., Ph.D., 1993
DeAsla, Richard, B.S., 1991
Deaver, Dawne, M.S., 1996
DeBaun, Barbara, M.S., 1992
DeCaro, Joel, M.S., 1990
DeJager, Sarah, M.S., 1997
DeSaboiaSilva, Rodrigo, B.S., 1994
Doh, Lucius, B.S., 1989; M.S., 1990
Donner, Janet, B.S., 1994; M.S., 1998
Driscoll, David, M.S., 1995
Druckenmiller, Daniel, B.S., 1990
Drummond, Iain, B.S., 1992
Du, Tu, B.S., 1990
Duckett, III, George, B.S., 1993
Dugan, Elizabeth, B.S., 1994
Dulnikowski, Christine, B.S., 1990
Dumas, Paul, B.S., 1990; M.S., 1992
Dunham, David, B.S., 1995
Dunn, Thomas J., Ph.D., 1994
Dwyer, Carol, B.S., 1990
Dziel, Andrew, B.S., 1990
Eastman, Clarke, M.S., 1991
Edick, Keith, B.S., 1997
Elefante, David, B.S., 1995
Ellis, Kenneth, B.S., 1990
Emmons, Robert M., Ph.D., 1992
Erdogan, Turan, Ph.D., 1992
Eron, Randall, B.S., 1990
Evans, Alan F., Ph.D., 1992

Everett, Jonathan, B.S., 1991
Fabrizzio, Robert, M.S., 1999
Faklis, Dean, Ph.D., 1990
Fanning, Andrew, B.S., 1991
Fargnoli, Joseph, M.S., 1996
Farmiga, Nestor, M.S., 1993
Farr, Keith B., Ph.D., 1994
Faust, Jessica, B.S., 1992; M.S., 1994
Felkel, Eric, B.S., 1997
Ferri, John, B.S., 1991; M.S., 1993
Feth, Susan, M.S., 1990
Fields, David, B.S., 1991
Fischer, David G., Ph.D., 1996
Fitzgerald, Gregory, B.S., 1994; M.S., 1995
Fladd, David, B.S., 1991
Franks, David, B.S., 1995
Freling, Ryan, B.S., 1994
Frosch, Ira, M.S., 1992
Gaeta, Alexander L., B.S., 1983; Ph.D., 1990
Gaeta, Zagorka D., Ph.D., 1995
Galuppo, Christopher, B.S., 1997
Gamliel, Avshalom, Ph.D., 1990
Gansen, Eric, M.S., 1998
Gardner, Craig, M.S., 1990
Gasal, Nermina, B.S., 1999
Gehr, Russell J., Ph.D., 1997
Gengenbach, Richard, B.S., 1990
Gerber, Ronald, B.S., 1990; M.S., 1992
Gobbi, Edward, B.S., 1988; M.S., 1991
Golding, Douglas, B.S., 1989; M.S., 1991
Gordon, Ronald, Ph.D., 1998
Govier, Jeremy, B.S., 1997
Gracey, Renee, B.S., 1990
Grice, Warren P., Ph.D., 1998
Grindel, Mark, B.S., 1991
Groglio, Jr., Nicholas, B.S., 1992
Guardalben, Mark, B.S., 1983; M.S., 1991
Gutierrez, Alina, M.S., 1991
Haag, John, M.S., 1993
Haas, Benjamin, B.S., 1997
Haddock, Joshua, B.S., 1998
Hagen, Colleen, B.S., 1996
Hahn, Michael, B.S., 1992
Hajek, Pavel, M.S., 1995
Hallerman, Gregory, B.S., 1990
Hand, Douglas, B.S., 1991
Hansotte, Eric, M.S., 1992
Harding, Harvard, M.S., 1997
Hark, Peter, B.S., 1997
Hartzell, Andrew, M.S., 1990
Haun, Niels, Ph.D., 1992

Hawthorne, Jeff A., M.S., 1990
Hayes, Jeanine, B.S., 1992
Headley, III, Clifford, Ph.D., 1995
Hendrick, Wyatt, B.S., 1991
Hendry, Michael, M.S., 1990
Heslink, Nathan, B.S., 1999
Hildebrandt, Michael, B.S., 1999
Hill, Andrew, M.S., 1993
Hilton, David, B.S., 1997; M.S., 1999
Hinrichs, Keith, B.S., 1993; M.S., 1994
Holmes, Robert, B.S., 1994
Homan, Russell, B.S., 1991
Hoppe, Michael, B.S., 1990; M.S., 1992
Horbatuck Suzanne, B.S., 1986; Ph.D., 1996
Houghton, Jennifer, M.S., 1995
Houk, Michael T., Ph.D., 1990
Hovorka, Richard, M.S., 1997
Howard, Joseph M., Ph.D., 1999
Hsu, Yuling, B.S., 1993; M.S., 1999
Hu, Ching Yee, B.S., 1997
Huang, Szu-Chi, B.S., 1991; M.S., 1993
Huber, Paul, B.S., 1991
Hubert, Jr., Charles, M.S., 1991
Hutcheson, Mark, B.S., 1990
Hutchins, Jamie, B.S., 1992
Hutton, Shannon, B.S., 1996
Iaconis, Christopher, Ph.D., 1999
Ingalls, Moria, B.S., 1999
Inman, Jill M., Ph.D., 1996
Isberg, Thomas A., Ph.D., 1990
Jain, Ajaykumar, B.S., 1992
James, Daniel F. V., Ph.D., 1992
Janisiewicz, Philip, B.S., 1999
Johnson, Aaron, B.S., 1994
Johnson, Frederick G., Ph.D., 1993
Jones, Andrew E. W., Ph.D., 1992
Jones, Mark, B.S., 1990
Jones, Michael, M.S., 1994
Jordon, Rebecca, Ph.D., 1995
Judge-Fanning, Jennifer, B.S., 1991
Kaczmarek, Crystal, B.S., 1990
Kadamus, Christopher, B.S., 1999
Kalenak, David, B.S., 1988; M.S., 1990
Kamanecka, Katherine, B.S., 1990
Karim, Adil, M.S., 1997
Kaufman, Gregory, B.S., 1996
Kauranen, Martti, Ph.D., 1992
Kavanagh, Suzanne, B.S., 1991
Kibler, Nelson, M.S., 1994
Killen, Margo, B.S., 1990
Kim, Mok, B.S., 1991

Kim, Tong, B.S., 1990
Kindred, Douglas S., Ph.D., 1990
Kitzke, Benjamin, B.S., 1997
Klaus, Jeffrey, M.S., 1991
Klein, Benjamin, B.S., 1990
Kleinstiver, Kimberly, B.S., 1994
Ko, Michael, B.S., 1991
Kobilansky, Anna, B.S., 1994; M.S., 1995
Koch, III, Karl W., Ph.D., 1990
Kohnke, Glenn, B.S., 1989; Ph.D., 1995
Korenic, Eileen, Ph.D., 1997
Koshel, R. John, B.S., 1988; Ph.D., 1997
Kosky, Nicole, B.S., 1992
Kotchick, Keith, B.S., 1993; M.S., 1994
Kowarz, Marek, Ph.D., 1995
Kreger, Stephen T., Ph.D., 1997
Kretschmann, Hanno, M.S., 1995
Krill, Daniel M., B.S., 1987; M.S., 1990
Krushbwitz, Brian E., Ph.D., 1998
Kubalak, David, B.S., 1991; M.S., 1993
Kubicek, Emily, B.S., 1991
Kulawiec, Andrew W., Ph.D., 1994
Kulleen, Seemant, B.S., 1998
Kunick, Joseph, B.S., 1991
Kuo, Shihjong, Ph.D., 1991
Kutner, Brian, B.S., 1999
Kuwa, Tomiei, B.S., 1998
Kuyucu, Omer, B.S., 1995
Kwak, Sun-Young, M.S., 1996
Lam, Jane, B.S., 1990
Lamkins, Timothy, M.S., 1997
Landau, Igor, B.S., 1994; M.S., 1995
Landry, Joseph, B.S., 1990
Langanke, Kristen, M.S., 1996
Lasche, James B., Ph.D., 1998
Latimer, David, B.S., 1995
Laverty, Denise, M.S., 1992
Law, Joanne Y., Ph.D., 1998
Lawn, Stephen, B.S., 1992
Le, Long, B.S., 1996
Lee, Augustine, B.S., 1994
Lee, Jae-Cheul, Ph.D., 1990
Lee, Je Choon, B.S., 1994
Lee, San Hun, B.S., 1996
Leung, Chin-man, B.S., 1989; M.S., 1990
Levene, Michael J., B.S., 1992
Li, Fai, B.S., 1991
Liao, Zhi Ming, B.S., 1995; M.S., 1996; Ph.D., 2001
Lightenberg, Julie, M.S., 1991
Lin, Ying, M.S., 1991
Ling, Maurice, B.S., 1990

Liodice, Christopher, B.S., 1999
Liou, Lisa, Ph.D., 1996
Lo, Koon K., M.S., 1990
Lopez, Ali, M.S., 1993
Lu, Ngoc, B.S., 1991
Lui, Cynthia, B.S., 1999
Lutter, Matthew, B.S., 1998
Macaluso, Robert, B.S., 1997
Machado, David, B.S., 1992
Madsen, David, M.S., 1992
Maislin, Seth, B.S., 1990; M.S., 1992
Mak, Oxcar, B.S., 1999
Maki, Jeffery J., Ph.D., 1991
Malach, Joseph, B.S., 1996
Mallalieu, Mark R., Ph.D., 1994
Mandra, Robert, M.S., 1993
Marasco, Peter, B.S., 1991
Marciante, John R., Ph.D., 1997
Margolies, Jeffrey, B.S., 1994
Marleau, William, B.S., 1998
Martino, Anthony J., Ph.D., 1990
Masters, Julie, B.S., 1994
Mastriani, Paul, B.S., 1995
Maywar, Drew N., B.S., 1993; Ph.D., 2001
McHugh, Timothy, B.S., 1994
McIntyre, Kevin, B.S., 1988; Ph.D., 1998
McKeever, Christopher, B.S., 1996
McKeon, Amanda, B.S., 1993
McMahon, Matthew, B.S., 1993
McMahon, Shaun, B.S., 1991
McMichael, Ryan, B.S., 1994
McNeil, Brian, B.S., 1995
McShane, Thomas, B.S., 1999
Mellberg, Laura, B.S., 1991; M.S., 1993
Melocchi, Michael L., B.S., 1997; Ph.D., 2003
Mercado, Alvaro, M.S., 1990
Merle, Cormic, B.S., 1991
Merwin, Kenneth, M.S., 1992
Meyer, Jon, M.S., 1999
Meyers, Mark, M.S., 1993
Michaels, Elise, B.S., 1991
Michaels, Robert, B.S., 1991
Michniewicz, Mark, M.S., 1991
Miller, Donald, Ph.D., 1996
Miller, Edward J., B.S., 1985; Ph.D., 1991
Miller, Michael, B.S., 1994
Miller, Paul O., B.S., 1990
Missig, Michael, B.S., 1992; M.S., 1994
Modavis, Robert A., M.S., 1982; Ph.D., 1990
Moi, Michael, B.S., 1998

Moon, Jeffrey, B.S., 1996
Moore, Sean, B.S., 1998
Moore, Thomas R., Ph.D., 1993
Moore-Sullivan, Karen L., B.S., 1990; Ph.D., 1998
Morelli, Taryn, B.S., 1993; M.S., 1995
Morrison, Jeffrey, B.S., 1990
Mount, Susan, B.S., 1990
Munro, James, M.S., 1990
Murnan, Andrew, B.S., 1996; M.S., 2003
Murnane, Michael, B.S., 1991
Murphy, Paul E., B.S., 1995; Ph.D., 2001
Myoungsik Cha, M.S., 1990
Nasir, Amir, B.S., 1991
Naso, Mark, B.S., 1990
Nelson, Robert, Ph.D., 1999
Ng, Siu-Yan, B.S., 1991; M.S., 1993
Ng, Willy, B.S., 1994
Niedzielski, Peter, B.S., 1992
Noel, Michael, Ph.D., 1996
Norton, Scott M., Ph.D., 1998
O'Neill, Mark, B.S., 1988; M.S., 1993
O'Shea, Kevin, B.S., 1994
Oey, Daniel, B.S., 1990
Oliver, Brian, M.S., 1994
Oliver, James, B.S., 1992; M.S., 1997
Olmstead, Ty, M.S., 1993
Olmsted, Brian L., Ph.D., 1993
Olofsson, Lars M., Ph.D., 1992
Olson, James, M.S., 1990
Olson, Jennifer, B.S., 1992
Olson, Stephen C., Ph.D., 1999
Onisk, Cynthia, B.S., 1994
Orband, Daniel, B.S., 1993
Pack, Thomas, M.S., 1990
Pantano, Joseph, B.S., 1990
Papademetriou, Stephanos, B.S., 1986; Ph.D., 1993
Park, Jeong, B.S., 1998; M.S., 2002
Parker, Jonathan S., Ph.D., 1990
Pascale, Michael, B.S., 1990
Pasquale, Bert, B.S., 1991
Passalugo, James, B.S., 1998
Patel, Falgun, B.S., 1995
Patience, Jennifer, M.S., 1994
Pedulla, Lesley, B.S., 1992
Peer, Aaron, B.S., 1998
Peng, Song, Ph.D., 1996
Pentico, Clark, M.S., 1992
Pentolino, Samuel, B.S., 1993
Perman, Rachelle, B.S., 1991
Perricelli, Ann M., B.S., 1992

Pete, Alexander, B.S., 1993
Peters, Philip, Ph.D., 1999
Pfenning, Michael, B.S., 1991
Pierce, Gregory, M.S., 1996
Pinyan, Christopher, M.S., 1991
Plescia, Joseph, B.S., 1994
Pomykai, Michael, B.S., 1991
Porat, Tamar, M.S., 1992
Poremba, Geoffrey, B.S., 1991
Porter, Jason, B.S., 1997
Portisch, Kuang-Chang, B.S., 1991
Powers, Jeffrey, M.S., 1991
Pradhan, Apurba, M.S., 2002
Prelewitz, David F., Ph.D., 1992
Proctor, Douglas, B.S., 1993
Pugliese, Lenore, Ph.D., 1990
Rabin, Mark, B.S., 1998
Radesi, Felix, B.S., 1990
Radic, Stojan, Ph.D., 1995
Ragg, Wolfram, M.S., 1992
Raguin, Daniel H., Ph.D., 1993
Raymond, Brion, B.S., 1992
Reed, David, B.S., 1990
Reid, Ellen, M.S., 1991
Ren, Jun, M.S., 1997
Rice, Kevin, B.S., 1997; M.S., 1998
Rich, Lisa, B.S., 1990
Rigatti, Amy, B.S., 1990; M.S., 1996
Roberts, Benjamin, B.S., 1997
Roberts, William, B.S., 1992
Robles, David, M.S., 1994
Rodney, Paul J., Ph.D., 1998
Rogala, Eric, B.S., 1990; M.S., 1992
Rouse, Andrew, B.S., 1994
Rubinoff, Greg, B.S., 1992
Rueckwald, Eric, M.S., 1997
Russo, Michael, B.S., 1990; M.S., 1991
Ryan, Andrew T., Ph.D., 1997
Ryan, Kenneth, B.S., 1990
Saaf, Lennart, Ph.D., 1992
Sabharwal, Yashvinder, B.S., 1992
Sales, Tasso R. deMelo, Ph.D., 1998
Sampath, Deepak, B.S., 1997
Sandruck, Scott, B.S., 1994
Sankey, Norris D., Ph.D., 1993
Sano, Koichi, M.S., 1999
Sanson, Mark, M.S., 1998
Santwani, Sheila, B.S., 1991
Sarama, Scott, B.S., 1991; M.S., 1993
Sato, Akira, M.S., 1992
Saunders, Rene, B.S., 1990
Sauther, Eric, B.S., 1999

Saxer, Christopher E., Ph.D., 1998
Sayer, Gregory, B.S., 1990
Schaad, Ian, B.S., 1993; M.S., 1994
Scheffel, Laurie A., M.S., 1990
Schertler, Donald J., Ph.D., 1993
Schiff, Roy, B.S., 1993
Schott, Peter, B.S., 1995
Schuberg, Darren, B.S., 1990
Schwarz, Richard, M.S., 1991
Schwiegerling, James, B.S., 1990; M.S., 1991
Sczupak, Robert, B.S., 1991
Segler, D.J., B.S., 1994
Selent, William, B.S., 1990
Seo, Katsuhiro, M.S., 1994
Shaffer, James, Ph.D., 1999
Shank, Steven M., Ph.D., 1993
Shea, James, M.S., 1991
Sherman, James, M.S., 1997
Shieh, Mun, B.S., 1990
Shipley, Jeff, B.S., 1995
Shukes, Scott, B.S., 1991
Shum, Frank, M.S., 1991
Shuman, Timothy, M.S., 1999
Siew, Ronian, B.S., 1997; M.S., 1999
Singel, Diane, B.S., 1996
Siryk, Walter, B.S., 1990
Smith, Corey, B.S., 1997
Smith, David, B.S., 1990
Smith, Robert E., Ph.D., 1993
Smith, Scott, B.S., 1990
Smith, Steven, M.S., 1996
Snyder, Shane, B.S., 1996
Sowder, Andrew, B.S., 1990
Spaker, Kurt, B.S., 1994
Spaulding, Kevin, Ph.D., 1992
Squier, Jeffery A., Ph.D., 1992
Srour, Donna, M.S., 1990
Stagnitto, Steven, B.S., 1998
Stamper, Brian, B.S., 1994
Stanley, Matthew, B.S., 1998
Stanley, Patricia, M.S., 1990
Statt, Bryan, B.S., 1990
Steckroat, Thomas, M.S., 1994
Stelick, Scott, B.S., 1993
Stentz, Andrew, Ph.D., 1995
Stevens, Colleen, M.S., 1996
Stevens, James, M.S., 1995
Stevens, William, M.S., 1990
Stossel, Bryan J., Ph.D., 1995
Stuart, Howard R., Ph.D., 1998
Stuehler, Alexandra, B.S., 1995

Stull, Corey, B.S., 1993
Sucha, Gregg D., Ph.D., 1992
Sullivan, Kevin G., B.S., 1989; Ph.D., 1994
Summa, Mark, B.S., 1990
Sun, Keung, M.S., 1991
Sweetser, John N., Ph.D., 1994
Taber, Afshin, B.S., 1990
Tamaddon, Houman, B.S., 1996
Tanis, Todd R., B.S., 1993
Tesar, Joseph, M.S., 1990
Theilmann, Rebecca, M.S., 1994
Thompson, Daniel, M.S., 1999
Thorson, Michael, B.S., 1990
Thurman, Samuel T., B.S., 1996; Ph.D.,
    2003
Tocci, Michael, B.S., 1990
Tomkinson, Todd, M.S., 1993
Tompkin, Wayne R., Ph.D., 1990
Torpey, Matthew, M.S., 1993
Traylor, Jennifer, B.S., 1989; M.S., 1995
Turgut, Suleyman, B.S., 1992
Van Leeuwen, Michael, Ph.D., 1998
Vanderloske, John, B.S., 1990
VanLieu, Neil, B.S., 1990
Varriano, John A., Ph.D., 1993
Vaughn, Mark, M.S., 1993
Velazquez, Belimar, B.S., 1992
Vizgaitis, Jay, B.S., 1998
Vogler, Scott, B.S., 1991; M.S., 1998
Wagner, Julianne, B.S., 1996
Wallace, J. Kent, M.S., 1992
Wamsley, Charles C., Ph.D., 1999
Wang, David Y-H., B.S., 1985; M.S., 1986;
    Ph.D., 1992
Warner, III, Frederick, M.S., 1994
Watson, Edward, Ph.D., 1991
Watson, Lee, B.S., 1993

Waxer, Leon J., Ph.D., 1999
Weaver, Daniel, M.S., 1993
Weber, Aaron, B.S., 1997
Wegner, Matthew, M.S., 1992
Wehr, Kristina, B.S., 1991
Weiss, Sharon, B.S., 1999
Wells, Conrad, B.S., 1989; M.S., 1991
Wernick, Miles N., Ph.D., 1990
Weslander, Michele, M.S., 1994
West, James A., Ph.D., 1998
Whalen, Michael, B.S., 1990
Wheeler, Benjamin, M.S., 1997
Whitcomb, Kevin, M.S., 1995
Williams, Christopher, M.S., 1992
Wilson, Brian, B.S., 1993
Wilson, Debra, B.S., 1994
Wittman, Mark, M.S., 1991
Wolff, Roger G., B.S., 1994
Wong, David, B.S., 1990
Wong, Michael, B.S., 1991
Wong, Minchuan, B.S., 1994
Wong, Victor C., Ph.D., 1996
Woo, Seungbum, B.S., 1995; M.S.,
    1997
Wrobel, Sandrine, M.S., 1990
Wu, Rucong, B.S., 1996
Wyatt, Suzanne, M.S., 1990
Yarussi, Richard, M.S., 1994
Yoder, Lars, B.S., 1991
Young, Moira, B.S., 1999
Yu, Ming, M.S., 1994
Yugama, Koji, M.S., 1995
Zaidi, Shoaib, B.S., 1990
Zainul, Mohamed, M.S., 1994
Zhang, Eugene, B.S., 1991; M.S., 1993
Zoref, Jonathan, B.S., 1994
Zuegel, Jonathan, Ph.D., 1996

PART VIII

Now: The New Millennium

VIII. Now: The New Millennium

In 2001 Wayne Knox became director of the Institute, returning to his alma mater after seventeen years in industry. At this writing he has been in that position for three years, enough time for his enthusiasm and relentless energy to begin to make their mark. In the first essay of this section we review the beginnings of his tenure as director. We then present a photographic essay of the people who inhabit the department in its seventeenth year. We review the credentials of the faculty who lead the department at this juncture in its history, and finally we present a series of remembrances of experiences as undergraduates in our program by alumni with a special distinction.

62. New Direction for a New Millennium: Wayne H. Knox Becomes Director

Carlos Stroud

Early in 2001 Wayne H. Knox was appointed director of The Institute of Optics. His connections with the Institute were long and deep, but he had just spent the previous seventeen years on the technical staff at Bell Labs in Holmdel, New Jersey. Wayne is the son of Robert Knox, a professor in the Department of Physics and Astronomy who himself was the recipient of a joint Ph.D. degree in physics and optics from the University. The family resemblance is remarkable, so that few of his father's acquaintances fail to recognize the son on first meeting. Wayne received his B.S. in Optics in 1979 and his Ph.D. in 1983 from The Institute of Optics. His thesis research was jointly supervised by Professors Teegarden and Mourou.

At Bell Labs Knox had a remarkable record in research, for a long time holding the record for the shortest laser pulse ever produced, and publishing some 140 papers. He also had some administrative experience as director of the Advanced Photonics Research Department at Bell Labs. While these accomplishments are impressive, they were not really what led to his appointment, but rather the energy, intensity, and optimistic enthusiasm that characterized him from at least the time that he was an undergraduate. All of those who knew him, and those who were just meeting him, felt that his metabolism as well as his talents were needed at the Institute at this juncture.

Wayne H. Knox.

During the last few years of Dennis Hall's directorship, and throughout the interim period during which Ian Walmsley served as acting director, the relationship between the Institute and the University administration was uneasy, with frequent disagreements over budget, appointments, and general direction of the department. The photonics boom had enticed several tenured faculty members to give up their faculty positions or take long-term leaves to work in industry. Michael Morris and Turan Erdogan left, Susan Houde-Walter and Duncan Moore took extended leaves. Dennis Hall left to become associate provost at Vanderbilt while Ian Walmsley assumed the chair of Experimental Physics at Oxford University.

Ian Walmsley served as Acting Director.

As expected, Wayne Knox "hit the ground running." In short order Jim Fienup joined the faculty as the first holder of the Robert Hopkins Chair, Assistant Professor Chunlei Guo was added to the faculty to work in the area of intense field-matter interactions, and Assistant Professor Miguel Alonso strengthened the Institute in the area of mathematical optics. Jim Zavislan was appointed Associate Professor of Optics and director of the Institute Ventures Program. Sadly, Parker Givens finally decided to stop instructing the teaching laboratory some fifty-five years after he first joined the faculty.

The Institute Ventures Program is described in a later essay in this volume. It was part of a general effort of the University, and the Institute in particular to couple research and innovations more directly and quickly to entrepreneurial activities. The University was anxious to tap into royalty income from campus inventions as well as to retain faculty who were being attracted away to start new companies. Not all of the faculty are comfortable with this development, but it is certainly consistent with the economic climate in Rochester and the nation. The University of Rochester is now the second largest employer in the Rochester area. Regional economic development plans depend heavily on University innovations to lead to new industries to replace jobs lost in more mature industries. Medicine, optics, and the interface between the two are natural places to look for such innovations. As earlier essays in this volume document, this is hardly a new activity for the Institute.

A new University department of Biomedical Engineering had recently been founded and needed a new building to house it. The Institute had long been crowded in Wilmot and overflowed into the small annex, teaching laboratories in Dewey Hall, and laboratories and student offices in Gavett Hall. The increased collaboration between optics and medicine and the common need for a new building by Optics and Biomedical Engineering led to a joining of efforts to build one new building to house additional space for Optics and a home for the new department.

In a separate essay Wayne Knox describes plans for this new building and for other developments in the future of The Institute of Optics. These plans will be supported by a major fund raising effort. It is indeed clear that Wayne "hit the ground running" and is continuing at his usual frenetic pace.

63. Faculty, Students and Staff: A Photographic Essay

Faculty, staff and students, February 2004.

Fifteen of the twenty-four full time faculty of the Institute.
Back row, left to right: Chunlei Guo, James Fienup, Lukas Novotny, Robert Boyd, Miguel Alonso
Second row: Thomas G. Brown, James Zavislan, Joseph H. Eberly
Third row from back: Carlos Stroud, Govind Agrawal, Andrew Berger
Front row: Wayne Knox, Nicholas George, Kenneth J. Teegarden, Susan Houde-Walter
Not pictured: Nicholas Bigelow, Philippe Fauchet, Thomas Foster, Stephen Jacobs, Duncan Moore,
Wolf Seka, Gary Wicks, David Williams, and Emil Wolf
In addition, the adjunct faculty includes Julie Bentley, Dale Buralli, John Marciante, James Oliver,
and Ian Walmsley.

Staff of the Institute.
Back row, left to right: Per Adamson, James DePinto, Michael Koch
Center row: Sylvia Schattschneider, Noelene Votens, Brian McIntyre
Front row: Betsy Benedict, Joan Christian, Maria Schnitzler
Not pictured: Gina Kern, Gayle Thompson.

Graduate students of the Institute. Fifty-five of the 89 graduate students in Optics.

Class of 2004, recipients of the B.S. in Optics.
Top row: Jason Kay, Alexander Gondarenko, Zachary Hoyt, Michael Quijano, Kevin Gemp
2nd row: Edwine Michel, Gary DeVries, Wei Qian, James Parke, Prof. James Zavislan
3rd row: Daniel Eversole, Jeff Virojanapa, Daniel Vickery, Matthew King, Katherine Lilevjen, David Lee
Front row: John Jackson, Kevin Mille, Jennifer Chen, Ankur Pansari, Tara Pajoohi, Salvatore Guarnieri
Missing: Laura Elgin, Joshua Fink, Dustin Hsu, Rong Liu.

64. Undergraduate Life from a Faculty Perspective

Carlos Stroud

Many alumni of the Institute have remarked on the profound effect their education had on their lives. There is one exclusive group who one might expect were most profoundly affected by their time spent in The Institute of Optics. The group includes at least seven: James Forsyth, Steve Jacobs, Wayne Knox, Alex Gaeta, Dan Gauthier, Mark Biermann, and Mark Beck. Each began his higher education as an undergraduate optics major, continued all the way through the doctorate at Rochester, and then went on to hold a faculty position. Reflecting on this list, it occurred to me that there must be something about our undergraduate program that inspired this group to continue their optics education and emulate their mentors in an academic career, so I asked some of them to recount the formative experiences that they had.

Mark Beck received his B.S. in optics from the University of Rochester in 1985, and his Ph.D. in 1992. He is now associate professor of physics at Whitman College in Walla Walla, Washington. He writes:

> I vividly remember my first Optics course—Geometrical Optics with Duncan Moore. Working on that ray tracing program using punch cards and the old IBM mainframe was quite a challenge. I even remember one of our exam questions that asked about the eye of an anablebs fish. It lives on the surface and its eye sits half in the water and half out, yet both halves are in focus! I actually saw some of these fish in an aquarium a couple years ago and instantly recognized them.
>
> One thing I really appreciated as an undergraduate was the opportunity to work on a research project. I wasn't alone in this, a number of my friends had research jobs, either at the Institute or at the Laboratory for Laser Energetics. Working on this project hooked me on research, and strongly influenced my decision to pursue a Ph.D. It influences me to this day, as I teach at an all-undergraduate institution and nearly all of my current research involves undergraduate students. I'm glad to be able to provide them with an opportunity similar to the one I had.

Mark L. Biermann is associate professor of physics at the U.S. Naval Academy. He began his studies in the Institute in 1980 and completed his Ph.D. in 1991.

> I was an undergraduate in The Institute of Optics from 1980 to 1984. I have many memories of that time, from our first freshman Optics course with Dr. Chris Dainty, to our senior Optics Laboratory with Dr. Parker Givens. However, one of my most vivid memories is associated with the Geometrical Optics I course, Optics 241, with Dr. Duncan Moore. Anyone who took this course during this time period will immediately know the single component of Optics 241 that I am about to refer to. This assignment was a touchstone for Optics majors for years and was clearly seen as a key rite of passage. The assignment was, of course, the computer ray tracing and aberration analysis project. The "computer program," as it was generally referred to, was an important part of Optics 241 for years. Our class was in a unique position, however. In taking the course in the fall of 1981, we were the last class to do the program almost exclusively on punch cards. The use of terminals

to talk to the IBM mainframe had just been introduced, but terminals were tough to come by and the safest approach in the fall of 1981 was to rely on the tried and true punch cards. The use of punch cards, while inconvenient, actually helped to forge a clear sense of community among the Optics majors of the class of '84. During the week or two leading up to the due date for the program, I could always count on finding a dozen or more fellow 241 students in the computer work room where the punch-card reader was located. Anytime of the day or night, there was a strong Optics presence to be found. Working in that small space in Taylor Hall, we all felt great when somebody's "a-ray" made it through correctly, and shared the disappointment of the wrong value for the Petzval field curvature. The experience helped us to see ourselves not just as college students, but more importantly, as Optics students. While the "computer program" was not always fun, it certainly helped to give us a strong sense of what it meant to be an Optics major in The Institute of Optics.

Alexander Gaeta is associate professor of applied and engineering physics at Cornell University. He received his B.S. in 1983, M.S. in 1984, and Ph.D. in 1991.

When I started as an undergraduate in the fall of 1979, I had intended to major in Physics and Astronomy. An upperclassman told me that there was this cool major called Optics which involved lasers and the sort. I took Optics 100 that Spring taught by Conger Gabel, and within a week I knew that optics was what I wanted to study. The optics classes were the ones I enjoyed the most and although my tennis pursuits interfered with my academic performance, I still remember well the material I learned in all these courses. Inspired by Duncan Moore's lectures, I offer "Shorts" in all the classes I now teach.

Curiously it was fate that intervened my senior year and led me to my career in nonlinear optics. I was considering applying to the Master's program and was told by a straight-talking faculty member that I would have to work in a faculty member's lab if I was to have any chance of being admitted. My undergraduate advisor, Prof. Chris Dainty, wrote down a list, in alphabetical order, of faculty who he thought would be looking for undergraduates to work in their labs. Bob Boyd's name was at the top of the list and I went to see him, having no idea what nonlinear optics was. The rest, as they say, is history. I'll always be immensely grateful for the opportunity to work in his lab as an undergraduate. His encouragement and the experience of seeing and working with his graduate students inspired me to focus my efforts on more intellectual endeavors which culminated in receiving my Ph.D. under his supervision.

Daniel J Gauthier is the Anne T. and Robert M. Bass Associate Professor of Physics and associate professor of biomedical engineering at Duke University. He received his B.S. in Optics in 1982, his M.S. in 1983, and his Ph.D. in 1989.

The Class of 1982 was part of a growing movement in optics, both in the Institute and around the country. Our class was substantially larger than previous years (just under thirty) and was an indicator of much larger classes to come. Yet, the class size was small enough so that we received a lot of attention from faculty while it was large enough to take on new activities. We started the first Student Chapter of the Optics Society of America for the expressed goal of learning more about careers in optics, networking, and having good parties (which Dean Thompson was more than willing to support). The chapter was very active in bringing in speakers from local industry and taking tours of their facilities, and hosting evening pizza parties and an occasional faculty/student social get together (usually surrounding a keg . . .). On the job front, we were most impressed by the number of companies willing to wine and dine us as soon as we declared the Optics major; little did we know of the boom and bust cycles of the optics industry!

One fond memory of life as an undergraduate in the Institute were the laboratories associated with most classes. While time consuming, it was great to get our hands on the real thing, even when the rail for the "Fourier Transform Processor" was a bit wobbly, for example. While independent study projects weren't emphasized, many of us found a job working on some small project, such as playing around with a small CO_2 laser (which we never were able to get working). All in all, we had a great time together and managed to get in quite a bit of fun in between classes and homework!

Stephen Jacobs, 38 years and counting as an optiker.

Stephen Jacobs is senior scientist at the Laboratory for Laser Energetics and professor of optics and chemical engineering at the University of Rochester. His connection with the Institute is the longest of the group, dating back more than halfway to the founding of the department.

Thank you for the opportunity to share some thoughts on what it was like for me to be an undergraduate in Optics at The Institute during the 1960s. I entered the U of R as a freshman in 1966 and graduated with a B.S. in 1970. I must have enjoyed the experience, because I never left.

Our first introductory optics class was taken in the beginning of the sophomore year. I remember that this was the first contact I had with an Optics professor. We met on the fourth floor of B&L in a small room. Of the approximately six of us students, I recall Cynthia Barnes, Jay Eastman, Mark Westcott, and Jim Buran. It was kind of like magic when W. Lewis Hyde showed up for lecture. He was the director of the Institute and what a gentleman! Always dressed in a coat and tie, he had these special felt markers to use on the overhead projector. There was this continuous roll of transparency that he wrote on during class. He seldom made mistakes or crossed anything out. His printing was neat and easily read. The book was Jenkins and White. It was much drier than his lectures, which were always well organized. I credit him with conveying to me the elegance of optics.

Two of the classes I took during the junior year were also held in this small lecture room on the fourth floor of B&L. They were taught by Peter John Sands, an assistant professor from Australia who was learning everything he could about advanced lens design during his time at The Institute. Prof. Sands taught us atomic and molecular spectroscopy, and for the second semester he offered the six of us a course on polarized light. This turned out to be my favorite course, and he was a great teacher. He used Shurcliff's book that had just come out in 1966. I still remember his fondness for the pop quiz, and my marginal performance on these surprise tests. We argued about giving them. I lost. I credit him with conveying to me the excitement in optical engineering.

In the late 1960s the undergraduates received a lot of attention, because our numbers were so few. That put us in a great position do well in our Senior year, when we took the same classes as the graduate students. I'll never forget Senior lab in Gavett Hall. [No one forgets Senior lab!] Cynthia Barnes was my lab partner, and she often had to leave somewhat early to attend a graduate course in lens design. She was always irritated with me, since the labs seemed to drag on until after her departure. This made her writing a difficult endeavor. Sorry Cynthia.

Congratulations to The Institute on seventy-five years of excellence. It has been my good fortune to have shared thirty-eight of them.

James Zavislan, currently associate professor of optics at the University of Rochester, received his B.S. in Optics in 1981 and his Ph.D. in 1988. He worked in industry for several years and recently returned to the Institute as an associate professor.

I arrived as an undergraduate at the University of Rochester and the Institute of Optics in 1978 from Colorado. At the time the twenty-four-beam Omega Laser system was being completed at the Laboratory for Laser Energetics. I was interested in working in optics so I applied for a job at the laser lab as soon as I arrived. My first job was copying the pencil-on-vellum engineering drawings onto blue prints. It was a tedious job involving spending hours aligning large sheets of paper into a noxious ammonia-spewing duplicator. However, it was a wonderful introduction to a large-scale engineering project. I can honestly say that I saw every part that went into the laser system. I also saw how many revisions were required on seemingly simple parts. The drafting area and duplicator was located in the future target bay for the laser fusion system. It was exciting to think at some point in the future twenty-four laser beams would be replicating the conditions of the Sun inside a laboratory. My affiliation with the laser lab continued throughout my undergraduate years. Because I was previously trained as a machinist, I later worked for several scientists machining mechanical parts for various laser or optical metrology systems. Everyone with whom I worked was helpful in teaching me about their research. I learned about and worked on instrumentation to make ultra-fast laser pulses and high damage threshold optical coatings.

James Zavislan.

In my junior year I took the optical interference coatings class taught by Professor Jay Eastman, then the director of the LLE. I remember one homework assignment was particularly difficult: Design an anti-reflection coating for 1ω, 2ω and 3ω. Nobody in the class was able to meet the specifications, although some of us came close. When we remarked to Prof. Eastman how challenging the design was, he told us, "Yes, we need this coating for Omega but we have not come up with a solution yet so we thought we would give the class a try. We don't know if a design exists." It was a great lesson that not all problems have solutions.

Taking classes from famous faculty could be intimidating, but I remember many lighthearted moments: Professor Givens wore a honey bee tie tack when he taught about the optics of the honey bee. Professor Kingslake told us that we could call him at home before 10:30 if we had any questions, "I don't hang out at the bars anymore." Professor Thompson would give an annual skit on "How not to give a technical presentation," and commenting that for a successful career one should cultivate a British accent.

I often encourage students to develop fundamental understanding and intuition about the behavior of light in different environments and systems: I tell them to "be the photon." As an undergraduate at The Institute of Optics and the Laboratory for Laser Energetics, I was surrounded by photons in myriad of circumstances. The combination of theoretical and applied understanding I learned at the Institute and LLE helped develop a deep appreciation for breadth and depth of optical engineering and optical sciences. I am deeply thankful for the education and the experience.

The experiences of two others among this group, Wayne Knox and James Forsyth, are recounted in separate essays in this volume.

65. Faculty Honors

Carlos Stroud

One of the timeless traditions of The Institute of Optics is the international recognition of the stature of its faculty, a stature which has been recognized by countless awards over the years. A number of those awards are mentioned in earlier essays in this volume. In the current essay we will limit ourselves to cataloging some of the accomplishments and honors received by current twenty-five full-time and five adjunct faculty members. Of the full-time faculty members, sixteen hold their principal appointments in the Institute, while nine have joint appointments with their primary appointments in other departments in the University. Of the twenty-five full-time members, seven hold endowed professorships.

Two faculty members edit important series of books: Emil Wolf, whose series *Progress in Optics* will soon reach fifty volumes, and Brian Thompson, who is an editor of series published by SPIE and Marcel Decker that list more than 175 and eighty volumes, respectively. Other faculty have also edited a number of conference proceedings and compilations so that the total is well over three hundred volumes. In addition, the faculty have written a number of popular textbooks and monographs, including: *Principles of Optics* by M. Born and E. Wolf; *Lasers* by P. W. Milonni and J. H. Eberly; *Nonlinear Optics*, and *Radiometry and the Detection of Optical Radiation* by R. W. Boyd; *Semiconductor Lasers, Nonlinear Fiber Optics*, and *Fiber-Optic Communication*

President Clinton and Duncan Moore in the Oval Office.

Systems, and *Applications of Nonlinear Fiber Optics*, all by G. P. Agrawal; *Two-level Atoms and Optics Resonance* by L. Allen and J. H. Eberly; *Optical Coherence and Quantum Optics* by L. Mandel and E. Wolf; and *New Physical Optics Notebook: Tutorials in Fourier Optics* by G. O. Reynolds, J. B. DeVelis, G. B. Parrent, and B. J. Thompson.

The faculty also serve as current or past editors, topical editors, associate editors, and members of the editorial boards of some twenty journals. One was founding editor of a popular optics journal. Publications include at least four citation classics—papers which have been cited in more than five hundred other refereed publications. When *Optics Letters* recently published the list of the most cited papers in the twenty-five-year history of the journal, two papers authored by current faculty members were among the top ten.

Fourteen of the faculty members are fellows of the Optical Society of America, four are fellows of SPIE, seven are fellows of the American Physical Society, and nine are fellows of various other professional societies around the world. Faculty members have served as presidents of both the Optical Society of America and SPIE. Notably in the current rotation for the president of the Optical Society of America, Michael Morris, who was until recently on the faculty, is past president; Peter Knight, who was a postdoctoral fellow in quantum optics, is president; and Susan Houde-Walter is president-elect. This brings to eight the number of faculty members or former faculty members who have served as president of the Optical Society of America.

The faculty have received too many awards and medals to list individually, including most of the top prizes of SPIE and the Optical Society of America. Notably, two faculty members have won the Rudolf Kingslake Award of SPIE, which itself was named for a former faculty member. One current faculty member, M. Parker Givens, has an endowed

Her majesty, Beatrix Queen of the Netherlands presents honorary doctorates to Emil Wolf and Andrei Sakharov.

chair named in his honor. The chair was generously endowed by alumnus James Wyant and his family.

Many of the faculty serve and have served on various governmental advisory committees, and one, Duncan Moore, served for three years as associate director for technology in the White House Office of Science and Technology Policy (OSTP) during the Clinton administration. Professor Moore is now chief executive officer of the Infotonics Technology Center Inc. The center, structured as a consortium of industry and universities, is formed by Eastman Kodak Co., Corning, Inc., and Xerox Corp. as a not-for-profit corporation to operate New York State's Center of Excellence in Photonics and Microsystems.

The University has recognized the accomplishments of the faculty with various prizes including two graduate education awards, two undergraduate teaching excellence awards, two School of Engineering and Applied Science lifetime achievement awards, and two University mentor Awards.

Professor Eberly is a foreign member of the National Academy of Science of Poland, and Professor Moore is a member of the National Academy of Engineering. Three different faculty members have been awarded a total of nine honorary doctorates.

The faculty have scores of patents, and Professor Jacobs and Professor Willams have won the prestigious R&D 100 award for their patents; others have won the Rochester Engineer of the Year award and the National Engineering Award.

Several years ago the Rochester *Democrat and Chronicle* carried Professor Dennis Hall's quip that the faculty of the Institute were "just 12 guys out to save the universe." If their qualifications do not quite match up with the requirements for that job, they would seem to match up well to the task of continuing the tradition of excellence set out by the founders in 1929.

The Institute of Optics
Faculty 2000–

Agrawal, Govind P., 1989–
Alonso, Miguel A., 2003–
Bentley, Julie L., 2000–
Berger, Andrew J., 2000–
Bigelow, Nicholas P., 2001–
Boyd, Robert W., 1977–
Brown, Thomas G., 1987–
Buralli, Dale A., 2002–
Eberly, Joseph H., 1979–
Erdogan, Turan, 1992–2001
Fauchet, Philippe M., 1994–
Fienup, James R., 2002–
Foster, Thomas H., 2002–
George, Nicholas, 1978–
Givens, M. Parker, 1948–
Guo, Chunlei, 2001–
Hall, Dennis G., 1981–2002
Hopkins, Robert E., 1943–
Houde-Walter, Susan N., 1987–
Jacobs, Stephen D., 1988–

Kingslake, Rudolf, 1929–2003
Knox, Wayne H., 2000–
Mandel, Leonard, 1978–2000
Marciante, John R., 2001–
Moore, Duncan T., 1974–
Morris, G. Michael, 1980–2002
Novotny, Lukas, 1999–
Oliver, James B., 1998–
Seka, Wolf, 1994–
Smith, Douglas, 1989–92, 1999–2002
Stone, Bryan D., 1994–2000
Stroud, Jr., Carlos R., 1969–
Teegarden, Kenneth J., 1955–
Thompson, Brian J., 1968–
Walmsley, Ian A., 1988–
Wang, Shen-ge, 1994–2000
Wicks, Gary W., 1987–
Williams, David R., 1988–
Wolf, Emil, 1978–
Zavislan, James M., 2001–

The Institute of Optics
Degrees Awarded 2000–2003

Adams, Marc, M.S., 2000
Allaire, Laura, B.S., 2002
Aronstein, David L., Ph.D., 2002
Baer, Jennifer, B.S., 2003
Bampoe, Sidney, B.S., 2001
Baum, Seth, B.S., 2003
Berfanger, David M., Ph.D., 2000
Berlinghieri, Joel, B.S., 2003
Bingham, Adam, B.S., 2003
Birnkrant, Dashiell, B.S., 2001; M.S., 2002
Boland, Daniel, B.S., 2000; M.S., 2003
Calvert, Lance, M.S., 2003
Campbell, Shawn, B.S., 2000
Cerami, Loren, B.S., 2002
Chambers, John, B.S., 2000
Charles, Kevin, M.S., 2000
Chen, Jack, B.S., 2003
Cobb, Joshua, M.S., 2000
Cocola, Anthony, B.S., 2001
Consentino, Bert, B.S., 2002
Constantino, Paul, M.S., 2000
Coskun, Mustafa, B.S., 2002; M.S., 2003
Cottrell, William, B.S., 2000
Crawford, Mary Kate, Ph.D., 2000
Davis, Arthur, B.S., 1996; M.S., 2000
DeAraujo, Luis' Eduardo E., Ph.D., 2001
DeCastro, Michelle, B.S., 2001
DeGroote, Jessica, B.S., 2002
Delorenzo, Michael, B.S., 2003
DeRose, Christopher, B.S., 2001
Dionne, Andrew, B.S., 2003
Doyle, David, B.S., 2003
Fales, Gregg, B.S., 2000
Fischer, David J., Ph.D., 2002
Fitzgerald, Daniel, B.S., 2002
Florence, Louis, M.S., 2002
Froggatt, Mark, Ph.D., 2001
Galime, Michael, B.S., 2002
Gifford, Dawn K., Ph.D., 2003
Goren, Evan, B.S., 2003
Gray, Daniel, B.S., 2002

Guimaraes, Marcelo, M.S., 2002
Hakrider, Curtis J., Ph.D., 2000
Hayes, Jennifer, B.S., 2003
Heaney, Alan D., Ph.D., 2000
Heebner, John, Ph.D., 2003
Hesterman, Jacob, B.S., 2002
Hill, Elizabeth, B.S., 2003
Hofer, Heidi, Ph.D., 2003
Hossain, Muntashir, B.S., 2000
Janchaysang, Suwatwong, M.S., 2001
Jani, Parthiv, B.S., 2002
Jehanno, Annick, M.S., 2001
Jenkins, Matthew, B.S., 2002
Johnson, Carleton, B.S., 2000
Johnson, Joshua H., Ph.D., 2003
Johnson, Kerry, B.S., 2000
Kanesaka, Tomoki, M.S., 2002
Kaylor, Brant, B.S., 2002
Kent, Haskell, B.S., 2003
Kosc, Tanya Z., Ph.D., 2003
Kwiatkowski, Joseph, B.S., 2001
LaFortune, Kai N., Ph.D., 2002
Lee, Esther, B.S., 2002
Lee, Joe, B.S., 2002; M.S., 2003
Lesniak, Mark, B.S., 2000
Liao, Zhi Ming, B.S., 1995; M.S., 1996;
    Ph.D., 2001
Lin, Wincheng, B.S., 2002
Maywar, Drew N., B.S., 1993; Ph.D., 2001
McMurdy, John, B.S., 2002; M.S., 2003
Melocchi, Michael L., B.S., 1997; Ph.D.,
    2003
Monacelli, Brian, M.S., 2001
Moore, Eric, M.S., 2001
Moskun, Eric, M.S., 2001
Moy, Alexander, B.S., 2003
Murnan, Andrew, B.S., 1996; M.S., 2003
Murphy, Paul E., B.S., 1995; Ph.D., 2001
Muthukrishnan, Ashok, Ph.D., 2002
Nagasako, Elna, Ph.D., 2001
Naradikian, Markar, B.S., 2000

Nguyen, Thanh, B.S., 2001
O'Donohue, Stephen, B.S., 2003
Oles, Catherine, M.S., 2003
Palit, Robin, B.S., 2003
Park, Jeong, B.S., 1998; M.S., 2002
Park, Mi-Young, B.S., 2003
Puth, Jason, M.S., 2001
Putnam, Nicole, B.S., 2003
Quinn, Daniel, B.S., 2003
Radunsky, Aleksandr, B.S., 2000
Rma, Jason, B.S., 2000
Romano, Joseph, B.S., 2001
Rouke, Jennifer L, Ph.D., 2001
Rustmann, Jenny, M.S., 2000
Sabia, Yi, M.S., 2003
Salisbury, Cedric, B.S., 2000
Schnidt, Greg, B.S., 2001
Schultz, Kathrine, B.S., 2003
Shmoys, Dmitry, B.S., 2000
Sickler, Jason, B.S., 2000
Smith, Zachary, B.S., 2002
Soller, Brian J., Ph.D., 2002
Sommer, Andrew, B.S., 2001

Spilman, Alexis, B.S., 2000
Spilman, Joseph, B.S., 2003
Stegall, David B., Ph.D., 2001
Steinberg, Jennifer, B.S., 2000
Stoll, Robert, M.S., 2000
Strandberg, Brian, B.S., 2003
Stromsky, Steven, B.S., 2000
Sykora, Daniel, Ph.D., 2003
Tardiff, Matthew, B.S., 2002
Thurman, Samuel T., B.S., 1996; Ph.D., 2003
Turner, Micholas, B.S., 2002
VanVenRoy, Jesse, B.S., 2000
Vaughn, Brendan, B.S., 2002; M.S., 2003
Verdoni, Luigi, B.S., 2000
Vigneaux, David, B.S., 2003
Vrakas, John, M.S., 2002
Wang, Ligang, M.S., 2001
Watson, Jonathan, B.S., 2002; M.S., 2003
Williams, Elizabeth, B.S., 2003
Yang, Chau-Shyang, B.S., 2000
Youngworth, Kathleen, Ph.D., 2003
Youngworth, Richard N., Ph.D., 2002

PART IX

TIMELESS TRADITIONS

IX. Timeless Traditions

There are some constants that really cannot be localized to any decade in a history. This section deals with three of those: basic attitudes that prime one for success, educational programs that prepare one for the problems to be faced, and the cadre of dedicated people who help along the way. The first essay is a graduation speech by alumnus Paul Forman that puts forward a set of lessons to be mastered if one hopes to be successful after graduation. We then follow with two essays describing the undergraduate and graduate educational programs in the Institute. Finally we review the contributions of two groups of individuals who have not received as much attention as other groups but have been essential to the success of The Institute of Optics, the part-time faculty and the staff. In addition, we review an important part of any program involving young people—athletics. The *optics jocks* have been almost as impressive in their accomplishments in the athletic fields, the tracks, and the mountainsides as they have been in the laboratory.

66. Address to Class of 2003

Paul Forman

Thank you. I am both honored and somewhat overwhelmed by this award.

I was in your place forty-seven years ago—this university gave me a wonderful grounding for my life's work, for which I am extremely grateful.

In those forty-seven years, I have done a number of interesting and significant things—some apparently noteworthy enough to have landed me up here today. It is a privilege to address you at your graduation.

For what it is worth, and this may be somewhat encouraging to some of you, I was certainly not the smartest in my class. So, what made me successful? That's what I am going to talk about today—and maybe it will be helpful to some of you.

1. *Persistence*: I learned one of my most important lessons in life here—but not in the classroom. I was a research assistant to Dr. Shina Inoue. I assisted him with a polarizing microscope he was developing, and once complained about the awkwardness of the focus mechanism. Two days later he handed me a gadget that completely eliminated the cause

Paul Forman is joined by Gary Wicks, Duncan Moore, Wayne Knox and Jim Zavislan in full academic regalia for Commencement 2003.

of my complaints. It was a sophisticated, not-at-all-obvious solution, and I asked how he came up with that solution. He explained that he simply believed there must be a good solution and worked at it until he found it. "I don't understand," I replied. He asked me, "Can you balance a raw egg on end?" "Sure. Just sprinkle salt on the counter and the egg can be balanced," I replied. "No, no. No tricks. A raw egg—balanced on a steady table-top." "No, I do not think it can be done. I've tried it before without success," I replied. He took a deep breath, looked me in the eye, and asked whether I trusted him. "Of course." "Well, then trust me when I tell you it is quite possible to balance a raw egg on end, no tricks. Now, go to the biology refrigerator down the hall, get an egg, bring it back here, and try it," he demanded. It took me less than a minute of trying to balance that egg, because I had perfect confidence it could be done. That lesson has guided me so many times in my life, in so many important ways.

Lesson learned: If you believe something can be done and it is worth doing, be persistent and just do it.

2. *Aim to be the best*: Perhaps most people know me as a co-founder of Zygo, a company three of us started thirty-three years ago. Today it is a public company, doing about $100 million in revenues annually, and known for its precision measurement instrumentation (particularly interferometers) and the fabrication of large, plano optics (such as all the laser amplifier slabs for LLE and the National Ignition Facility at Livermore). There is not enough time today to tell the Zygo story but a few highlights might be instructive.

- Contrary to what is today considered necessary practice, we did not have a product identified as the basis of starting the company. Instead we had a philosophy: We will be successful if we provide outstanding products and services. Our vision was to be the best at whatever we set out to do.
- We started out with the intent of building the best plano optics fabrication shop in the world and today many of our customers would agree that we have accomplished that goal.
- If we were going to make the best optics, we needed to be able to measure them—and we felt there were no adequate ways at that time. We began to develop an interferometer for our own use. We needed sales, so I went out and sold an identical instrument. Today, thousands of interferometers later, our various measurement instruments are used around the world.

Lesson learned: Aim to be the best and never lower your sights.

3. *Teamwork pays dividends*: As I said, there were three founders: a scientist, an optician, and I. We divided responsibilities in a logical fashion: all engineering and technical matters for the first, all fabrication matters for the second, and all sales, marketing, and administrative matters for me. An interesting fact: never were there three people who are so fundamentally different. We had differing views about almost everything and different ways of finding solutions. But, and most important, we all respected each other. We were each more or less free to do our jobs, but when we faced overarching issues, we had the benefit of complementary skills and viewpoints. Our diversity turned out to be our strength—and it would not have worked if we did not have a high regard for each other and had we not had the same vision—to be the best. Today, amazingly enough, all three of us continue to contribute to Zygo and enjoy good relationships between us.

Lesson learned: Teamwork, and employing complementary skills, usually pays dividends.

4. *Choose your partners carefully*: When it came time to raise capital to fund the start of Zygo, we were careful to seek out sources of funding that would have a long-term benefit

from the success of Zygo. We purposely did not pursue Venture Capital funding because we knew their time horizon was short and they would be in it to make a profit for themselves. We interested Canon Inc., the Japanese optics company—who was intrigued by the prospect of what collaboration with Zygo might produce, and we interested Wesleyan University—who was expanding their science curriculum and was interested in starting a sort of mini industrial collaboration ala MIT/Route 128. We chose partners, not funders, and in retrospect it was exactly the right thing to do. Wesleyan's approximately $600,000 investment grew to over $30 million and they finally sold out when it became too large a percentage of their portfolio. Canon today remains a major shareholder in Zygo, and a major customer.

Lesson learned: Choose your partners, in business and in life, very carefully.

5. *Smarts in hiring*: It took a while to learn it, but we found it important to hire better people than we needed at the time. First of all, two junior engineers cannot substitute for one senior engineer. But, more important, there needs to be an experienced mentor for others, since learning by your mistakes is expensive and discouraging. I used to opt on the side of promoting an employee, even before he or she was ready, instead of hiring his or her boss—but soon learned that was not fair to the employee or to the organization. Creating a culture where you can hire a person's boss, with their encouragement, is desirable.

Lesson learned: Be sure, in your next job, you have a mentor from whom to learn.

6. *Importance of a can-do attitude*: Some people attack each new problem with a vengeance. This is particularly evident in successful new start-ups where every employee is gung-ho and enthusiastic. Some big companies manage to maintain a culture where this enthusiasm thrives, while others ossify into what I call the "twenty reasons why it cannot be done" syndrome. Don't be one of those people. They are for hire by the dozens, while the person who consistently figures out how to get something done is a rarity, is more highly rewarded, and has more job satisfaction.

Lesson learned: an enthusiastic, can-do attitude is contagious and drives creativity.

7. *Exceed customer expectations*: Those of you who have become familiar with aspects of the quality revolution of the past ten to fifteen years are familiar with the term: exceeding customer expectations. It was not in the lexicon thirty-three years ago when we started Zygo. As part of being the best we set out whenever possible to "exceed customer expectations." If you can do it without disproportionate effort, it pays dividends.

Lesson learned: Always try to exceed expectations.

8. *Sense of urgency*: At least in business, and probably in most of life's activities, time is of greater value than money. Sufficient time enables you to do the job right, to be the best, to exceed expectations. The lack of time erodes all options. Some tasks deserve more time and care than others. Know how to prioritize. Some daunting tasks can be accomplished quickly with a bit of common sense. I often use the rule: get ninety percent of the benefit in ten percent of the time. For example, how often have I watched a group of engineers labor for days over a quotation, which they ultimately complete two weeks later than when it was needed but accurate to the nearest decimal point—when an educated guesstimate, backed up with a checkout of the major purchased items, would have yielded a more timely and more useful result.

Lesson learned: Time is precious. Learn how to use it efficiently.

9. *Integrity and trust*: Integrity must be your guide star. Your performance must be trustworthy. Say what you'll do—then do what you say. Don't hide problems or mistakes. Mutual agreement is not necessary, but mutual respect is.

Lesson learned: Make integrity your middle name.

Pilfered street sign returned.

10. *Communicating well is essential*: Part of your success will depend upon how others perceive you. Your communication skills have a major role in your personal success as well as that of your team. Write well, speak well, and appear well. And if you can't, there is still time to learn how. Your education does not stop today.

Lesson learned: Good communication skills are a lifelong investment and asset.

11. *Be responsible for your own success*: There is nobody more important than you in determining your success. Take charge and make yourself successful at whatever you decide to do. Set an example by your own actions. Take ownership of the work you do. Don't accept mediocrity. Take initiative when necessary. Don't keep a good idea to yourself. Create your own luck. Be passionate about what you are doing.

Lesson learned: Be all you can be—make yourself successful.

I hope my remarks are not perceived as lecturing to you. I am not interested in doing that. I am trying only to convey those specific attitudes and principles that I have found important to my success in hopes that they may be helpful to you as you transition from this great university to what you have chosen as the next step in your career.

In conclusion, I have a confession to make. When I entered the University in 1952, there was the men's campus on River Boulevard and a separate women's campus on Prince Street. Until the time when the two were merged, there were frequent forays to Prince Street for dates. Well, probably after a particularly hot date, and undoubtedly helped by suitable libation, I shinnied up a light pole for a souvenir to mark the evening. Integrity also means not to lie, cheat, or steal—and this event has been increasingly on my conscience ever since it happened. I felt that perhaps today is the time to make amends and I want to atone by giving back my ill-gotten souvenir to the University.

Lesson learned: It is never too late to act with integrity.

Good luck and good work—to all of you.

Paul Forman received his B.S. from the Institute of Optics in 1956. He was awarded the 2003 SEAS Distinguished Alumnus Award and gave the 2003 commencement speech. He currently serves as an independent consultant.

67. Undergraduate Studies in Optics

Thomas G. Brown

To study light in all its phases: what it is and where it comes from; how light behaves; how it can be split into parts; how light registers in human vision, in color phenomena; how light can be applied and used . . .

These words graced a publicity booklet, printed in color with the aid of a new Eastman Kodak process, advertising The Institute of Optics as it entered its second decade. As we celebrate the seventy-fifth anniversary, those of us preparing students for optics in the twenty-first century still identify with this broad mission. Indeed, while we have always had a multifaceted mission—research, graduate teaching, and undergraduate teaching—we on the faculty are reminded that the Institute was first founded to train undergraduates in optical science and engineering.

The balance of the fundamental and the applied was present from the beginning of the optics curriculum. The 1929–30 announcement of the undergraduate optics program described three distinct tracks of study—industrial applications of optics, the design and construction of optical instruments, and optometry. The first optics students were expected to take five to six courses per semester, including requirements in rhetoric, German, or French (a history alternative was available for the language-challenged), mechanical drawing and shop, and psychology. Two years' study in both mathematics and physics rounded out the core requirements.

Consistent with curricula of the time, students took no optics courses until they had successfully completed two years of the general curriculum—after that, the curriculum was saturated with studies in optics or related areas of physics. The significant European heritage in both optics and physics encouraged most students to take one or more courses aimed at reading the German or French literature in optics.

As is the case today, the optics courses of 1929 reflected a balance between the fundamental concepts (geometrical optics, physical optics, and radiometry) and the important technological themes and applications of the late 1920s (photography, optical fabrication, optical design, and physiological optics). The Institute made extensive use of local experts, including elective courses in such areas as microscopy, refractometry, pyrometry, and military fire control instruments.

A glance through the history of the Institute shows that advances in science and technology, along with the associated changes in faculty specialty, significantly modified the applied components of the curriculum. In turn, the advances in optical physics expanded and modified the fundamental components of the curriculum. A student entering our optics program in 2004 is expected to study geometrical optics, scalar wave optics, electromagnetic theory and vector-waves, quantum optics, laser systems, and optoelectronics.

The Changing Face of Undergraduate Education

While the broad educational mission remains largely the same as seventy-five years ago, both the student population and the technology with which they are educated have changed dramatically. The early student population had only the occasional female member—a fraction that remained low until the last twenty-five years. Recent classes have consisted of 20 to 25 percent women and, more importantly, have seen dramatic increases in leadership spots occupied by women. While much of this can be attributed to overall societal trends, the increased number, and involvement, of role models among the women alumni and the supportive departmental environment have combined to provide an excellent learning environment for women.

The laboratory experience has remained a central component of our undergraduate education. As these experiments are upgraded and replaced with newer technology, the students are able to carry out scientific and engineering activities that only a few decades ago belonged to the world of Nobel laureates and multibillion-dollar research programs. Students assemble the components of a mode-locked fiber laser and study its behavior. Others assist in a demonstration of scanning probe microscopy, observing single atoms of carbon on a graphite surface. A recent participant in our summer research experience for undergraduates (REU) studied single photon sources for quantum communication, while another employed state-of-the art computers to precisely control optical finishing. In short, the opportunity which increasingly sophisticated technology brings to the teaching and undergraduate research laboratories is unprecedented.

The Optics Pipeline

The undergraduate population at The Institute of Optics has always been a barometer of the national supply and demand. Throughout much of our history, demand for well-trained optical engineers has outstripped supply. The archives of the Institute contain letters and articles emphasizing this national need. In the 1940s, optics was critical to wartime technologies. In the 1950s, it was the increasing need in optical materials, metrology, and the photography industry. The 1960s brought the laser, the photocopier, and the first serious implementations of computer-aided design.

Despite perennial demand, the optics student population has gone through cycles not unlike (and sometimes correlated with) business cycles. From a low population of six graduates in 1976, the program exploded to a peak of ninety-seven in 1987, and is currently at a relatively steady twenty-five to thirty graduates per year. (During the same period, the number of faculty in the Institute has remained between twelve and fifteen full-time equivalents.) During this time, most undergraduate optics majors discovered optics after coming to the campus, usually enrolling in the introductory freshman course after being introduced to the major by other undergraduate students. The small number who came to campus intending to major in optics usually had some family connection with the optics industry.

One cannot overestimate the significance of family influence on technical career choice. The academy award-winning movie of the late 1960s featured a young Dustin Hoffman mulling over career options. The most familiar clip in that movie shows an older relative repeating one word, "plastics, " to the recent graduate. In my annual talk given to

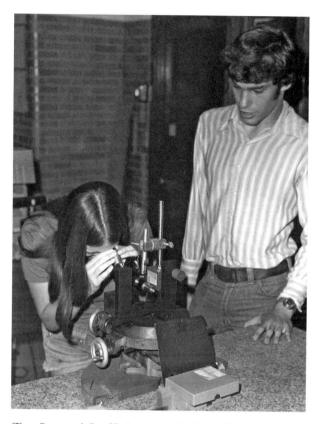

Tom Stone and Sue Horbatuck in the Optics Teaching Lab, 1977.

parents of entering freshmen, I emphasize this by showing the clip with the word "optics" dubbed in as the modern equivalent. The message is simple: Parents and friends want the best for young people, and if optics is perceived as a good home for the best and the brightest, we have solved the pipeline problem.

However, most alumni (graduate or undergraduate) of The Institute of Optics can identify with the following scene. You have just encountered Aunt Mabel at a family wedding, she asks you about your latest activities, and you respond that you are an optical engineer at Corning Tropel Corp. While the conversation may well drift toward the latest designs in dishware, you will inevitably be asked to check her bifocals. This stereotype became so prevalent that, by the early 1990s, alumnus Robert Modavis (B.S., M.S., Ph.D.) had designed a new logo for the Institute—a pair of spectacles surrounded by the universal *verboten* symbol. No ophthalmics here, if you please. (It was, ironically, only a few years later that a team of researchers from the Institute and the Center for Visual Science began a revolution in ophthalmics through the use of adaptive optics.)

The reality is this: Throughout most of our history, and despite the best efforts of faculty and alumni to spread the word, optics has remained a "hidden" technology. The birth of the movie industry focused much more on film than the sophisticated optics required for sharp, color-corrected projection. The invention, and subsequent development, of the integrated circuit chip focused much more on electrical engineering and computer science than on the powerful optics required to print subwavelength features and then provide inline inspection.

It was not until the telecommunications "bubble" of the 1990s that the growth (and subsequent collapse) of optics-related technologies came to the forefront of the public consciousness. Now, despite the doldrums in the telecommunications sector, it seems everyone wants to know more about optics.

Community Outreach: The Optics Road Show and the Optics Suitcase

The desire of the broader community to learn more about light could not come at a better time for The Institute of Optics. Outreach efforts, in which faculty, undergraduates, and graduate students work together to show the light to the wider community, is a rich part of the Institute tradition. In the 1960s, Professor Parker Givens and colleagues launched the "Optics Road Show," a portable set of demonstrations of light-related phenomena that could be taken to classrooms and museums. Over the years, experiments have been reorganized, redesigned, and added to form an impressive array of optics lessons used both for on-campus groups (science summer schools, etc.) and off-campus outreach activities to schools and museums.

It was Professor Ian Walmsley who, in the early 1990s, spearheaded an effort to revive the road show, including such things as optical fiber communications, elementary principles of lasers, and spectroscopy. The local undergraduate student chapter of the Optical Society took this effort and, with the further help of faculty and graduate students, began taking the show to elementary schools throughout the Rochester region. In the years since, the show has appeared at summer camps, made annual appearances in the science museum, and been incorporated into enrichment programs in several local elementary schools. The road show also formed a basis for several on-campus summer programs: The various University summer science camps, some emphasizing outreach to underrepresented groups, have regularly featured optics.

In a parallel effort, Professor Steve Jacobs has, with the close participation of undergraduates, introduced the "Optics Suitcase" to classrooms in Rochester and across the country. It features lessons in optical materials and basic optical elements, and incorporates activities that tie concepts of optical energy together with mechanical and electrical energy. If the road show has had a local impact, the optics suitcase has had a national impact.

A Twenty-first Century Challenge

While modern technology is indeed revolutionizing undergraduate education, the twenty-first century also brings unprecedented challenges. Students have never before had such sophisticated technological toys at their disposal—the same technology that revolutionizes instruction also presents enormous distractions to learning. For example, the wired

The REU Program allowed these undergraduates to join Optics research groups for the summer of 2003.

classroom not only provides unprecedented instructional tools, it lets students instant-message, web surf, and carry out all manner of other activities during a time intended for learning. The educational challenge of the twenty-first century is this: How do we, as faculty and alumni, construct a learning environment which makes us master and not slave to technology?

We have found that an undergraduate student's willingness to shed these distractions and focus on learning can be significantly enhanced by interaction with the professional community of optical engineers and scientists. Such interactions are often centered on summer employment or internships at optics companies and research experiences in which students rub shoulders with senior engineers and scientists. They can also be centered on outreach activities at science museums and schools. All such engagements instill a sense of pride in being part of a community of optics professionals and an appetite for deeper knowledge.

This emphasis on gaining early exposure to the industrial arena is not a new one. For many years, students have been encouraged to seek summer employment or internships with optics professionals. The formation of the industrial associates of The Institute of Optics has been instrumental in providing cooperative educational experiences for our students. What is new is the ability of students, with the aid of our industrial associates and alumni databases, to locate opportunities all over the country—indeed, all over the world. These students return with a practical view of many of the tools of modern optical engineering and a broader perspective on the fundamentals of the discipline.

It truly takes a committed professional community to educate the next generation of optical scientists. We are fortunate that The Institute of Optics has such a community among its alumni, and can look forward to many more generations of excellent undergraduate students in our future.

Thomas G. Brown is associate professor and chair of undergraduate studies.

68. Graduate Studies in Optics

Carlos Stroud

Before the Institute was even set up, various optics experts in the United States were asked to recommend the nature of the proposed academic program. There was a diversity of opinion among these advisors as to whether the new institute should be a separate entity or part of the physics department. The tension between optics as a sub-field of physics and optics as a branch of engineering has energized the Institute and its academic programs from this beginning. Dennis Hall, faculty member and director of the Institute in the 1980s and 1990s, liked to say that the department was organized along a different axis from conventional physics and engineering departments. Physics departments are concerned with *basic research* in all the various disciplines in physics, while electrical engineering departments are concerned with *applied research* in all areas of electrical engineering. The Institute of Optics is rather concerned with all areas of optics from the basic to the applied. Optics is also to be loosely defined as electromagnetic phenomena with wavelengths in the range from about one centimeter to one angstrom. This broad view of the scope of the discipline and of the appropriate program of graduate studies means that the students study fundamental physics as well as design, fabrication, and testing of optical systems. To use modern jargon, one would characterize the academic program as *culturally diverse*.

The original academic program of the Institute called for degree programs leading to bachelor's, master's and doctor of philosophy degrees in optics. In spite of this the first

Graduate student Ab Smith takes data the hard way in the late 1950s.

doctoral degree in optics was not granted until 1939, a decade after the founding of the department. The delay was not due to the students taking an extraordinarily long time to graduate, but rather to the fact that the early students were physics department students and got their degrees in that department. The students also took a great deal of their course work in the physics department. As Brian O'Brien began to greatly expand the research activities of the Institute in the years leading up to World War II, graduate research in optical engineering quite separate from physics grew rapidly, as did the separate graduate program. During the war the research programs greatly expanded, but student theses were delayed until after the cessation of hostilities. Students were often recruited to set up assembly lines for putting together some instruments needed urgently in the field. The fourth floor of the Institute where most of the research took place was restricted by wire grills, and everyone needed clearance to enter.

Following the war the graduate program in the Institute grew rapidly for several reasons. The program was considerably enlarged and had better facilities than before, there were many veterans returning to school, and the physics department was increasingly dominated by nuclear and particle physics. Solid state physics was growing in importance. The Institute had developed some experience in the area during the war so that the field was now a part of the Institute instead of physics. Several faculty members were added in this area. For a while there was even debate as to whether astronomy would be part of the Institute; astronomer Malcolm Savedoff had a faculty appointment in the Institute for a short while before moving to physics. For several years the written qualifying examination in optics included an option in the second day in which the students could choose either the optical engineering or the solid state optics version.

In about 1970 the curriculum was extensively reorganized into a form that has remained essentially unchanged since. A unified core curriculum was set up in which every doctoral student took the same set of eight required courses: two semesters of geometrical and instrumental optics, two semesters of physical optics and image processing, one semester each of radiation and detectors, mathematics, quantum mechanics, and laser engineering. This core was what the faculty felt that every Ph.D. graduate in optics from Rochester should know. After completing this common core the students took various specialty courses depending on their research interests, but this core was what was covered on the written preliminary examination for every student.

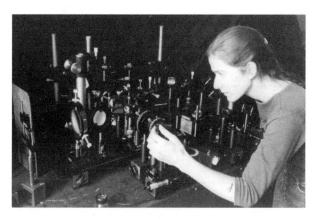

Lenore Pugliese (McMackin) tweaks her experiment, 1989.

Laura Weller-Brophy and Bob Holland confer about sample preparation, 1985.

The master's degree in optics could be obtained with Plan A, the thesis option, or Plan B, the course work and examination option. Part-time students from industry generally took the Plan B option and in addition were exempted from the teaching laboratory requirement. The course work requirement for the M.S. was very similar to that for the core for the Ph.D., with the exception that mathematics and quantum mechanics courses were not required, and instead the teaching laboratory was required. Eight courses were required for the Plan B degree, including these seven requirements and only one elective. For several years the thesis plan was required for graduates of our undergraduate program. Few other students chose this option because it was possible to complete the eight-course requirement in nine months whereas a thesis generally required from twelve to twenty-four months. There were also relatively few research assistantships to support the M.S. theses because faculty members had available plenty of Ph.D. students who stayed around longer and thus made a larger contribution to the research program.

A further attractive option was started for the master's degree program, the M.S. co-op. In this program the students would take their first semester of course work and then go out and work for a company for one year, drawing an industrial salary, and then return to the Institute for the final semester of course work. With these options the M.S. program grew in popularity in the 1970s and 1980s, eventually reaching a peak enrollment of more than thirty students per year in 1990. It allowed well-prepared graduates in physics or electrical engineering to become sought-after optical engineers in just nine months. Active programs in local industry in which employees were allowed time off from work to come to the Institute to take two courses per also increased the numbers of students in the M.S. program during this period. The enrollments in the M.S. program are always out of sync with the employment situation. When the job market is tight, B.S. graduates decide to get an M.S. degree, and the M.S. co-op is especially popular. On the other hand, when the employment situation is good, students decide to go to work immediately on getting their B.S. and there are fewer students in the M.S. program, except for part-time students.

Another innovation in the Ph.D. program proved very popular with applicants. All admitted students were offered full fellowships with no teaching or research obligations during their first year. They could spend the whole year taking courses and learning the basics of optics. After learning about all areas of optics they made their choice of research areas and advisors. During the second year the students fulfilled their one-year teaching assistant requirement while beginning research. This sped up the course work completion and allowed students to take their preliminary examination in the summer before the beginning of the second year. These innovations, along with a strong recruiting effort including bringing top applicants to campus with all expenses paid, improved the quality of students in the program dramatically in the 1980s and 1990s. The average grade point average of the incoming students rose to almost 3.9/4.0. In some years the Graduate Record Exam scores averaged as high as 2200. Optics won as many as three of the ten Sproull Fellowships, the top fellowships offered in the University. The faculty often commented that it was good that they got their degrees when they did because they would not be admitted to the department today. It was true that many students entering some years had turned down offers from Stanford, MIT or both, not to mention Arizona.

The quality of the students was a great boon to faculty research productivity. Graduating students landed top positions in industry. A number went to Bell Labs, IBM and other top industrial labs. Similarly, a number went to faculty positions in top schools such as Cornell, Duke, Georgia Tech, Penn State, Arizona, and Sidney, among others. Remarkably these students became faculty members not only in optics departments, but in physics and electrical engineering departments in these top schools. The quality of the broad education that the students received in the Institute was recognized even by these departments in excellent schools.

The quality of the programs of the Institute was recognized in another most remarkable fashion. In 1997, the most recent ranking of physics departments in the United States by the National Research Council, The Institute of Optics was ranked as the twenty-fifth best *physics department* in the country! It was ranked higher than some of the best known departments in the country. It even marginally outranked the University's Department of Physics and Astronomy. This was probably due in part to some confusion on the part of the rating panels, which were unable to distinguish between the two Rochester departments, but it showed indisputably that optics in Rochester, whether optical engineering or optical physics, was recognized as excellent in the physics community.

The dual success of graduates in industry and academia, as well as the fact that quantum optics theorists often become successful engineers and optical engineers often become successful academic researchers and teachers, attests strongly to the basic correctness of the model that combines basic optical physics and applied optical engineering in one department and sees that every student experiences the whole range of disciplines. Changing of the areas of application of optics will no doubt require modification of the core curriculum. It is remarkable that the core has remained stable in course title, if not necessarily course content, for thirty years. Of course, the advanced specialty courses change year by year. It is unlikely that the basic model of mixing basic and applied optics in the faculty and in the curriculum will change. It is very much a part of what it means to have a graduate degree from The Institute of Optics at the University of Rochester.

69. Optics Jocks

Carlos Stroud

Long hours in the laboratory and even longer bouts with Rochester winters do not encourage outdoor activities, but from early in the history of the Institute there were those who were very active in sports. Bob Hopkins was famous for the competitiveness of his downhill skiing and his horseshoe matches. Joe Eberly is still playing noontime basketball after thirty-five years at the University—his height, elbows, and skill are known to hundreds who have played in these games over the years. Problems like a ruptured Achilles tendon have not kept him off the court for long. It would be hard to say which faculty member was the most ruthless competitor, but certainly Dwayne Miller's cross-checking in the intramural hockey games would put him in the running. At least one faculty member has coached a University team. Ken Teegarden coached the sailing club when he was a young assistant professor. Ian Walmsley is a black belt and taught a class in Tae Kwan Do. At least one former faculty member played on a varsity team as an undergraduate—Professor Michael Lea was a member of the varsity croquet team at Cambridge.

Without doubt the greatest athletic daring was exhibited by New Zealander Peter Gough, who was a postdoc and part-time assistant professor in the 1970s. He took time off from his Rochester duties and led an expedition to climb an unclimbed peak in the Andes, but was thwarted when one of his comrades was killed falling into a crevasse. He had another close scrape when climbing an ice face in the Adirondacks. Another group climbing the same face above Peter's group fell and got their lines tangled with Peter, who ended up dangling a hundred feet up the cliff face with a compound fracture of his leg. Rescuers had to be called to get the climbers down as Peter's wife Janet watched from below.

Not all the faculty are so competitive in their athletic endeavors. Both Emil Wolf and Bob Boyd have had notorious pictures taken of their dancing at conference banquets. Bob seldom passes up a conference with a surfing beach nearby, nor a hotel hot tub. Carlos Stroud has a picture of himself waterskiing on his group web page, but rumors are that it is two or three years old.

Graduate student Steve Kreger competing in Orienteering, 1994.

Of course, the real athletes in the department are mostly students. At least one under-graduate optics major won All-American honors at the University, Alex Gaeta in doubles tennis. Anna Hrycin was the star in one of the University's outstanding women's basket-ball teams. Anna went on to get a master's degree and Alex a Ph.D. at the Institute. When Alex was a graduate student in Bob Boyd's group he injured his ankle and was unable to compete in the Rochester Open Tennis Tournament. No matter: Mark Kramer, another member of Boyd's research group, entered and won the tournament. They tried to chal-lenge the graduate students at the Optical Sciences Center in Tucson to a match at the annual meeting of OSA, but someone tipped off the Arizona team, which wisely declined.

One graduate student, Stephen Kreger, competed in a world championship meet in 1994. He competed in the World Championship of Orienteering in Fiesch, Switzerland. The event for college students, sponsored by the International Orienteering Federation (IOF), is held once every two years. The sport of orienteering, more popular in Europe, especially Scandinavia, than in the United States, involves running a course through the countryside using a compass and map to navigate between a series of intermediate points.

Chris Saxer scales a rock face in the 1980s.

Steve began competing in the sport as an undergraduate at Rose Hulman Institute, and continued competing in Rochester as a member of a local club.

There were a number of serious runners, especially in the 1980s and 1990s. Graduate student Alan Evans was one of the dominant forces in the Upstate running scene, winning a number of races and competing in some national marathon events. Perhaps the most remarkable runner, though, was Anne Forbes, wife of Professor Greg Forbes. She was one of the top-rated runners in the Rochester area, and like any successful competitive runner, she was a bit obsessive in her training. Shortly after one of their children was born she was a familiar sight on snowy winter days in southwest Rochester, running along a path pushing the baby in a big wheeled stroller through the snow. Both Alan and Anne continue their serious competition more than a decade later, Alan as a Corning employee, and Anne back in Australia.

Peter Gough was not the only climber. During the 1980s a number of graduate students got to be very serious about rock climbing, well before climbing walls were a familiar sight in every suburban mall and school gymnasium. Campus security had to remain vigilant to keep them from climbing up the outside of Hoyt auditorium without safety ropes, using the decorative bricks protruding a half-inch or so as handholds. Graduate students Chris Saxer, Karl Koch, Dan Gauthier, Maurice Pessot, Steve Chakmakjian, and Mark Beck were the most serious of this bunch. Happily, they never had accidents quite at the level of Gough's.

Softball has been a perennial favorite. The Incoherents were a softball team that played in a city of Rochester league for a number of years. Their alter ego was Zelda and the Zoneplates, a much less serious group of folks who played intramural softball. Zelda had one of the simplest, yet profound, rallying cries ever used by a sports team: "Don't screw up!"

Frisbee has been a perennial favorite since the '60s. Ultimate Frisbee matches are serious business as Optics students Jay Anzelotti and Tom Dunn demonstrate.

70. The Part-time and Joint Faculty

Carlos Stroud

From its founding, one of the goals of the Institute has been to be of service to the optics industry. Providing educational programs relevant to the needs of this industry has remained a central theme. Servicing these needs is problematical to a top-ranked research department for two reasons. First, the faculty must be in close touch with current trends in industry, and second, courses must be taught at a high level on topics that are not currently the subject of academic research. Over the years the Institute has done a pretty good job of meeting these demands with very significant assistance by part-time teaching by practicing engineers from local industries.

In the first decade of the Institute's existence C. E. K. Mees, the director of the research laboratory at Eastman Kodak, taught a course in photographic processes that was the most popular course offered. Of course, Rudolf Kingslake left the full-time faculty in 1937 to become director of the photographic lens department at Eastman Kodak but continued teaching on a part-time basis his famous course in lens design for another fifty years; he also taught in the summer school until about 1990.

It is not practical to list here all of those who have taught optics courses as part-time faculty, but their names are included in the listings of faculty in the various chapters of this book. There have been some notable contributions from this group. Joseph Altman and John Hamilton followed the tradition of Mees in teaching courses on photographic processes

Erwin Loewen talking with Zheng Wu Li (Ph.D. 1989) at an Industrial Associates Meeting.

for nearly twenty years, from 1969 until the late 1980s. These courses were taken by hundreds of Kodak employees in the part-time M.S. program and by full-time students. A number of noted optics industrial researchers such as David MacAdam, Erich Marchand, and Erwin Loewen joined the part-time faculty after retiring from local industry. MacAdam spent several years working in the Institute teaching colorimetry and working on research and book writing. Marchand taught engineering mathematics and was very active in the University Chess Club.

The lens design laboratory course, Optics 444, has often been taught by part-time faculty. Bob Hopkins taught it for many years after he left the full-time faculty. Presently Julie Bentley from Tropel-Corning is teaching the course to record numbers of students; Dale Buralli of Apollo Optical Systems is teaching the introductory geometrical optics graduate course, Optics 441.

Another group of part-time faculty members who have been important to the teaching

M. Parker Givens in the teaching lab.

program are non-faculty staff members of the University. Many of these are part of the technical staff at the Laboratory for Laser Energetics or the Center for Optics Manufacturing. Most notable among these is Stephen Jacobs, who has served in this capacity since 1978, regularly teaching the fabrication and testing course and a course on liquid crystals. His appointment is properly classified as a secondary appointment as professor of optics so that he also supervises student thesis research. John Marciente and Jim Oliver of the laser lab both are teaching specialty courses.

Faculty members who specialize in optics-related fields are hardly limited to The Institute of Optics. Many of these faculty members in other departments throughout the University hold joint secondary appointments in the Institute. The Institute has always been close to the physics department so there have been many such appointments, particularly in quantum optics which overlaps both departments strongly. Currently Nicholas Bigelow, Joseph H. Eberly, and Emil Wolf from physics hold joint appointments, as do Govind Agrawal, Robert Boyd, and Carlos Stroud in the other direction. David Williams, who is director of the Center for Visual Science in the Department of Brain and Cognitive Sciences, is the latest in a long line from this center to hold joint appointments in optics. Tom Foster from radiology, Philippe Fauchet who is chair of Electrical and Computer Engineering, and Wolf Seka from the Laboratory of Laser Energetics round out this important component of the faculty.

There is one special category exemplified by M. Parker Givens: the emeritus faculty. Parker formally retired from the University in 1981 but continued instructing the teaching lab, Optics 256, until 2003, fifty-five years after he joined the faculty. He was loved and respected by the students for the entire period. Even in the last year students were in awe when he walked over to the balky experiment that they had unsuccessfully toiled over all afternoon—and with one little tweak of a knob he made it work.

71. The Staff of the Institute[1]

Maria J. Schnitzler

There is a saying that "behind every great man is a great woman." Something similar can be said for The Institute of Optics: "Behind this great department is a great support staff." There were, and continue to be, men and women who made a lasting impression in the department, through their passion for their job, their outstanding skills, and their longevity. This essay pays tribute to these people, the technical staff, and the administrative staff, who put in the extra effort from World War II and continuing on into the twenty-first century.

The Shops and Shop Staff of The Institute of Optics: The Early Years

In the beginning, the Institute of Applied Optics was established "to train students in the various fields of optical science" and "to prepare candidates for work in the optometric and ophthalmic fields. . . ." To assist in this endeavor, the University of Rochester agreed to set apart, without cost, the whole fourth floor of Bausch & Lomb Hall, which was currently under construction, with facilities and service staff to be available for use by the Institute. Any special tool, apparatus, widget, or whatchacallit that was needed for teaching or research had to be fabricated in-house. E-Bay didn't exist, neither did Newport, VWR, or other manufacturing firms to supply these items (though many optics alumni started their own businesses to fill this niche). Specialized shops were established and extraordinary people found to staff them.

Glass shop

One of the first facilities was the glass shop, with the emphasis on the design and construction of eyeglasses. This shop was overseen by Ernest Petry (formerly dean of the Rochester School of Optometry) and his instructor in optical shop work, Herbert E. Wilder. The partitioning of the floor was completed as quickly as possible. Petry's clinic rooms and offices for optometry were divided off at the east end, and the glass workshop was at the west end, leaving the center for the work in applied optics. It wasn't long before the top floor of the B&L building was inadequate and the glass shop had to be moved and reassembled in Gavett Hall. In 1936, the last class graduated from the division of optometry. Ernest Petry's work with the University was concluded at the end of the 1935–36 year, but Herbert Wilder continued to have charge of the glass workshop until his retirement in 1938. Around 1938–39, the large room in engineering lent since 1930 for the optics glass shop had to be vacated to make room for the new Department of Chemical

Engineering. The glass shop was moved once again—another in a long series of moves—to the basement of the Library.

Machine shop

Space on the fourth floor soon became limited, and a metal workshop for making small research apparatus and special laboratory equipment was located on the third floor and shared with physics. Clarence McVea was the machinist in charge for some years, to be succeeded by Paul John, a very precise gentleman who had just two standards, good and perfect. One had to specify which was required. A story floating around goes something like this. Paul was encouraged to take on an apprentice, as he was nearing retirement age. In the shop was a machine that had been tweaked and twitched to the nth degree of calibration, all done by Paul himself. As the story goes, the apprentice had the machine "untweaked" by the end of his first day of work. Needless to say, the apprentice was not seen again, and Paul was left alone in his beloved workshop.

Design shop

In 1929, then University President Wilkins reported the appointment, part time, of Gustave Fassin, an employee of Bausch & Lomb, to teach mechanical design of optical instruments. A Belgian who had taught at the Technical School of Ghent and had charge of workshops in the Societe Belge d'Optique, he was an original and competent designer. After the close of the optometry school, more prominence was given to Fassin's work: instruments designed and completed for use in research involving optics. In 1938, there was another major change in the faculty: Gustave Fassin left town to join another company and so had to relinquish his superb teaching of instrument design at the University. He was a great personality, and his loss was a serious one for the Institute.

World War II to the Present

By the end of 1940, the Institute was already working on optical problems for government agencies in an effort to avoid the serious shortages of optical devices that occurred during World War I. At the height of activity, some fifty people—scientists, technicians, machinists, research students, and others—were involved in the Institute's program of cooperation with the government.

Optics shop

The optics shop (formerly Glass Shop) once again moved, from the basement of Rush Rhees Library to Gavett Hall. The primary purpose of the optics shop was to grind and polish lenses, prisms and other optical elements for The Institute of Optics. Hugo Guenther, from Bausch & Lomb, headed the optics shop, followed by Bill Klingert.

Herb Graf joined the staff of the optics shop in 1943. I had the opportunity to sit in on the taped interview of Mr. Graf's reminiscences of his time in the optics shop which are included in essay 16. He was brought on board by Professor Fred Paul after a chance meeting while duck hunting on Irondequoit Bay in Rochester. He was here during the hectic years of World War II, working on various projects for the war effort. He talked about doing the work on the optics that were put in the tubes for the range finder on the battlewagons and of the triple mirrors used to outline an airfield at night. He also spoke of the ninety-degree angle flashlights that were mounted with a unity telescope on top that had an area in the middle that was sensitive to infrared light. When the flashlight was turned downward, it became an infrared light source. When the paratroopers dropped behind enemy lines, they couldn't do anything one by one, so they had to get together as a force. These flashlights were used to re-assemble the group. These flashlights were made in the optics shop.

The shop still exists today, moving once again, this time to the Laboratory for Laser Energetics.

Instrument shop

Rudolf Hamberger came to the University in 1949, to the Institute's instrument shop. Over and above sheer mechanical skill, his strong point had been his close concern with the research operation, and the active interchange which existed between himself and the people in the laboratories. He came into the lab, observed what was there, and listened to the scientists' needs and wants. He could deduce what was required, often with insufficient information, and then produce a component or instrument to do the job. Rudi retired at age sixty-six in 1965. Pat Borrelli joined the instrument shop around 1962, following in the footsteps of Rudi. Pat enjoyed the creative process. After Pat's retirement, Ken Adams took over the instrument shop, whose current reincarnation not only provides support for optics but also for the entire University. The instrument shop is currently housed in a separate one-story building next to Wilmot. And, yes, it will be moving soon again.

The Optics Instrument Shop, 1966.

Helen Tobin and John Leone.

Photography shop

The Institute even had its own darkroom and photography shop. This shop had the responsibility for producing graphs, pictures, and tables in accordance with the requirements of the various journals to which articles were submitted, as well as for the slides that were used at technical presentations and conferences. Alan Knapp was the photographer and David McCumber was an illustrator. Then came along computers and publishing programs.

Administrative Staff of The Institute of Optics

Directors' assistants

No history of the Institute would be complete without mentioning the various directors' personal assistants. Helen Tobin was the first administrative assistant. Helen was a native of Victor, New York, and joined the University as a staff member shortly after she received her B.A. degree at the University in 1929. She started out in the physics department but transferred to optics when the department was relocated from Prince Street to the River Campus. In an article at the time of her retirement, it was noted that "Her service to the department has lent much in the way of stability and quality consistent with the Office of the Director, while at the same time retaining enough flexibility to cope with the individual differences of successive administrations." (What a gentile way of putting it!). Helen remained secretary to the director for the next forty-three years, retiring in July 1972. Lois Greene succeeded Helen, then Gina Kern, Imelda Panzer, Jean Conge, and again Gina Kern. It is interested to note that in the seventy-five years of the Institute, there have been only five directors' assistants.

Karin Strand, department administrator.

Department Administrator

About 1965, Institute Director W. Lewis Hyde made the appointment of a new kind of department administrator, a member of the staff who would relieve the director and other faculty members of much organizational work. Susan Raup was the first such appointment; she was followed in due course by Karen Strand, David Child, and the current occupant, James DePinto.

Department Secretary

Anyone who worked at or attended classes in the department between 1952 and 1987 will remember Evelyn Snyder, the vivacious and dynamic department secretary. She was extremely well liked and respected. She started as a temporary employee, but the friendship which developed between Evelyn and the students, staff, and faculty kept her here as a permanent worker for twenty-five years. Evelyn passed away in 2003.

The Institute grew by leaps and bounds during the last quarter of the century, and there was a large secretarial staff to support the faculty. The advent of the personal computer decreased the need for basic secretarial assistance, allowing administrative staff members to become more specialized to make the best use of their particular talents.

Undergraduate and graduate administrative assistants: As the student enrollment of the Institute increased, administrative positions were created to facilitate the student's journey towards getting their degree. The full-time position of undergraduate secretary was first occupied by Joan Christian, then Betsy Benedict. The position of graduate secretary was originally filled by Beverly Holloway; upon Bev's retirement, Joan Christian moved over. All of these women exhibited patience and compassion with and for the students. Bev had the added benefit of a prior naval career background, which came in handy keeping the students in line.

Special Events Planning

Gayle Thompson joined the staff in 1982 as an assistant to George Fraley and worked her way up the ladder. She currently provides invaluable assistance as the special events coordinator (unofficial title—party planner). Gayle coordinates the semi-annual meetings of the industrial associates, the annual two-week summer school, and other special events held or sponsored by the Institute. If you need a room on campus for a specific event, Gayle can rattle off capacity, amenities, and the location of the nearest rest room.

Sponsored Programs Administration

Maria Schnitzler joined the Institute in 1986 as administrative assistant for the ARO-URI Center for Opto-Electronic Systems Research, which had a budget of $20 million over its lifetime. Maria provided the financial administration needed for a large, multi-investigator program as well as coordination of agency review meetings. She has since provided the same services to other faculty members in the Institute. Her presence at meetings prompted one faculty member to remark, "When I saw Maria in the conference room organizing meeting materials, I knew everything was going to be just fine."

Purchasing and Bookkeeping

The current bookkeeper and "purchasing person" is Noelene Votens, who came to optics in 1999. Noelene is the keeper of the pencils and erasers and works well amidst the chaos of faculty, staff, and students.

The Great Ones

An essay on staff members of The Institute of Optics would not be complete without mentioning Johnny Leone and George Fraley. These gentlemen didn't fit into any neat job description. They provided invaluable service, loyalty, and imagination to the department.

John Leone

The first "great support staffer" was John Leone. Hilda Kingslake, in her history of the Institute, stated that Johnny was "a very young man of great good will, who was appointed technician and general factotum as soon as teaching at the new campus began (1930)." While his job description was technician, he was the jack of all trades, and one of the department's prime movers. He continued in this capacity until his retirement in 1975; sadly he died that same year. Johnny's dedication can be summed up in this story, which is unsubstantiated. George Eastman was to visit the Bausch & Lomb building (yes, *that* George Eastman). Now remember, this was the Mr. Eastman who split his house in half in order to move it several feet to make it bigger—he paid attention to detail. Everyone in the department wanted all to go well. Elevators in those days were manually operated, and sometimes the level of the elevator floor didn't quite match with the level of the chosen floor. No one wanted Mr. Eastman to trip. So Johnny spent a whole day stopping and starting the elevator, matching up floor and elevator levels. Johnny was rewarded for his efforts; Mr. Eastman did not trip or fall during his visit.

George Fraley

George joined optics some time in 1941, when the war effort was geared up and the Institute did military restricted classified research. George played an important part in most of the research being conducted: driving around town with the forerunner of night vision goggles on his head (see "Man from Mars"); detonating explosions in Mendon (see "Let Sleeping Cows Lie"); hunting prairie dogs on a naval base in the middle of the country (see "Hunting Prairie Dogs"); and almost imitating men in their flying machines (see "Accidental Launching").

Maria J. Schnitzler has been a member of the staff of the University of Rochester since 1974.

Reference

1   The history of the early years and staff of the Institute was based, in part, on excerpts from "The Institute of Optics, 1929–1987," by Hilda G. Kingslake and from interviews with retired staff members George Fraley, Herb Graff, and Pat Borrelli.

PART X

THE FUTURE

X. The Future

As we look forward to the next twenty-five years leading to the centennial of The Institute of Optics we take out our crystal ball and make some predictions of what the future will bring. This is always risky, but we have four essays that undertake that task. The first is an essay by alumnus Douglas C. Sinclair in which he sets out his vision for the future of optical design that is rather different from its past. Faculty member James Zavislan then describes a new program the *Institute Ventures* which promises to turn the ideas developed in the Institute's laboratories into marketed products quickly without the faculty having to leave and start new companies. Professor Stroud suggests that the time for quantum optics to leave the laboratory and become the basis for completely new technologies is rapidly approaching. Soon there will be a field of *quantum optical engineering*. Finally, Director Wayne Knox lays out his vision for the coming decades leading up to the Centennial.

72. Whither Optical Design?[1]

Douglas C. Sinclair

The twentieth century is likely to have witnessed both the birth and the death of traditional lens design. By traditional lens design I mean the process of balancing the aberrations of centered spherical systems to achieve maximum image quality. In traditional lens design, physical optics provides only a termination condition. When the Rayleigh diffraction limit is reached, the design is good enough.

Until recently, the dimensions of typical optical systems were much greater than optical wavelengths. Specialists in geometrical optics studied refraction using aberrations and rays, and specialists in physical optics studied images using waves, with neither group having much in common with the other. Now, however, optical wavelengths are not considered as short as they used to be. At the same time, there is a lack of people competent in both geometrical and physical optics. We have the tools to tackle challenging and exciting problems of much greater scope and interest than ever before, but fewer and fewer people know how to use these tools. Nearly twenty years ago, Warren Smith wrote an article entitled "The Vanishing Lens Designer"; today, the dwindling number of expert lens designers has become a problem that is even more keenly felt.

At the beginning of the century, the mathematics and physics relevant to traditional lens design were already pretty well established, and early designs like achromatic doublets and the Petzval lens had already been developed. But it was during the first half of the twentieth century that the theory and practice of lens design were really established, chiefly in Europe.

By the time computers appeared in the 1950s, the basic design forms used today were pretty well developed. It is a tribute to the inventors that lenses like the Cooke triplet, the Petzval and the Double-Gauss are still widely used, mostly in the form of computer-optimized derivatives. There are some new forms, of course. Gradient-index and diffractive lenses, and the ubiquitous zoom lens, were known but not well developed until the second half of the century. It is interesting but perhaps not surprising that although computers have made possible the development of lenses of greater complexity, today most lenses still operate within more or less conventional guidelines. The modern lithographic lens is a sterling example of such a design. With nanometer distortion tolerances, incredible illumination and wavefront requirements, lithographic lenses are part of a recursive cycle, in that they are designed to produce chips fast enough to design the next generation of lenses. On the other hand, they tend to be variations of double-humped Gauss lenses, an established form.

Two mid-century inventions, the laser and the computer, have expanded the scope of optical design so much that optical design as it is traditionally conceived will likely soon be relegated to a minority position. Today, the laser provides the work for the optical designer, while the computer provides the necessary support. The importance of the laser is not to be found in the intrinsic characteristics of the device itself, but rather in its impact on optics. Until fairly recently—with the exception of a few established military, visual and photographic applications—optics was essentially a service discipline for other sciences. As we enter the new century, optics is rapidly becoming a consumer technology.

To meet with market success, consumer technology must be both "good" and "cheap." Many lens designers are not used to working under such pressure: they're comfortable with good—but not with cheap. In the future, designers will not be called upon to design the lenses that form the best images, but rather those that form satisfactory images and are cheapest to manufacture. This is an important distinction, one that under-scores the need for development of a whole new design methodology. If a lens for a consumer product is over designed, it will be too expensive to be competitive. Yet optimizing this aspect of production is outside the boundary of traditional optical design.

Tolerancing, the most challenging and traditionally the most neglected aspect of optical design, is obviously becoming more important. In packaging, small size is increasingly in demand. The quest for smaller and smaller sizes has led to unusual geometries, and the consequent replacement of analytic design methods with numerical techniques, often tailored to the particular task at hand. In some applications, size restrictions may necessitate placing lenses in spaces where they can have dimensions of only a few wavelengths. In this case, geometrical design methods are inadequate, but current physical optics methods are too slow. These are the types of problems that optical designers can expect to confront in the future.

Designers won't be able to solve these problems without wide-ranging knowledge of optics as a discipline. In the future, it will be necessary to combine the lens designer's meticulous methodology with the broader perspective of the optical engineer. Outside the optical design community, there is a tendency to consider lens design a problem that has been solved: there are those who believe that if you purchase an optical design software package and press the "global optimize" key, you can be done with it. The reality, of course, is different.

The optical design problem presented to participants in the 1998 International Optical Design Conference, involved the optimization of a system characterized by chromatic aberration. Participants had the choice of using a few surfaces but lots of different glasses, or a few glasses and lots of surfaces. As expected, experienced lens designers came up with the top five solutions. Four of the designers used commercial optical design software, one an in-house proprietary program. Although three of the designers noted that they had used the global exploration features of their software as an aid, all the solutions reflected the detailed personal involvement of the designer. In this respect, the results were comparable to those of similar contests held over the course of the past twenty years.

Two designs submitted as solutions to the lens design problem posed at the 1998 International Optical Design Meeting in Kona, HI. John Isenberg's winning design (top) achieved superb performance, but a typical solution from an unknown designer (bottom) lacked the essential apochromatic correction. In the drawings, higher index glasses are shown in darker shades.

More interesting are some of the losing designs among the few dozen that were submitted. It is apparent that many of the designers were unaware of some of the basic principles of apochromatic correction, or else that they tried to let the software do the thinking for them—and in this case, it didn't work. Of course, apochromatic correction of lenses is not something that you expect the average engineer to be familiar with, but we're talking here about a group of optical design specialists. These are the people who presumably will take

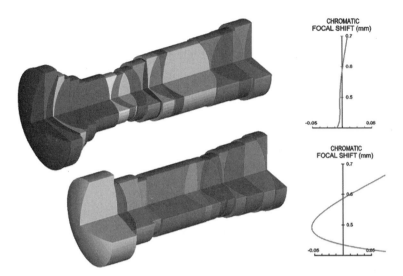

Two designs submitted for 1998 International Optical Design Conference problem. Above is the winning design by John Eisenberg. Below is a typical submission lacking apochromatic correction.

over optical design when today's top lens designers vanish. It seems reasonable to ask what happened here. The obvious response is that the software didn't provide the answer: its standard built-in capabilities were insufficient and needed to be supplemented by designer-developed workarounds.

As the scope of optical design widens, this type of situation will become increasingly common. To deal with it, we need to re-conceptualize optical design and ensure we are educating students in such a way as to provide them with the ability to meet the challenge. In particular, it's not a good idea to start by teaching geometrical optics and then progress to physical optics: better to start with waves and then introduce rays as a useful approximation when the dimensions of the elements are large compared to the wavelength. It's true that learning is facilitated when students progress from simple to more complicated subjects, but the truth of the matter is that ray optics isn't any simpler than wave optics.

In fact, starting with rays implies the use of Snell's law. Snell's law is elegant, but when you try to use it to describe imaging systems you are led to series expansions that very quickly become unmanageable. At this point, with a limited degree of familiarity with paraxial optics, and believing that only lens designers with a penchant for algebra can understand the subject, the vast majority of students opt out. Optical design is difficult because it involves modeling a continuous non-linear system using discrete numbers, not because the algebra is hard. Computers can do the algebra.

Starting with waves means beginning with Huygens' principle and arriving at geometrical optics through Fermat's principle, an approach that leads students to think about the physics of light rather than the algebra of ray tracing. This is good because it helps them understand how waves and rays are related, as well as how the systems needed to make sensible engineering decisions really work. If your job will one day entail circumventing the limitations of canned software, it's important to understand the physics of what you're doing. And it's not likely that this requirement will change in the future.

Jenkins' and White's Folly

First published in 1937 and still in print 63 years later, *Fundamentals of Optics* by Jenkins and White is probably the most widely used optics text ever published. In a field sown with thousands of what are known as "twig books," *Fundamentals of Optics* has been at the root, or at least the trunk, of the tree. Everyone trained in optics is familiar with it. Yet the first two sentences start us off on the wrong track:

> Optics, the study of light, is conveniently divided into three fields, each of which requires a markedly different method of theoretical treatment. These are (a) geometrical optics, which is treated by the method of light rays, (b) physical optics, which is concerned with the nature of light and involves primarily the theory of waves, and (c) quantum optics, which deals with the interaction of light with the atomic entities of matter and which for an exact treatment requires the methods of quantum mechanics.

What's the problem? It's not in the assertion that classical and quantum optics are based on different concepts. It's in the assumption that the difference between geometrical and physical optics requires a "markedly different method of theoretical treatment." Everyone agrees that the propagation of light is governed by Maxwell's equations: it doesn't matter whether you think in terms of wave surfaces or the normals to these surfaces. Although Jenkins' and White's "folly" has been detrimental to students trying to learn optics, the real problem is that the text seems to have been adopted as some sort of bible by suppliers of optical components. Real optical designers don't use Jenkins and White.

Lens Design vs. Optical Engineering

A few years ago, Rudolf Kingslake was named Engineer of the Year by the Rochester Engineering Society, not for anything he did during that particular year, but for a lifetime of professional accomplishment. When I congratulated him on an award justly deserved, he replied that he felt indeed honored to have been selected, and was somewhat surprised, because he had always thought of himself as a lens designer, not an optical engineer.

Kingslake had a clear picture of the difference between the two. The lens designer was the one who balanced the aberrations; the optical engineer worked on layouts and negotiated with the marketing and mechanical departments to get enough room for the design to be implemented within the laws of physics. As we enter the new century, that distinction is disappearing. At the moment, it is leaving a void that is not being filled. Both lens designers and optical engineers need to confront this issue.

The profession of lens design *per se* is likely to disappear. The reality today is that very few companies can afford to employ a full-time lens designer from the traditional mold. The problems that these companies face are not the aberration-balancing problems solved in traditional lens design—they're much broader in scope. At the same time, the optimization of optical systems is not a problem that lends itself to casual solution, as the results of recent lens design contests demonstrate. There's much demand for people who can work at a professional level in optical design, but who also have a broad engineering perspective.

A few years ago, the Japanese trade ministry came up with the slogan "Electronics is the science of the twentieth century—Optics is the science of the twenty-first century." Now, at the turn of the century, optics is looking pretty good, but we need to be confident that we're working on the right agenda. We do indeed have the opportunity to make optics the science of the twenty-first century, but it will be primarily an engineering science, and we need to understand that.

Including lens design as a part of optical engineering is not easy. Although changing the way that geometrical optics is taught may be of some help, it is not sufficient. More important is raising the level of optical design taught to optical engineers. There's a great deal to be learned from the past, and it's important to learn it. But there are wonderful opportunities in optical design, and surely there's never been a better time for a young person to enter optics.

Douglas C. Sinclair received his Ph.D. from the Institute of Optics in 1963. He was a member of the faculty of the Institute of Optics from 1965 until 1980. He is currently employed at Sinclair Optics, Inc., Fairport, NY.

Reference

1   Reprinted from *Optics and Photonics News*, June 2000, with permission.

73. Institute Ventures

James Zavislan

Optical sciences and engineering have been key enablers in the high-growth technologies of the last half-century such as integrated circuits, consumer electronics and high-speed communications. Optics continues to play a major role in these technologies and is positioned to be both a foundation and catalyst in the next generation of high-growth markets. Optics presents a wide "footprint" in the development of new materials, medical diagnostics and therapeutics and precision measurement. In many businesses, novel optical systems and devices have provided the advantage that enables a company's success.

Throughout its history, The Institute of Optics has been closely aligned with the commercial applications of optics. Initially formed with input from the Eastman Kodak Co., and Bausch & Lomb Corp., the Institute, through its students, staff, faculty and alumni, has contributed to many companies. Over the years, commercial applications of optics have evolved to include photographic imaging, military equipment, cinematography, remote sensing, electro-optics, lasers, digital imaging, optical storage, telecommunications, and biomedical optics. The diversity of optical applications has attracted individuals from many technical and cultural backgrounds; within the Institute these backgrounds have mixed. The resulting environment has led directly or indirectly to the founding of many new companies or contributed to the growth of new markets. Table 1 shows a partial list of companies that have been formed by Institute of Optics faculty, staff or students.

Before 1980, much of the commercial activity at the Institute was ad-hoc and driven by individual circumstances. Students and faculty established commercial links depending on their backgrounds, sponsored research contracts, and consulting relationships. While the University of Rochester nominally administered these relationships, it did not actively manage or encourage them. Occasionally a student's research became the basis of a commercial product (or even a new company) or a faculty member participated in the formation of a new company. However, with the passage of the Federal Bayh-Dole Act in 1980, which granted universities rights to intellectual property developed from Federal funding, the University had additional incentive to commercialize its inventions. The technology explosion of the 1990s, especially in optical telecommunications, encouraged the Institute's faculty to start or develop their own companies. These two conditions have encouraged the University to develop strategic programs to develop and transfer commercial technologies. One such program is the Center for Institute Ventures (CIV).

CIV was developed by the Institute and the College of Arts, Sciences and Engineering to provide new entrepreneurial opportunity to its students, staff and faculty, to assist in the efficient transfer of technology as well as to mitigate the risk of technology business formation. CIV was started in 2001 at the suggestion of Bala Manian (entrepreneur, venture capital investor, and Institute alumnus and former faculty member) in response to the exuberant investments made in technology companies in the late 1990s. As Manian pointed out, technology companies were being formed and funded based on specialized technology

Table 1. Partial list of company formation from The Institute of Optics.

Tropel	1953	Hopkins, Evans	Alumnus/Faculty
Optical Research Assoc.	1963	Harris	Alumnus
Velmex	1967	Evans	Alumnus
Zygo	1970	Forman	Alumnus
Burleigh	1972	Klimasewski	Alumnus
Sinclair Optics	1976	Sinclair	Alumnus/Faculty
Digital Optics Corp.	1980	Manian	Alumnus/Faculty
Gradient Lens Corp.	1980	Moore	Alumnus/Faculty
Optikos	1982	Fantone	Alumnus
WYKO	1983	Wyant	Alumnus
Coherent Optics	1984	Hercher	Faculty
Optel	1985	Eastman	Alumnus/Faculty
Hampshire Instruments	1985	Forsyth	Alumnus/Faculty
VISX	1986	Munnerlyn	Alumnus
Lumisys	1987	Manian	Alumnus/Faculty
Molecular Dynamics	1987	Manian	Alumnus/Faculty
LaserMax	1989	Houde-Walter	Alumnus/Faculty
Optra	1990	Hercher	Faculty
Biometric Imaging	1991	Manian	Alumnus/Faculty
Lucid	1992	Eastman	Alumnus/Faculty
ASE Optics	1994	Cotton	Alumnus
Rochester Photonics	1995	Morris	Faculty
QED Technologies	1997	Golini	Alumnus
Quantum Dot Corp.	1998	Manian	Alumnus/Faculty
SurroMed	2000	Manian	Alumnus/Faculty
Semrock	2000	Erdogan	Alumnus/Faculty

that had often not been validated. The specialized nature of the technology challenged the traditional methods of due diligence performed by the investors prior to committing resources. Many companies were funded without thoroughly understanding the background of the technology. The lack of validation clouded the commercialization timetable. Together these factors blended to impede the success of the company in the marketplace.

Structurally CIV is a partnership between venture capital investors and the University through the Institute. CIV provides technology services to venture capital investors and their client companies, leveraging the unique strengths of academic excellence and creativity at the Institute to facilitate efficient technology and economic development in the field of optical sciences and engineering. Initially, CIV is targeting biomedical optics, life science instrumentation, and photonics. These areas provide symbiosis with the University's medical center, Department of Biomedical Engineering, Center for Future Health, Center for Electronic Imaging Systems, and Laboratory for Laser Energetics. It also provides collaboration with the micro-fabrication and packaging infrastructure developed at the Center of Excellence in Infotonics. CIV aligns applied-research activities with business opportunities and attracts new optical technologies to the University and the Rochester community.

Operationally, CIV partners with groups of venture capital (VC) firms to form a for-profit business partnership (IV Partners). The structure of the relationship is shown in the figure. Each partnership is active for three to four years. The partnership hires a project scientist familiar with optics and the technology space of the venture firms. CIV coordinates due-diligence technology evaluation, technology validation, and research for the partnerships. The partnerships fund these services. The project scientist, as an employee for a for-profit business, can apply for Federal Small Business Innovative Research (SBIR) funding for technology projects of interest to the venture capitalists, or collaborate in Federal Small Business Technology Transfer (STTR) funded research at the University. The University owns the new intellectual property (IP) reduced to practice through these activities. The venture capital firms retain first negotiation rights to IP. Technology validation and research results will be published.

CIV administers three programs for the business partnerships. The first program is due-diligence consulting to mitigate the time and money risk of venture capital investments. Venture capital partners select business plans that are both potentially fundable and that include optics as a key component or enabler. Faculty and CIV project scientists review these business plans. They offer reports and opinions on these business plans, providing the investors with background to the technology, context for its potential, and questions that should be addressed prior to funding. Faculty act as independent contractors to the business partnership as allowed by their academic appointment. While many Institute faculty already provide consulting services to investors, this program coordinates this activity and introduces to the venture capital firms the full breadth of our optical understanding while offering expert opinions about business plans under consideration.

The second program is technology validation to accelerate the technology milestones of venture-backed companies. CIV project scientists, Institute students (predominantly M.S. candidates), staff, and faculty participate in technology validation research and technology reduction to practice. This work involves small-scale lab experiments and modeling to verify the optical technology or technologies that are at the core of the venture-backed companies. These activities, administered as sponsored research contracts, utilize the existing infrastructure of the University of Rochester to understand and demonstrate the full extent of the technology and to identify the risks to commercialization. The companies and their

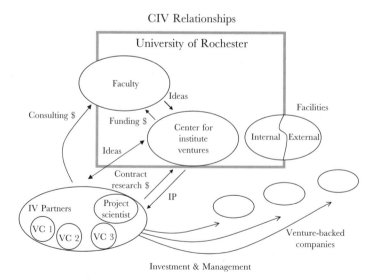

CIV Structure.

investors benefit by concentrating the companies'efforts and resources on customer acceptance, strategic partnerships, and manufacturing, rather than investing time and money setting up laboratory facilities to prove their technology. Students benefit by participating in research experiences similar to the experiences that they would face as an employee in a technology company. These projects provide a layer of entrepreneurship to our educational program and personal contacts that will be useful to the students after they graduate. Faculty and staff will have opportunity to survey technologies on the cusp of commercialization, many of which may assist their research or help refine new research directions.

The third program is platform technology research for venture capital groups. Institute students (predominantly Ph.D. candidates), post-doctoral fellows, faculty, staff, and CIV project scientists respond to "unmet needs" requests from the VCs and propose research projects to VCs. Because VCs seek to identify early high-growth markets, they are in a unique position to identify consistent and pervasive technology shortcomings that limit the scope or slow the growth of new technology markets. Thus, VCs can suggest research projects that when successful could form a platform technology for a particular market.

The research projects in this third program are consistent with the time frame and scope of Ph.D. research. They provide a source of funding for applied research. Students interested in applied research are given the opportunity to identify the problems associated with a current technology and develop a new solution with potentially large application. After completing their degrees, students who participate in this research would be well suited to work as a CTO of a company commercializing the platform technology or to apply their experience to a new technology field.

It is important to note that CIV is not a business incubator. Businesses are not started by CIV nor housed in CIV research facilities. Instead, CIV focuses on technology at the foundation of high-growth markets. Our VC partners collect technology opportunities from around the country; CIV helps them understand the background, context, risks and opportunities provided by the technologies. Our VC partners fund businesses and build business teams; CIV validates and augments the technologies of the funded companies. Our VC partners identify unmet technology needs; CIV provides the organization and facilities to research these opportunities and develop platform technologies for high-growth markets. By focusing on technical foundations rather than business formation, CIV provides entrepreneurial opportunities for our students, staff and faculty that augments the educational mission of the Institute and the University.

As an undergraduate and graduate student of The Institute of Optics in the 1980s, I had the fortunate opportunity to participate in a start-up company, Optel Systems, founded by my advisor, Jay M. Eastman; and to consult for various companies and develop a surface profilometer instrument that was the foundation of another start-up company, Chapman Instruments. These experiences expanded the education I received at the Institute and helped me understand how my training at the Institute could be used in a variety of technical fields from bar-code scanning to machining. CIV hopes to bring additional opportunities to members of the Institute to expand the breadth of applications of optics.

James Zavislan received his B.S. and Ph.D. from the Institute of Optics in 1981 and 1988, respectively. He has been a member of the faculty of the University of Rochester since 2002.

74. Quantum Optical Engineering

Carlos Stroud

From a historical perspective the title of this essay is an oxymoron. The Institute of Optics has long been the home of both quantum optics and of optical engineering, but they have occupied the opposite poles of the axis that runs from pure basic research to applications-driven research and advanced development. The assignment of quantum optics to "pure" research with no application in sight is changing rapidly and a new field called *quantum optical engineering* or even *quantum technology* is growing rapidly. It promises to be a central player in the technologies of the new century.

There are two separate forces driving the development of this new field. The first is miniaturization and the second is quantum weirdness. Each requires some comment.

The processes underlying most technologies are rapidly being miniaturized. Photolithography is producing circuit elements on silicon chips well into the nanometer range. Semiconductor devices are fabricated atomic layer by atomic layer. Nanotechnology has made imaging and manipulation of single atoms commonplace. The nanometer-scale devices that result from this research are central to new commercial applications: faster, more powerful, compact electronic devices; super materials that are stronger and lighter; medical devices that automate and simplify laboratory tests; chemical processing molecule-by-molecule. The scale of these new technologies is that of a few, or even a single, atom. This is the realm at which classical physics gives way to quantum physics. The discreteness of atoms, electrons, and photons as well as their complementary wave properties can no longer be ignored.

The ways in which quantum mechanics influences the behavior of nano-scale devices is sometimes surprising. Professor Lukas Novotny has a very active new group in the Institute working in the field of nano-optics. In many of his research projects he combines a metallic probe, which is only a few nanometers wide at the tip, with a focused laser beam to probe a surface optically with nanometer resolution. The laser beam can provide either high spectral sensitivity in the case of a narrow bandwidth cw laser, or femtosecond temporal sensitivity in the case of a pulsed laser. The high curvature of the metallic tip greatly enhances the laser field in the nanometer-sized volume near the tip. When moving the tip near the surface, even though there is no direct mechanical contact, a great deal of friction is experienced. Novotny and his student Jorge Zurita Sanchez have shown that the fluctuating thermal and quantum fields in the small volume are the source of the friction. Such fluctuations are intrinsic to the quantum scale and can be expected to show up in many related problems in nanotechnology. Even friction becomes quantum mechanical at this scale.

One trying to miniaturize a conventional technology might be inclined to view the appearance of quantum mechanics as a nuisance. It leads to friction, quantum noise, and a new academic discipline that must be mastered to keep up with the demands of Moore's law in computer development. That is true if your purview is simply that of pushing the boundaries of mature technologies, but there are associated new opportunities that may lead to completely new technologies that eventually replace the old ones.

Quantum mechanics is fundamentally different from classical mechanics and electromagnetic theory in that it describes a field that is weird from the perspective of our macroscopic classical world. A quantum particle has wave properties—it has a wavelength and can exhibit interference and diffraction. Similarly a quantum wave has particle-like properties—it is absorbed and emitted in discrete units. A quantum particle can be at two places at once. A pair of quantum particles can be *entangled* so that even when separated by large distances they share a common state and do not have definite individual states. Only when one particle is subjected to a measurement does the state of the other become well determined. These are the basic phenomena of *quantum weirdness*.

It is perhaps counter-intuitive but it is exactly these weird parts of quantum theory that offer the greatest promise for technological breakthrough. The reason is simple. The weird phenomena are those that do not occur in any classical setting and thus they enable processes that cannot be carried out by any classical means. They allow you to do things that cannot be done any other way. Quantum computing was the first such application to gain wide attention. There are problems such as factoring large numbers which are very difficult on conventional computers, with the time to compute growing exponentially as we go to larger numbers. Factoring a number of a few hundred digits would require a time longer than the age of the universe with the fastest existing computer. In part because of the ability of quantum theory to describe a particle as being many places at once, a quantum computer could theoretically speed up the computation exponentially. This is extremely important because the current standard method of encryption, the RSA scheme, is based on the difficulty of factoring large numbers compared with the ease of multiplying large numbers. Quantum computers are currently able only to handle a few bits, but the field is progressing very rapidly. At the same time that quantum weirdness threatens conventional encryption schemes it offers new methods of communication that are secure against any form of eavesdropping that is consistent with the laws of quantum mechanics. This sort of secure communication is currently being used in military and commercial applications.

Carlos Stroud and quantum information calculation.

It seems very likely that we have not thought of the really earthshaking applications of quantum weirdness. The whole idea that this is a reasonable subject to pursue is itself quite new, but the situation is not unprecedented. In the closing decades of the Nineteenth Century Maxwell had just proposed his equations which tied together electricity, magnetism, and light into one unified theory which predicted waves propagating in a vacuum. This was considered weird. There cannot be a wave unless there is something to vibrate. In a vacuum there is no medium to vibrate, thus it cannot support a wave. Many of the eminent scientists of the day rejected the idea and insisted that there must be an aether. Of course it was exactly this weird property of electromagnetic theory that led to wireless communication which continues to lead to major changes in our lives today. This was a tremendous breakthrough exactly because it was something that could not be done any other way. In 1870 a ship that passed over the horizon was out of communication. It was certainly not clear that Maxwell's weird theory would lead to a cell phone in every pocket, or a wireless modem in every computer, but it did. I would venture to predict that quantum weirdness will also lead to a similar technological blockbuster.

This argument makes the idea of quantum technology plausible, but it is perhaps not clear why I refer to quantum *optical* technology. The reason has some close ties to the history of the Institute. Tunable narrowband lasers provide a marvelous way to control a quantum system. Isolated atoms and other systems in which quantum effects are important are generally very high Q systems with narrow resonances. A laser tuned precisely to one of these resonances can interact so strongly with the atom that it can control it. This is illustrated dramatically in laser cooling of atoms—a subject that has earned six recent Nobel Prizes. In a room temperature gas the atoms are moving with an average velocity of about 600 meters per second, more than 1000 miles per hour. If a resonant laser beam is scattered off of one of the fast moving atoms the force is sufficient to stop the atom in a distance of about one foot. Such interactions can also strongly affect the internal states of atoms. One can gain exquisite control of the quantum system and manipulate it in ways that are difficult to accomplish any other way. As usual the laser and optics more generally are enabling tools for the new technology.

It is not surprising that Rochester has been a center for the development of quantum optics. When Ben Snavely, Otis Peterson, and Sam Tuccio were developing the first cw dye lasers at Eastman Kodak Research Laboratories and Michael Hercher, Alan Pike, Felix Schuda, and Conger Gabel were developing the narrowband tunable version in the Institute they certainly did not envision that they were enabling a method for cooling atoms to nano-Kelvin temperatures, or breaking the most secure codes, but they were. Certainly Leonard Mandel and I were quick to see how we could exploit the new tool to study some quantum mechanical problems that we had been puzzling over.

Without having a crystal ball I cannot know what the big breakthrough will be in quantum technology, but the odds that optics will play an important role in it are very high and those of us who have been the "poets of optics" are likely to be in the middle of a new twenty-first century technology.

75. Looking to 2029

Wayne H. Knox

Here in Rochester, as we celebrate our seventy-fifth anniversary, we are looking back over a distinguished past, as well as forward to an exciting future leading to our one hundredth anniversary in 2029. The Institute of Optics was born in a very turbulent time in September 1929. In October 1929, the stock market Dow Index dropped by a factor of two, and then began a long decline. Throughout the Depression that followed, the newly formed Institute of Optics was busy gearing up and produced its first Ph.D. student in 1939. The figure below shows the Dow Index during these years.

In what ways does the stock market affect an academic institution in general, and in what ways should it specifically impact an optics department? A private academic institution such as the University of Rochester relies on its endowment for part of its income. This is a very

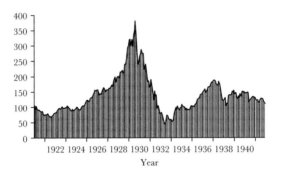

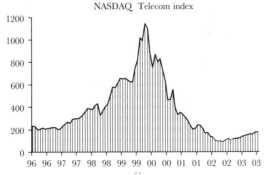

Top is the Dow Jones Index from 1921 to 1940, bottom is the NASDAQ Telecom Index from 1998 to 2003. There are strong similarities in peak-to-valley ratio as well as duration of the peak.

direct tie to the market. Other factors such as corporate revenues are important. In good times of large corporate profits, it is much easier to get corporate donations and contributions to the University and the department. In addition, our industrial associates program revenues follow these general economic trends. In any case, there is a striking similarity between the market conditions in 1929 during our founding, and the market conditions in 2000. During this time, many entrepreneurs were looking into a "new world" in which it was very easy to obtain venture capital funding. It was also easy to hire people by luring them away from relatively secure jobs at large corporations and very secure jobs in tenured positions at universities into startup companies with very uncertain futures. Many university departments were dealt a severe blow by faculty egress. At The Institute of Optics, several faculty members left around the year 2000 to start and manage companies, Director Dennis Hall had been promoted to associate provost for research at Vanderbilt University, and Professor Ian Walmsley left for Oxford University. During this period, my Advanced Photonics Research Department at Bell Labs in Holmdel was undergoing very much the same process, with many scientists leaving to go to start-up companies. Shortly after I was appointed director of the Institute in April 2001, we hired several new faculty members to regain our required faculty strength. We have recently hired Assistant Professor Chunlei Guo, Professor James Fienup, Associate Professor James Zavislan, and Assistant Professor Miguel Alonso. Also, Professor Susan Houde-Walter has returned from her two-year leave of absence as president of LaserMax. We anticipate more faculty hiring in the future.

Since the founding of the Institute seventy-five years ago, the field of optics has changed considerably, yet the Institute has changed along with the field. Although optics is a relatively specialized field, there is a wide range of activity in the field, ranging from lens and optical system design to quantum optics and semiconductor optoelectronics, ultrafast and adaptive optics, telecommunications and biomedical optics, physical and geometrical optics, theoretical and experimental optics, high intensity optics, imaging and optical fabrication/testing, and nano-optics. The Institute is unique in that it covers much of the field of optics, while maintaining significant depth in these areas. It is a Big Tent of Optics, a very dynamic and active place, very much in tune with the optics industry through several channels such as industrial associates meetings, seminars, corporate visits, corporate sponsored research, etc. It is also a free-wheeling academic department where faculty are free to pursue, and well-supported in building, whatever research program they wish. It is a collegial and supportive department in which junior faculty are hired into tenure-track positions with appropriate conditions and every expectation that they will achieve tenure. It is a department in which graduate students are admitted in the expectation that they will finish their degrees with a high success rate. We expect that they will look back at their time as a student as a happy but challenging and rewarding time, yet one that is perhaps a bit scary at times, too. When Tiger Woods recently played the Eighty-fifth PGA championship in Rochester, he commented that the course at Oak Hill was *"the toughest and fairest course I have ever played."* I would certainly like to think that our students would say the same about our optics program well past the year 2029.

As we celebrate our seventy-fifth anniversary, we are in the midst of a very exciting expansion of our facilities that will have a significant and lasting impact on our department well into the future. The Institute of Optics spent most of its first fifty years housed in a single floor of Bausch & Lomb Hall and moved into the current Wilmot Building in 1975. After twenty-five years in the Wilmot Building (fig. 2a), the department had outgrown its space. As I write this, we are starting construction on the Optics-BME building project that will expand the available optics research and teaching facilities as well as provide a home for our biomedical engineering department. This project came about as a result of several factors. Our biomedical engineering program became an official department in the year 2000 (note the coincidence in the first figure, that BME was also founded during a market peak). They had landed a Whitaker Foundation faculty development grant as well as a three million dollar Whitaker challenge to assist in the building of a new BME building. The original plan was to put the new BME building next to the Wilmot Building. When I arrived, a number of discussions with the chair of BME, Rick Waugh, and BME faculty members made it clear that there were many new opportunities in the field of biomedical optics, an area in which we already had significant optics faculty interest and strength, as well as significant BME faculty interest. So, we began investigating the possibility of building a combined Optics-BME complex as our expansion. This project is scheduled for completion in June 2006.

This building will provide optics with expanded state-of-the-art research space as well as expanded lecture halls and greatly improved meeting spaces. The figure on the next page shows a draft plan of this project as of this writing.

The expansion of optics space (Wilmot currently offers us only 25,000 square feet) will allow us to significantly increase our research output, modernize and expand our teaching laboratories, create new centers, expand our lecture halls, and create new environments for our undergraduate and graduate students to hang out, study, and meet with teaching assistants. In addition, the new space will allow us to increase the size of our faculty over time, allowing us to expand into new areas of optics as they evolve. And, there is a national need to increase emphasis on K-12 education. The new building will allow us to host groups of students for visits with lectures, demonstrations and perhaps even some hands-on experiments with optics.

We are also expanding and enhancing our industrial associates group to include more companies. Currently, we have twenty-two companies signed up, with as many as twenty-five more pending. The economic climate at the time of this writing is pretty tough, and many companies find that funding for these kinds of academic programs is the first to disappear when times get tough. But, The Institute of Optics has always had strong connections to the optics industry, and it makes it very unique in the University setting. The Institute of Optics has been responsible for producing people who have founded quite a large number of

Current Wilmot Building.

Architect's sketch of new building.

companies. Moving forward, we find ourselves in a University of Rochester that is significantly changed as a result of greatly increased intellectual property revenues. Recently, the University has catapulted into the top ten list of universities for IP revenues, with $40 million in revenue in 2002. This has caught the attention of many here, and the timing is right to launch a new entrepreneurship initiative here in the Institute. We hired Associate Professor James Zavislan for many reasons—one of them is his interest in optics entrepreneurship. We are working to create a much smoother channel for carrying out the normally difficult transitioning part of research once the early concepts have been shown. (Jim writes more about that in essay 73). I think that, over time, our Institute ventures program could have considerable impact on the economic development climate in Rochester.

The optics education environment has changed markedly since the founding of the Institute in 1929. The figure on the next page shows the number of institutions that offer optics degrees. The data from this is contained in a 2001 *OE Reports* survey.

As can be seen from this figure, after the founding of The Institute of Optics, the next addition was the University of Arizona in the early 1960s. After that, there was a rapid rise in the 1980s. We can only presume that the number of optics degree-granting institutions will continue to rise through the year 2029. In the face of this increasing competition, The Institute of Optics needs to continue to maintain the great traditions and standards of optics that we have developed, yet at the same time continue to expand and add new elements. We have recently added several new graduate courses such as nano-optics and biomedical optics, as well as new undergraduate courses in computing for optics and optics in the information age. We continue to develop and implement new courses in the optics curriculum.

In her distinguished last writing of the history of The Institute of Optics on the occasion of our fiftieth anniversary, Hilda Kingslake didn't mention about our seventy-fifth

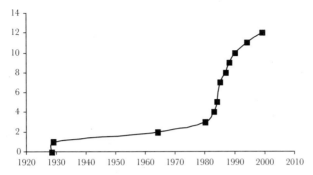

Number of institutions in the United States offering optics degrees of any kind.

anniversary; rather she made the comment, "ahoy and onward to our 100th Anniversary." So, as I write this, I have my hands full with planning our seventy-fifth anniversary events for October 2004. I'm not spending too much time planning for the details of the hundredth anniversary in 2029, but I would like to think that we are laying the groundwork well in advance. The Institute of Optics was born in a turbulent time and lived and prospered through many more exciting and turbulent times, and I am sure we will have a lot of interesting things to write in 2029.

Wayne H. Knox received his B.S. and Ph.D. from the Institute of Optics in 1979 and 1984, respectively. He has been a member of the faculty of the University of Rochester since 2001. He has served as the Director of the Institute since 2001.

Index

Page numbers in **boldface** indicate authorship.